THE ILLUSTRATED ENCYCLOPEDIA OF SEX

THE
ILLUSTRATED
ENCYCLOPEDIA OF
SEX

By

DR. A. WILLY
DR. L. VANDER
DR. O. FISHER

and Other
Authorities

CADILLAC PUBLISHING CO., Inc.
New York

PREFACE

A volume of similar theme first appeared some years ago. It represented a summary of sexual knowledge as it stood then. However, during the intervening period, after years of inertia following upon one war and preceding another, the science of sexology has made such rapid and brilliant progress that we consider it opportune to place before the public this volume, in order to make the results of newer scientific research available to the general reader in popular form.

Perhaps the most important new discovery in the sphere of sexology is that relating to Natural Birth Control which offers great hope in the solution to an age-old problem which, however, has become particularly acute in modern times. The section describing the work of Professors Kyusaku Ogino and Hermann Knaus, and the results achieved by them in their studies of Natural Birth Control, is a major contribution in this book.

But there is another, no less important aspect of our subject that claims universal interest: During recent years the failure of the intrinsically great works of Professors Eugen Steinach and Serge Voronoff, and other investigators of methods of rejuvenation has been definitely established. These scientists approached the problem of rejuvenation from the sexual angle, and practical experience has placed it beyond doubt that the biological process of gradual decay and death could not be delayed for any considerable length of time by temporarily re-invigorating the sexual apparatus, and, indeed, that "rejuvenation" is impossible. On the other hand, it has been proved that if it is beyond human power to *regain* lost youth, it is possible, by a rational mode of

5

life, and by the rigid observance of sexual hygiene, to maintain the youthful vigor both of the sexual apparatus and the organism as a whole far into old age, and that it largely depends on the individual whether he will decay and die at a comparatively early age, or whether he will live to be a happy and healthy centenarian. In the section devoted to this vital question we deal in a practical manner with the principles upon which the process of *maintaining* youth, of keeping young, must be based.

Closely linked with the subject of sex is, of course, the activity of the endocrine glands, about which the average educated person knows next to nothing, and concerning which the scientists themselves were largely in the dark until comparatively recently. Here again, our authors, each an expert in his particular branch of science, have combined to present to the reader, in a manner easily understandable to the layman, a clear survey of past and present knowledge, together with a practical interpretation of the importance of glandular activity, both as regards general and sexual health.

The prevalence of feminine sexual insensibility—frigidity and impotence—together with its causes and possible cure, is another aspect of sexual life which has been dealt with frankly and in great detail in the present work. This is one of those vitally important problems with regard to which ignorance is rife, and which false modesty, disastrous in its domestic and social consequences, has caused to be hushed up. Here, for the first time, the reader will learn about the nature and effects of feminine sexual insensibility and may perhaps find the solution of many a mystery that has hitherto darkened his or her life.

But there is one feature of this book of which we are particularly proud—the illustrations! One hundred seventy-six of them, representing every aspect of sex, but particularly the functional aspect, and explaining every process in the male and female organism so clearly that no one can fail to understand them.

We say, with every confidence, that this long series of illustrations, which includes twenty-three colored plates, is unique and unprecedented. Never has such a complete series of illustrations of the sexual apparatus of both sexes, at rest as well as in function, appeared in a single volume. Indeed, a large number of these illustrations, specially prepared for us for the purpose of this work, are unique in themselves. That we have been unable in each case to arrange the illustrations in the orthodox manner—close to the relevant text—is due to the fact, which the reader will no doubt appreciate, that sometimes a short portion of the text relates to a number of illustrations, while on the other hand several chapters require no illustration at all.

Originally this book was published in England, and it is printed for the first time in this country only with such modifications in the manuscript as were found necessary for more familiar American phraseology.

Although we do not claim to have achieved perfection in the present work, we offer THE ILLUSTRATED ENCYCLOPEDIA OF SEX in the confident hope that it will prove to be an important contribution to the cause of sexual enlightenment.

THE PUBLISHERS.

LIST OF ILLUSTRATIONS

9

COLOR PLATES

CONTENTS

BOOK I

SEXUAL ORGANS AND HOW THEY FUNCTION

How they influence your life and health—Detailed description
and illustrations of male and female sex organs—How they
work—Striking similarity of male and female sex organs—Importance of this resemblance.

How they function during coitus—How the testicles produce
semen—Active male sperm attacks and unites with the female
ovum—A single spermatozoon fertilizes a woman—500 million
sperm in a single male emission—How brain power depends
on healthy function of the testes—How sex fluids influence
vital energy and mental powers—Seminal reservoirs: their action during coitus—Function of prostate during coitus and
orgasm.

Marvels of erection mechanism—Development of genital organs—Anatomical differences between flaccid and erect penis
—How the feminine sex apparatus is excited—Factors that
cause normal erection—How the brain becomes stimulated—
Morning erections.

How they function to prepare for coitus and reproduction—
The ovaries in function—How the ova prepare for the marital
union—Uterus during coitus—Conception possible without
orgasm.

BOOK II

HORMONES AND VITAMINS

BOOK III

NATURAL BIRTH CONTROL

BOOK IV

THE SEXUAL IMPULSE

BOOK V

DELAYING SEXUAL DEATH

BOOK VI

DISEASES—ALCOHOLISM—STERILITY

BOOK I

Sexual Organs and How They Function

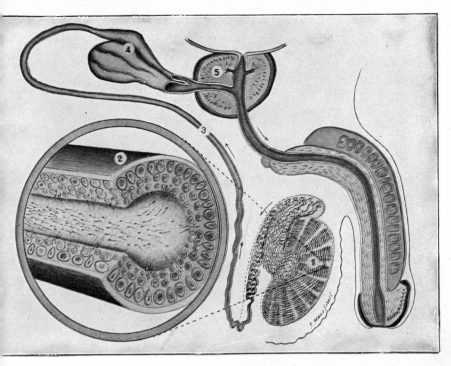

Sperm's travel through man's sexual organs.

Fig. C-1— (1) Testicle from which spermatozoa issue. (2) Small section, considerably enlarged, of vas deferens, showing spermatozoa (dark lines) in white fluid. (3) Vas deferens which conveys them. (4) Globus minor and seminal vesicle. (5) Ejaculatory duct through which fluid from globus minor and seminal vesicle passes.

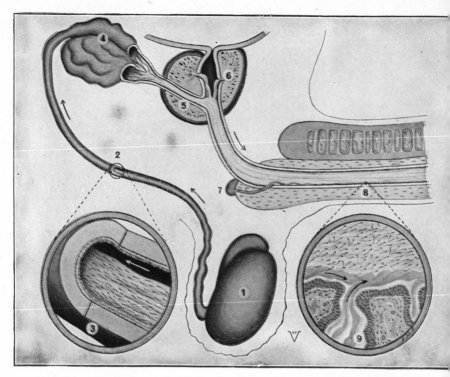

Fig. C-2— (6) Prostate fluid flowing from urethra. (7) Cowper's gland pouring secretion into urethra. (8) Gland of urethra which empties itself into the same. In the circle, ditto, increased by seminal fluid and spermatozoa (dark lines). (9) Urethral secretion enters urethra, in order to prepare way for semen.

CHAPTER 1

THE SEX ORGANS OF MAN AND WOMAN

THERE is an obvious difference, both as regards functions and purpose, between the genital or reproductive organs and the other apparatus of the human body. The groups of highly complicated organs constituting the human organism—the digestive, circulatory, respiratory and other systems, all of which function under the coordination of the nervous system—serve to preserve the individual; whereas the genital or reproductive system serves for the perpetuation of the race.

Naturally, this does not signify that there is no connection—beyond the purely physical—between these two kinds of organs. On the contrary, the genital apparatus exercises a very considerable influence on the other apparatus. For example, in the case of the female, the fecundation of an ovum produces certain changes in the mammary glands or breasts, so that by the time the child is born the most suitable food is available for it; while in the case of the male, the internal secretion of the testicles affects somewhat such masculine qualities as courage and physical strength. It is a well-known fact that loss of or injury to the testicles may lead to some impairment of the characteristically masculine attributes.

Less well known than the connection between the genital apparatus and the rest of the human mechanism is the close analogy that exists between the male and female genital apparatus. In order to emphasize its importance we will base the following detailed description of the male and female genital organs on an unorthodox main classification, in which these organs are grouped according to their functions.

Thus we have:

1. Sexual glands producing germinal cells. These are the testicles in the male and the ovaries in the female, collectively known as the gonads.

2. Ducts which transport these cells and render fertilization possible. These are, in the male, the vasa efferentia, the epididymis, the seminal duct or vas deferens, the ejaculatory duct and the urethra; and in the female, the oviduct or Fallopian tube, which carries the ovum from the ovary to the uterus or womb.

3. Organs of copulation, through which the semen reaches the ovum for the purpose of fertilization. These are, in the male, the penis, and in the female, the vagina. The uterus or womb retains the fertilized ovum until the new individual is sufficiently developed to be born.

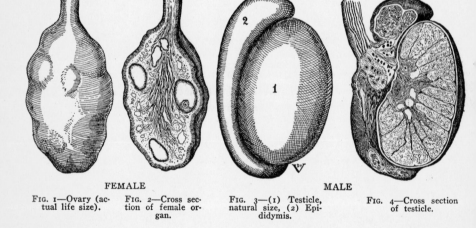

FEMALE　　　　　　　　　　　MALE

Fig. 1—Ovary (actual life size).　　Fig. 2—Cross section of female organ.　　Fig. 3—(1) Testicle, natural size, (2) Epididymis.　　Fig. 4—Cross section of testicle.

In the following pages all these organs will be described in detail, with an explanation of their precise functions, first separately in the male and the female, with the sexual apparatus in a state of rest, then in conjunction with the processes taking place.

At this stage, in order to impress upon the reader the analogy between the male and female sexual apparatus, we give comparative illustrations of the ovary and the testicle, showing an ovary in its natural size; a longitudinal section of an ovary; a testicle and epididymis in their natural size; a longitudinal section of a testicle and epididymis. It will be noted that, in accordance with their corresponding functions, the ovary and testicle are approximately of the same shape and size. The sections illustrating the internal structure of these organs will be explained later.

CHAPTER 2

THE MASCULINE GENITAL ORGANS

THE masculine genital organs are as follows:
1. Testicles or germinal glands;
2. Seminal ducts;
3. Penis.

The testicles are the most important organs of the masculine generative apparatus. They are a pair of oval-shaped glands which hang suspended in the scrotal sac by the spermatic cord. The scrotal sac, or scrotum, is a cutaneous bag consisting of several layers divided by a connective tissue into two compartments, each of which contains a testicle. The spermatic cord is the name given to the *vas deferens* and all the structures associated with it (blood vessels, lymphatic vessels and nerves).

The testicle is approximately 1½ inches long and about ¾ to 1¼ inches thick, its weight varying between ½ and 1 ounce. The left testicle may be slightly larger than the right and is suspended somewhat lower than the latter. Each testicle consists of a large number (about 300) of infinitely small convoluted tubules with blind origins, in which spermatozoa or sperms are produced. These tubules are the so-called seminiferous tubes, which form a network of considerable length; for the two testicles this length is more than 4900 feet. The spermatozoa or sperms, the principal elements of the semen, are produced in this intricate network of canals at a colossal rate, so that a single emission of normal semen contains anything from 400 to 500 million spermatozoa!

Thus the testicles perform the important function of producing the generative cells by means of which man is able to perpetuate his species with all its peculiar characteristics.

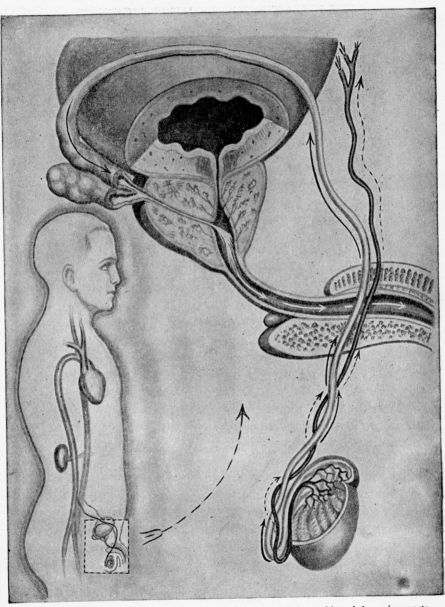

FIG. 5—Drawing of male sexual apparatus. The insert shows relative position of the various parts outside and inside the body.

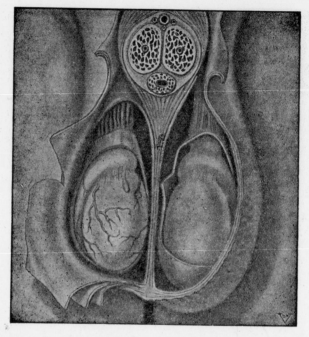

FIG. 6—The testicle and its suspensions.

At top of illustration a cross-section of penis can be seen.

The testicles and epididymis hang suspended from the spermatic cord. and are separated from each other by a partition. Several layers forming a covering envelop these organs. The cutaneous layer is called scrotum.

The product of the testicle, the spermatozoon, is a highly specialized cell that differs very considerably from all the other cells of the human organism. It is composed of an egg-shaped head, an intermediate segment, and a long tail, called the flagellum. The spermatozoon is extremely motile and can, by means of the flagellum, move forward with great rapidity in the seminal fluid or in the mucus of the vagina or the uterus. In addition, the spermatozoon is capable of propelling itself, as though consciously, in a direction favorable to itself. If, for example, we observe a number of live spermatozoa under the microscope with an infinitesimal piece of mucous membrane each from the vagina and the uterus, we shall find that the spermatozoa will immediately move in the direction of

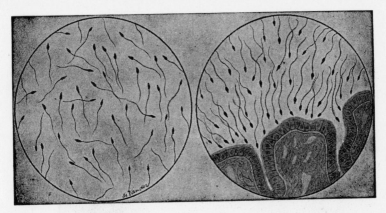

FIG. 7—Live Spermatozoa.   FIG. 8—How sperm are attracted by the uterus.

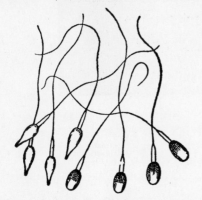

FIG. 9—Spermatozoa enlarged 1000 times.   FIG. 10—Semen and its elements.

the latter, and away from the former. The reason is that the vagina secretes an acid substance (lactic acid, and acid of any kind is injurious to the spermatozoa.

The spermatozoon, whose union with the ovum constitutes fertilization, appears to be seeking the female cell. When it succeeds in reaching the ovum, which is considerably larger than itself, the spermatozoon penetrates the ovum with its head. This attack is only carried out by the most vigorous of the spermatozoa, which engage in a regular war with each other in their efforts to reach their goal. Finally, a single spermatozoon, the strongest of the strong, wins its way to the female cell.

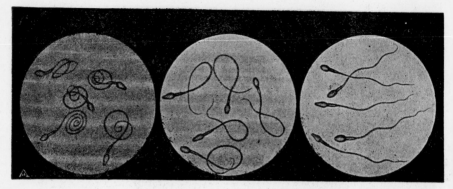

Male sperm under various conditions.

FIG. 11—Spermatozoa swimming in mucus.   FIG. 12 — Spermatozoa damaged by irrigation and distilled water.   FIG. 13 — Spermatozoa completely paralyzed by irrigation with diluted vinegar.

In this microscopic world the male element is far more active than the female, corresponding respectively to the active and passive roles played by the man and the woman in the course of physical union. The spermatozoon propels itself towards and, so to speak, fights for the opportunity to enter the ovum, while the latter is passive and appears to be condemned to immobility. Nevertheless, the ovum may be said to possess a certain selective capacity, for upon being attacked by the "pretenders" it forms an external zone facilitating ingress, perhaps to the most vigorous spermatozoon. Once the spermatozoon has penetrated the ovum this cellular membrane becomes closed to all other spermatozoa. Normally, only a single spermatozoon succeeds in penetrating the ovum.

When the spermatozoon penetrates the ovum it leaves its flagellum or tail outside, which confirms the fact that the actual life-germ is the head of the male cell, while the flagellum only serves to propel it towards the ovum, and decays once it has achieved its object.

The exact process by which the spermatozoa reach the ovum, how they live, fight and perish, is described in detail in Chapter 6.

This capacity of the male cell to go in search of and propel itself towards the ovum in order to fertilize it, distinguishes it from all

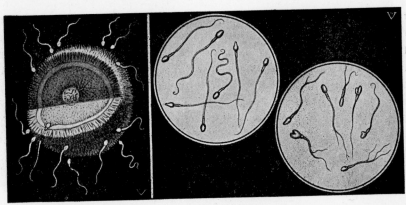

FIG. 14—Normal spermatozoa   FIG. 15—Abnormal spermatozoa.
Sectioned ovum showing head of fertilizing spermatozoon with detached flagellum.

others of the human organism. An interesting scientific achievement is the discovery that each spermatozoon contains chromosomes, twenty-four in number, by which the characteristics not only of the parents and grandparents but also of far more distant ancestors are transmitted to the new being. It is assumed that the chromosomes themselves have sub-divisions corresponding to the various hereditary intellectual, moral and emotional qualities, such as musical, mathematical or other talents. We shall not enter here into details on this subject, but may deal in a later work with the latest discoveries concerning the laws governing the transmission of various characteristics, good and bad, from ancestors to descendants.

To return to the spermatozoa, we have seen that a single spermatozoon suffices to fertilize a woman. That fact alone is nothing less than miraculous, since, as we have already mentioned, a single emission may contain anything from 400 to 500 million spermatozoa. Naturally, this number varies not only according to the individual but also in each sexual act. After days or weeks of abstemiousness the number of fertilizing cells is higher, while if the sexual act is repeated at frequent intervals, there is a corresponding reduction. Even then, however, the number of living cells is counted in tens of millions, and the process of fecundation remains one of the great miracles of nature.

Another miracle is the fact that a comparatively small gland like the testis should produce such a colossal number of spermatozoa per day. How this is accomplished may be gathered from the illustrations which show a longitudinal section of the testis and the epididymis with the countless convoluted tubules, already referred to above, forming a vast and intricate network of a total length, within a space of about 1½ inches, of nearly a mile for both testicles. These tubules unite to form a set of larger ones, the so-called *vasa efferentia* —because they lead the secretions *out* of the testis—while these larger tubules unite to form the epididymis, which will be explained below.

The spermatozoa are produced in these infinitesimally small tubules. Each inch of seminiferous tubule manufactures hundreds of germ cells—and the total length of the network of tubules amounts to over 5200 feet! And the "laboratory" in which this colossal work goes on night and day only weighs a few ounces!

What is the actual process by which the spermatozoa are produced? It would serve no useful purpose to go into that question in detail, and we need only know that there are special cells, which we will call mother cells, in the walls of the seminiferous tubules, which cells incessantly divide and multiply, finally producing spermatozoa. The mature spermatozoon detaches itself from the wall of the tubule and is gradually transported through the interminable convolutions of the tubules themselves, until it reaches—by a route which we will describe in detail in the following pages—the spermatic duct and its globus, from which it is expelled during the sexual act.

That is the function of the testicle as far as its exocrine activity is concerned; that is to say, the production of spermatozoa. The reader may be surprised to note that the testicle possesses a certain creative faculty, not, indeed, in the sense that it creates something from nothing, which would be impossible, but in the sense that it produces a superior thing out of inferior materials, in that it transforms simple cells into spermatozoa, into cells of differentiated structure. In this respect the testicle may be compared with the brain, which does not create in the literal sense of the term, but merely transforms existing ideas and concepts into higher, more original ideas and concepts. Artistic, scientific or mystic inspiration only means that the human brain acts as a sort of laboratory, in which psychical images and impressions are transformed and transmitted to the organic world.

Apart, however, from this analogy between the brain and the germinal glands, there is a close connection between the two, in that the creative capacity of the brain may be to some extent dependent on the proper functioning of the testes. We have already mentioned that physical injury to the testes may lead to some impairment of the characteristically masculine attributes of the male. In the same manner, if there is deficient endocrine activity in the testes, that is to say, if it produces and conveys to the blood its internal secretions in insufficient quantities, the psychical faculties of the individual so affected suffer accordingly, and many cases of loss of nervous energy and mental abnormality have been attributable to this cause.

This subject will be dealt with in greater detail in the following chapters. One point that we wish to mention at this stage is the contention of a great many authors that early development of the sexual instinct goes hand in hand with intellectual development. That is true in most cases, but we must be careful to distinguish between this entirely normal condition and more sexual surexcitation which in children frequently leads to the practice of masturbation.

We now have at least a rudimentary knowledge of the structure of the testicles and their functions in producing spermatozoa. But spermatazoa, while they are obviously the most important part of the seminal fluid, or semen, are not the whole of it. The seminal fluid is composed of a number of secretions with which the spermatozoa combines in the course of its journey from the testes, and through various other organs, to the penis, from which it is then ejaculated. In the course of the following description of this route we will see how the combination of the various secretions to seminal fluid occurs.

From the testicle to the urinary meatus or passage, the seminal duct may be regarded as a single duct, though its various parts are known by different names. The semen emerging from the testicle gradually passes into the bunch of tubules into which the network of tubules in the testicle unites, then into the epididymis. This is a long convoluted tube behind the testis, whose great length enables it to act as a reservoir for the spermatozoa. The *vas deferens* is a continuation of the epididymis. It is about eighteen inches long and runs upwards from the testis within the scrotum to pierce the abdominal wall. The *vas deferens*, together with the arteries, veins, lymphatic vessels and nerves associated with it, constitutes the spermatic cord.

The *vas deferens* transports the spermatozoa by contracting and relaxing. Before it penetrates the prostate gland—a gland at the neck of the urinary bladder—it widens into a pouch, or globus, in which part of the semen is retained as though in a reservoir. Near this pouch is another, called the seminal vesicle, which is considered by many as being another reservoir for the spermatozoa. The duct of the seminal vesicle unites with the *vas deferens* to form the ejaculatory duct, which penetrates into the urethra—the canal by which urine is discharged from the bladder—and perforates the prostate. Thus there is a double duct, one for each testicle, but the urethra is only a single canal, though it serves a double purpose— to discharge urine from the bladder, and also to expel the semen during copulation.

The seminal vesicles are symmetrical bodies located at the posterior base of the bladder. The seminal vesicles produce a fluid whose precise function is not known, apart from the fact that it increases the volume of the semen (spermatozoa) with which it mixes. Indeed, the greater part of the seminal fluid ejaculated during copulation consists of the secretion of the seminal vesicles. On the other hand, diseased seminal vesicles may be the cause of abnormal loss of semen (spermatorrhoea), as well as of sexual impotence accompanied by premature ejaculation.

The prostate is a musculo-glandular organ situated at the base of the bladder. It is traversed from top to bottom by the urethra,

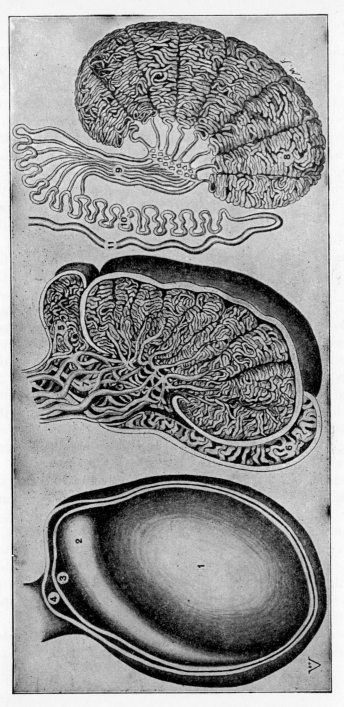

Showing how the sperm are reproduced and how the semen is carried out.

Fɪɢ. 16—(1) Testicle, (2) Epididymis, (3 and 4) their fibrous coverings.

Fɪɢ. 17—Section of the testicle and epididymis showing the numerous seminiferous tubules.

Fɪɢ. 18—Schematic illustration showing the tubules of the testicle in which the spermatozoa are produced. The various ducts (9, 10 and 11) through which semen is carried out.

this portion of which is called the prostatic urethra; the real part of the prostate is pierced by the ejaculatory ducts. It is generally accepted that the voluptuous sensation accompanying the emission of semen is localized in the prostatic urethra.

The prostate secretes a fluid which is a component of the seminal fluid. The secretion is called prostatic fluid. It flows in tiny drops into the prostatic urethra at the end of the sexual act, that is to say, during the orgasm, through a series of minute tubes, which are the apertures of countless glandular elements.

In this connection it should be noted that the spermatozoa do not possess the great motility mentioned above immediately upon emerging from the testicles; they only acquire this motility upon coming into contact with the prostatic fluid. Perhaps nature has arranged it so, in order to prevent the spermatozoa from moving or escaping prematurely or at an unsuitable time; that is to say, before they are propelled in the semen towards the vault of the vagina—the part that is in communication with the uterus—for the purpose of procreation.

It is the prostatic fluid that lends to the seminal fluid its characteristic odor.

As already stated, the seminal fluid is a mixture composed of spermatozoa and the secretions of various portions of the seminal ducts, i.e., the seminal vesicles, the prostate, the urethra, and of Cowper's gland, a tiny organ situated near the urethral bulb. All these secretions unite to form the seminal fluid, or semen.

The mechanism of ejaculation is rather complicated. At the present stage it will be sufficient to know that at the moment when sensual excitement, accompanied by a voluptuous sensation, reaches a certain intensity, an increasing automatism arises, so that the processes taking place from that point are entirely independent of volition. The glands, as well as the seminal ducts, contract and propel the fluids towards the prostatic urethra. The urethra instantly starts to perform a series of rhythmic contractions expelling the semen. During the entire process the sphincter of the bladder—the muscle that surrounds its lower orifice—is tightly closed. It is a well-known fact that at a certain degree of sexual excitement, long before orgasm and ejaculation occur, it is difficult if not impossible to pass urine.

CHAPTER 3

THE PENIS AND ERECTION

THE genital organs are not equally well developed throughout the animal world. In mammals the penis is fully developed, and in the majority of wild beasts, as in the case of bears, the member has a bony part. As regards humans, certain primitive tribes are said to still preserve traces of a bone in the form of a cartilaginous part, evidently intended by nature to endow the penis with greater firmness and facilitate its introduction into the vagina.

Rigidity of the penis is indispensable for perfect sexual union and most favorable to fecundation, since the process depends on the entry of the semen into the womb, and this is accomplished the more easily the deeper the seminal fluid is injected into the vagina.

Fecundation, if not impossible, is at all events very difficult if the semen is deposited on or in the external genital organs and not in the vagina itself. In any case, normal fecundation demands rigidity of the penis, i.e., erection. The friction of an erect penis against the walls of the vagina and the clitoris, excites the feminine genital

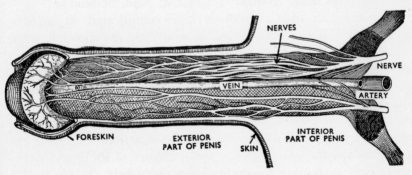

FIG. 19—Anatomy of penis.

47

apparatus, provoking rhythmic movements of the vulva, the vagina and the uterus, which facilitate the ingress of the semen into the uterus.

The normal penis consists of a central portion, which is long and thin, an anterior part which is known as the glans, and a posterior part deeply embedded in the abdomen which is called the root. The latter contains the urethral bulb and Cowper's gland. The glans is more or less covered by a cutaneous fold, known as the prepuce or foreskin, which is richly supplied with terminal nerves, and is therefore highly sensitive. Still greater, however, is the tactile sensitiveness of the fold which connects the glans with the foreskin. The glans has a close network of peripheral nerves which, together with those of the foreskin and the connecting fold, convey to the brain libidinous sensations. Between the prepuce and the glans there is a space in which secretions and residues of an objectionable odor may accumulate. The size of the prepuce varies according to the individual. Sometimes it is so large that it covers the glans entirely, while at others it covers it only incompletely or hardly at all.

The orifice of the prepuce is in some individuals so small that the glans is constantly imprisoned by it. When the penis is in the erect state, the prepuce cannot slip down the glans, or if it does so, with some difficulty, there is a danger that it may strangulate the penis. The undue tightness of the prepuce is called *phimosis*, which can be cured by a minor operations known as circumcision. This consists in removing part of the foreskin.

The age-old practice of circumcision among Jews and Moslems probably originated from consideration of sexual hygiene.

The immediate consequence of circumcision is to deprive the glans penis of its protective covering. The highly senstive terminal nerves of the glans gradually lose some of their sensitiveness, so that excitation of the glans may become more difficult. That is why, in the case of a circumcised man, coitus lasts longer, as orgasm is more difficult to attain. In recent years, circumcision has been widely practiced even among gentiles for health reasons. Uncircumcised men must, of course, be extremely careful to keep the part between the glans and the foreskin clean.

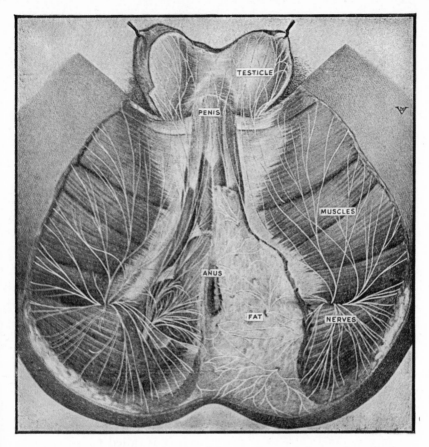

Fig. C-3—Picture of nerves network in man's zone of sexual excitation. The same terminal nerves transmit the impressions of the genital organs and those of the anus. This explains why the anus is considered as a secondary erogenous zone.

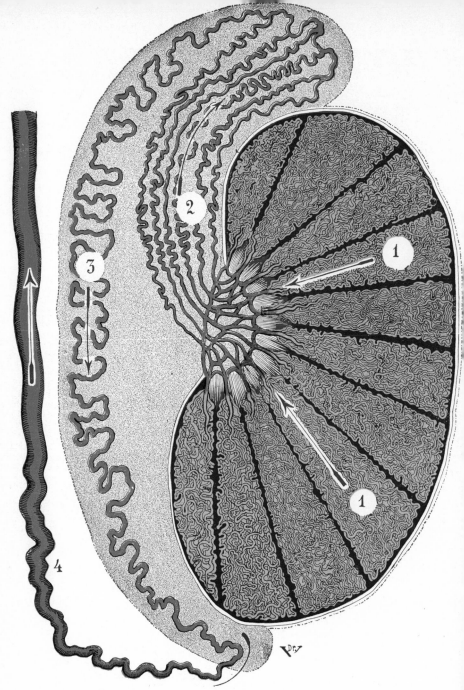

FIG. C-4—Larger than life-size picture of testicle, showing where the
male sperm is formed. The testicle, which is only about 1½ inches
long, contains no less than 400 yards of seminiferous tubules (1),
in which spermatozoa are formed. The latter, before they are expelled
into vagina, must pass through tubes of the epididymis (2 and 3) and
vas deferens (4).

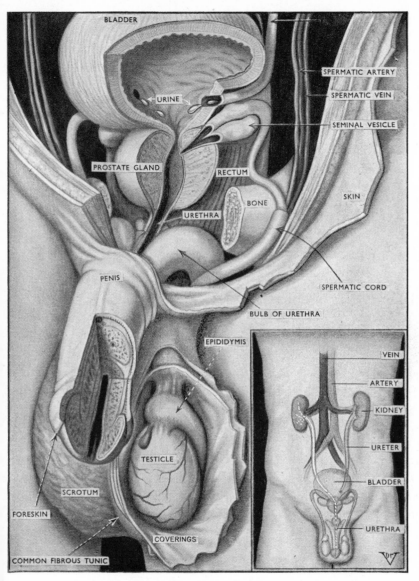

Fig. C-5—Man's sexual organs pictured simultaneously with urinary organs. Penis and its coverings are cross-sectioned to show interiors. Inset picture explains urinary course.

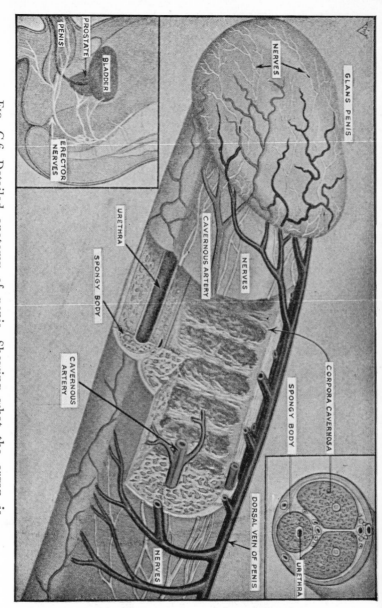

Fig. C-6—Detailed anatomy of penis. Showing what the organ is composed of, also its nerves network.

Inset pictures of cross-section of penis and the position of genital organs inside man's body.

GLANS PENIS

NERVES

URETHRA

SPONGY BODY

CAVERNOUS ARTERY

NERVES

CAVERNOUS ARTERY

CORPORA CAVERNOSA

SPONGY BODY

DORSAL VEIN OF PENIS

NERVES

URETHRA

PENIS

PROSTATE

BLADDER

ERECTOR NERVES

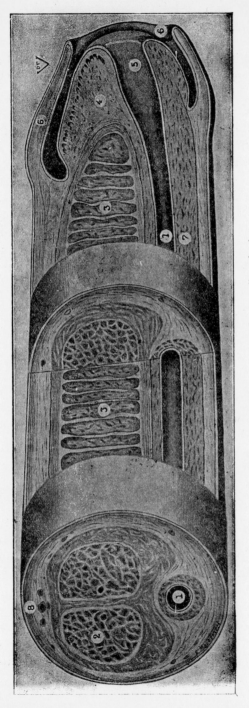

Fig. 20—Internal anatomy of penis; three dimensional.

(1) Urethra; (2) Corpora cavernosa; (3) Same in longitudinal section; (4) Glans penis; (5) Urinary meatus; (6) Foreskin; (7) Spongy body of urethra; (8) Dorsal arteries and veins of penis.

The penis is longitudinally pierced by the urethra, which is surrounded by a spongy body composed of erectile tissue. Above the urethra, also longitudinally, there are two cavernous bodies. It is through these and the erectile tissue mentioned above that the penis acquires volume and rigidity at times of sexual excitement.

We will now deal with the complicated mechanism of erection, which, as we know, is an indispensable condition of normal sexual intercourse.

The cavernous bodies of the penis, as well as the urethral spongy body, consists of highly resistant tissue forming a larger number of caverns known as areolae. When the penis is in a state of repose, i.e., flaccid, the areolae contain only a very small quantity of blood. When, however, the individual is sexually excited, the arteries and veins become flooded with blood, which they carry to the areolae. Thus the latter are filled through a nervous mechanism which governs all these vessels, which also prevents the blood from escaping before the congestion of the corpora cavernosa or cavernous bodies has produced erection in the penis. This condition of the penis prevails throughout the duration of the sexual excitement, after which the capacity of the vessels diminishes, the caverns empty, and the penis reverts to its normal state of flaccidity.

The illustration shows the penis in erection. It will be seen that the central portion looks like a three-barrelled gun, the two cavernous bodies and the urethral spongy body representing the three barrels. Part of the penis is shown in longitudinal section, and part in cross section. The former illustrates the manner in which the glans is joined to the penis and also that, in the erect state, this part is also congested with blood. The cross section illustrates the same in regard to the central portion. The arteries conveying the blood, and the veins receiving them, are clearly shown under the cutaneous covering of the penis. The smaller drawing in the bottom left-hand corner shows the part of the penis situated in the abdomen.

The anatomical composition shows, partly in longitudinal section, the connection that exists between all the male sexual glands as a result of the conjunction of the sexual ducts. The root of the penis in the abdomen, with the urethral bulb, is clearly indicated. The

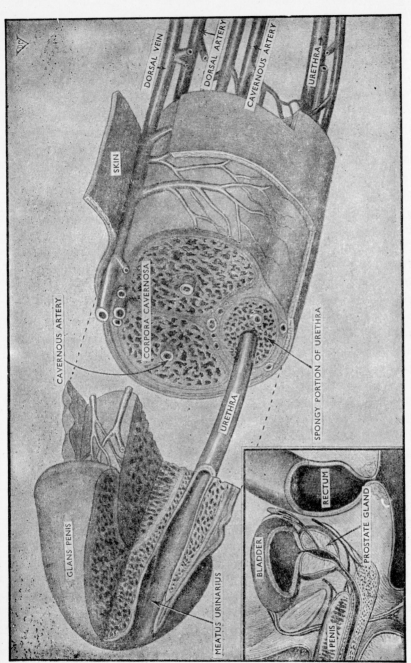

FIG. 21—Anatomy of male member in the erect state.

The areoles of the cavernous bodies and the spongy body of the urethra are full of blood. The arteries conveying blood to the penis, and the veins that collect it, are clearly shown. The smaller illustration shows the part of penis which is in the abdomen.

drawing in the top left-hand corner shows the position of all these organs in the body. It will be noted that a considerable portion of the penis is situated within the abdomen.

A normal erection occurs under the influence of a number of factors. It may take place when the sexual glands are charged and this particularly refers to the internal secretion of the testicles. The testicles, as already mentioned, produce a fluid, known as hormones, which they convey direct to the blood stream. When this product reaches the brain, the brain becomes eroticized, so to speak; that is to say, the action of the hormones induces in the brain sexual desire and also stimulates the centers of recollection in which are stored memories of sexual acts previously dreamt of, desired or actually experienced. When the brain is crowded with erotic images, the excitement is transmitted through the medulla—the pith of the spinal cord—and the nerves. The vertebral column contains for this purpose a center known as Budge's center, whose stimulation produces automatic erections. This center has a connection with the penis and the corpora cavernosa.

In order to make this process quite clear to the reader, we give two examples representing all its stages.

In the case which we are now going to consider the excitation does not originate in the testicles, but in the brain. This is called psychical sexual excitation, to which (by reason of impeded mechanism) psychical sexual impotence corresponds.

There are many external causes which may arouse sexual desire in the brain. These causes may be connected with sight, smell, hearing and the other senses, or with the memory. Sight of the loved person or of any other attractive woman, the sound of erotic music or any other sounds that recall previous impressions, the perfume or odor of the feminine body, are some of the causes that may produce the same effect. These and a thousand other factors may set the sexual impulse aflame without the immediate intervention of the testicular glands. The eroticization of the brain is transformed into sexual excitement which, when communicated to the reproductive organs, induces erection.

Thus erection may be induced either by the action of the testes

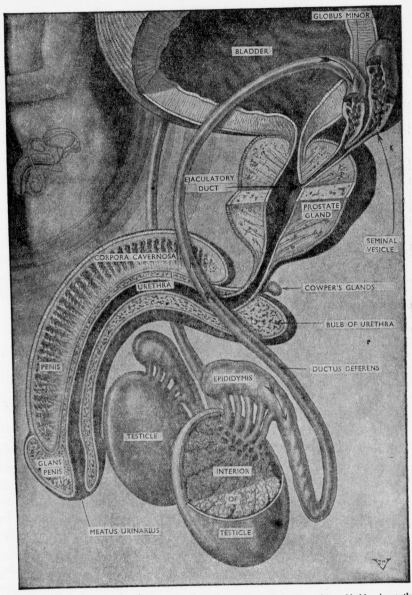

FIG. 22—Showing the correlation of all the sexual glands of man. The urinary bladder is partly sectioned, in order to show its interior.

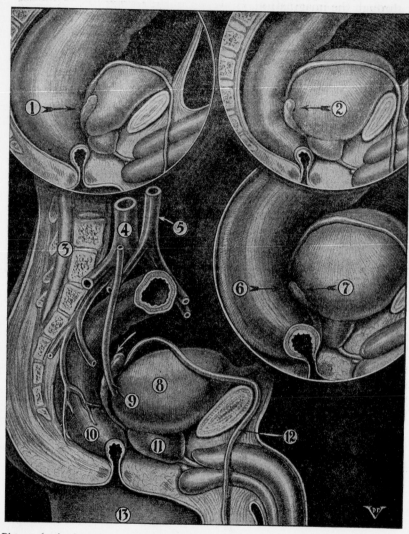

Pictures showing how erection is produced by pressure of various organs on the normal apparatus.

FIG. 23 (lower left)—Normal state of rectum (10) and prostate (11).
FIG. 24 (upper left)—Pressure of full rectum (1).
FIG. 25 (upper right)—Pressure of full bladder (2).
FIG. 26 (lower right)—Pressure of both (6) and (7).

or through the imagination. However, in the former case the genesic effect is immediate and it might be said that the testes are sufficient unto themselves, whereas if the process starts in the brain erection can only result if the sexual glands are functioning normally.

At the same time, there are other factors which may produce an erection, such as the repletion of the urinary bladder or the intestine (intestinal erection).

There are certain pathological conditions in this connection. When the penis is in a state of repose, the quantity of blood in the areolae, or caverns, is infinitesimal. Whereas, when the penis is in a state of erection, the areolae of the corpora cavernosa, as well as of the urethral spongy body, are congested with blood.

Morning erections, i.e., the erections that men frequently have upon waking, are of no erotic significance. They are produced by the pressure of a full bladder and/or rectum on the prostate, so that these erections are purely mechanical. Naturally, however, such erections, by an association of ideas, may, and frequently do, lead to genuine erections.

CHAPTER 4

THE FEMALE GENITAL ORGANS

IN describing the male generative apparatus we classified the component organs in the following groups:
1. Testicles or germinal glands;
2. Seminal ducts;
3. Penis, or organ of copulation.

Similarly, in the case of the female genital organs we find it more logical to base our description on a functional classification, instead of grouping the organs as external and internal. Accordingly we will deal with:
1. The generative organs or ovaries;
2. The ducts which transport the ovum; that is to say, the Fallopian tubes;
3. The organs of copulation, i.e., the vagina, vulva, etc., and lastly, the uterus or womb whose principal function is to accommodate and nourish the fertilized ovum until the new being is completely developed, i.e., during the period of pregnancy.

In this way the analogy and correspondence between the male and female generative apparatus will be completely demonstrated. Indeed, there is a stage in the development of the embryo when the two sexes resemble each other so closely that it is impossible to distinguish between them, and even fully developed men and women retain vestiges of the common origin of their sexual apparatus. Hence parallelism in describing the male and female organs is the logical procedure.

As the testicles in the male, so the ovaries in the female are the most important organs of the generative apparatus, and they therefore deserve careful study. Without a precise understanding of the

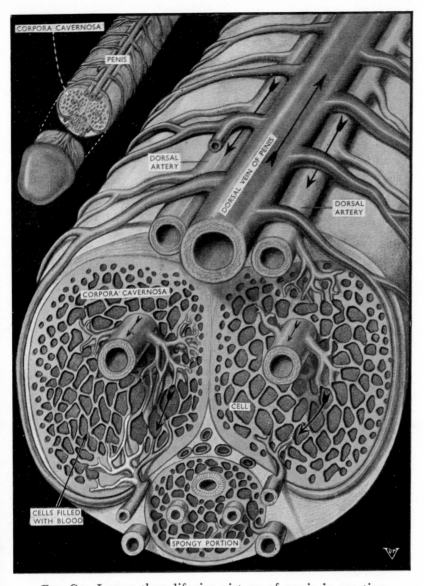

FIG. C-7—Larger than life-size picture of penis in erection.
Cross-section showing corpora cavernosa and spongy body congested
with blood.

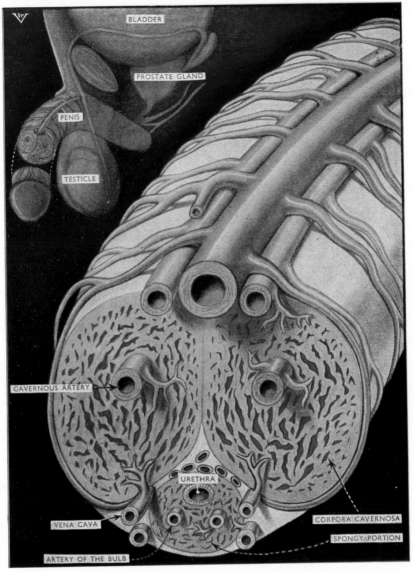

Labels in image:
BLADDER
PROSTATE GLAND
PENIS
TESTICLE
CAVERNOUS ARTERY
URETHRA
VENA CAVA
CORPORA CAVERNOSA
SPONGY PORTION
ARTERY OF THE BULB

FIG. C-8—Larger than life-size picture of penis at rest.
Cross-section showing corpora cavernosa and spongy body in the flaccid
state, also the arteries that supply blood to penis.

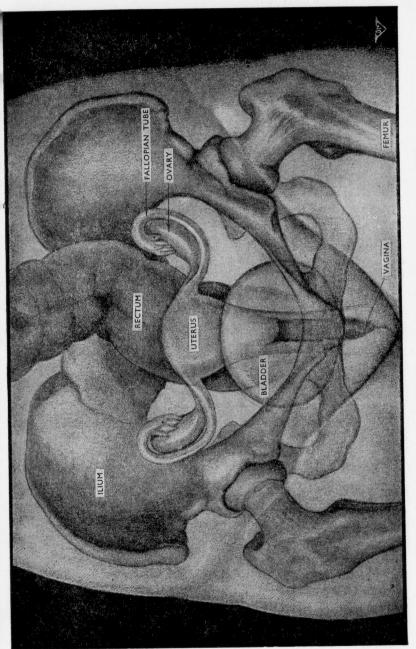

FALLOPIAN TUBE

OVARY

FEMUR

RECTUM

VAGINA

UTERUS

BLADDER

ILIUM

Fig. 27—How you would see the pelvic organs if woman's body were transparent.

function of the ovaries it is impossible to obtain a clear idea of the processes of fecundation, pregnancy, menstruation, etc.

The ovaries, of which there are two, are the female germinal glands. They are situated on both sides of the uterus, and are approximately almond-shaped. The length of an ovary is about 1½ inches.

As a result of scientific investigation, it has been found that each ovary contains about 30,000 ova.

The ovum is a globular cell which can almost be discerned with the naked eye. It is therefore larger than a spermatozoon, which can only be seen with the aid of a microscope.

Each ovum is enclosed in a tiny bladder known as the Graafian follicle, which is filled with fluid. The follicles containing the ova are situated on the outer layer of the ovary. The ovum, as it matures, causes the outer wall of the ovary to bulge.

Every four weeks, or, more generally, a few days earlier or later, an ovum matures. This introduces a considerable change in the internal genital organs of the woman. Nature prepares the organism for fecundation, which demands different processes from those involved in the maturing of the ovum.

As soon as the ovum is mature, contractions arise in the ovary, which cause the follicle enveloping the ovum (known after its discoverer as the Graafian follicle) to burst and shed its contents, together with the ovum, into the abdomen. At this stage the ovum has no envelope of any kind (somewhat like a hen's egg without its shell) and would soon perish, but Nature has ordained that another organ should produce an albuminous substance to nourish and protect it.

Before we proceed to describe the subsequent journey of the ovum, we must mention that the ova are not motile like spermatozoa.

From the abdomen the ovum is picked up by the funnel-shaped, fringed end of the oviduct, which is from 4 to 6 inches long. The funnel looks somewhat like a carnation. The fringes usually lie flaccidly over the entrance of the funnel-shaped entrance of the oviduct, closing it. The funnel only opens when the ovum has been shed, when it bounds in like a ball for which a pair of hands are

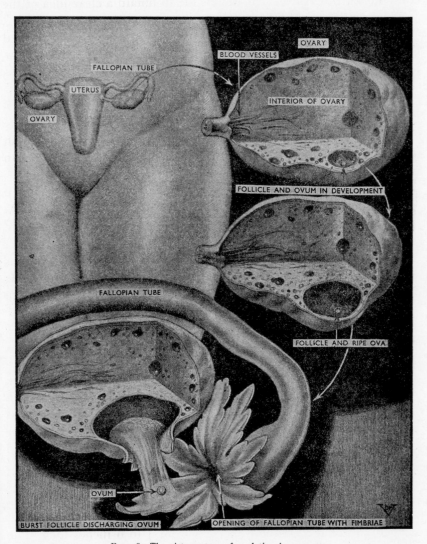

FIG. 28—The picture story of ovulation in woman.
A transparent female figure showing through the uterus, ovaries, fallopian tube. The follicle and ovum in development. The follicle and ripe ova. Burst follicles discharging ova, etc.

waiting. Thus the ovum usually only remains in the abdomen for a fraction of a second, as long as it takes for it to bounce from the burst follicle into the funnel of the oviduct.

Fertilization usually takes place in the oviduct, where the spermatozoa are already waiting. But regardless of whether it does or does not become fertilized, the ovum sets out on a journey lasting approximately eight days in the direction of the uterus.

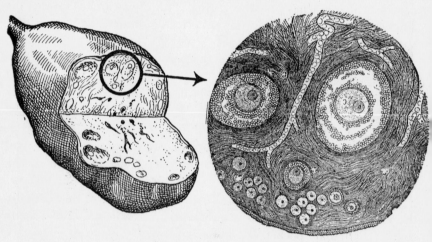

FIG. 29—Section of ovary.   FIG. 30—Section of ovary showing many unripe and two completely mature ova.

However, it may sometimes happen that the fertilized ovum is for some reason detained on this journey. In that case the ovum digs itself in in the mucous membrane of the oviduct, and the result, very dangerous to the health of the woman concerned, is extrauteral or ectopic pregnancy. The ovum, as it develops into an embryo, bursts the oviduct, with possible fatal consequences, due to hemorrhage, which can only be prevented by timely operative intervention.

The wall of the oviduct consists of three layers. First, there is a delicate mucous membrane studded with fine "feelers," which give the interior of the oviduct the appearance of velvet under the microscope. Under this there is a coarse muscular tissue, and finally a thin external envelope, which is connected with the pelvic membrane.

The two oviducts debouch into the uterus. The latter, a pear-shaped organ, is situated above the vagina. In front of the uterus is the urinary bladder, below it the rectum. In its normal position the uterus is slightly inclined forward.

We distinguish three different parts in the uterus, the upper part into which the oviducts open, the middle, and finally the neck or cervix, which reaches into the vagina. The upper arched part is the thickest and widest, the lower, spherically rounded downwards, is the narrowest.

In the center of lower end of the cervix, the part of the uterus reaching into the vagina, there is a small orifice, the so-called external mouth of the uterus. This has an anterior and posterior lip, both of which are smooth and lie close together in a virgin. During a menstruation these uteral lips part slightly, and there is then a somewhat larger circular orifice. In women who have had a child there are scarred, corrugated folds along the edge of the mouth of the uterus.

The walls of the uterus usually lie close together, so that actually there is no uterine cavity. It is only when the walls are drawn apart that a triangular, pocket-like space is formed.

The mucous membrane lining of the uterus secretes a slimy substance, which flows towards the mouth of the uterus, closing it up like a stopper. Most of this "stopper" is made up of a jelly-like clear mucous material excreted from the glands of the lining of the canal through the cervix. This canal extends from the external mouth to the upper uterine cavity. The mucous stopper, or plug, actually is constantly oozing from the external mouth. Its consistency varies greatly over the menstrual cycle. Following menstruation it is quite sticky, but very scant. About the time of ovulation it is relatively copious, crystal clear, and more watery but quite cohesive; and it is at this stage that this so-called endocervical mucus is in the most ideal state for spermatozoa to swim through on their way toward the ovum. Toward the end or the cycle the plug becomes more thickened, tenacious and opaque.

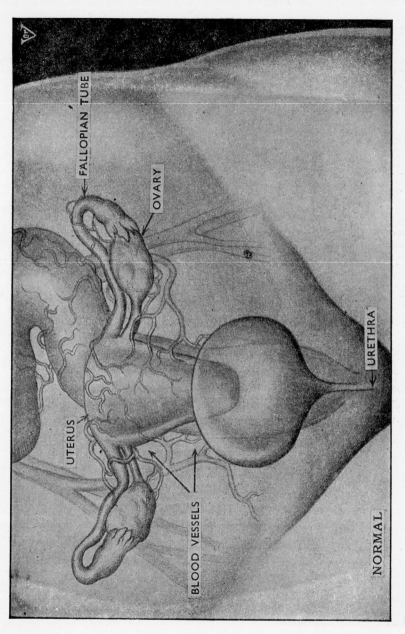

FIG. 31—Transparent female body, showing position of the pelvic organs.

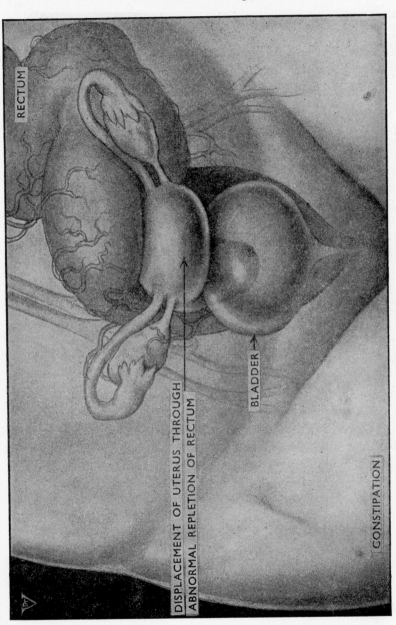

Fig. 32—How constipation affects female sex apparatus.

Infection and inflammation within the cervical canal, where the mucus is produced, may alter the character of the mucus so as to make it unfavorable to the spermatozoa by slowing their progress and causing many of them to die. This infection, called chronic cervicitis, which may follow acute infection such as gonorrhea, or that of an abortion, or laceration at childbirth, or sometimes just poor feminine hygiene, is considered nowadays by many authorities to be a common cause of infertility, or the inability to become pregnant. In other words, such a chronic infection may be a mechanical barrier to fertilization.

Under the mucous membrane from whose secretion the slimy substance is formed, there is a thick muscular layer, whose fibers are extremely elastic, and that is why the uterus can distend during pregnancy to several times its normal size.

The outer last layer of the uterus is a thin, smooth membrane which, proceeding from the rectum, continues forward into the bladder. From this membrane issue the ligaments by which the uterus, which lies rather loosely in the abdomen, is kept in position. If these ligaments loosen, the uterus may easily become displaced or bent. If, under conditions, the uterus bends backwards, it presses on the rectum, and constipation results. If in this position it comes into contact with the nerves of the pelvic bone, the consequence is backache, of which women frequently complain. Very frequently, the contrary process occurs. Owing to severe constipation the rectum becomes enlarged, exercises constant pressure on the uterus, and thereby loosens the ligaments, so that the uterus tips forward.

With regard to the mutual action of the uterus and the urinary bladder on each other, this is a matter of considerable importance. Women are usually very careless in the matter of relieving the bladder, and very frequently retain the urine for several hours, until the bladder becomes quite full. The full bladder exercises increased pressure on the uterus, which leads to a loosening of the ligaments, and a consequent bending of the uterus. Parents are advised to train their daughters in early childhood to avoid this bad habit. If girls acquired the habit of relieving the bladder morning,

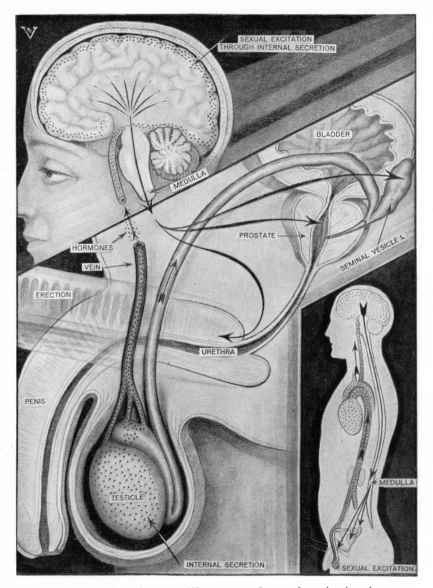

Fig. C-9—Two-color picture telling story of sexual excitation in man. Normally the testicle produces an internal secretion containing specific hormones which, through the bloodstream, travel to the brain and evoke erotic desires.

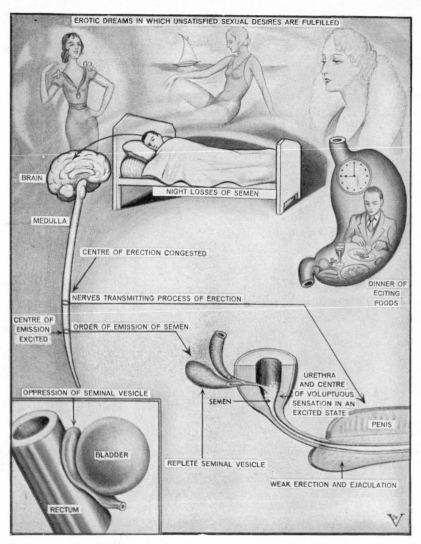

FIG. C-10—Why man has nocturnal losses of semen.

Schematic pictures illustrating the different causes.

noon and night, many genital and urinary complaints in later life would be avoided.

To revert to the ovum, we have seen that it has no motility. It is conveyed on its journey partly by the "feelers" with which the oviduct is lined, partly by the secretions of the oviduct which flow in the direction of the uterus, and partly by the rhythmic movements of the funnels in the direction of the uterus, which they perform during this period.

If the ovum is fertilized, it settles in the mucous membrane of the uterus. But if, within about eight to ten days after the bursting of the follicle, no fecundation takes place then the whole of the mucous membrane of the uterus, which had prepared for the arrival of a fertilized ovum, disintegrates and is discharged after a further six or eight days. This is called menstruation, with which process we deal in a separate chapter.

CHAPTER 5

FUNCTIONS OF THE VAGINA

THE vagina is the canal that connects the uterus with the external genital organs. At the posterior end the rounded neck of the uterus projects into the canal, like a stopper into a bottle. This circular space at the posterior end, into the center of which the external mouth of the uterus opens, is called the vaginal vault. The wall of the vagina, like the oviducts and the uterus, consists of three layers, the uppermost of which is lined with a mucous membrane. In the direction of the anterior opening of the vagina, this mucous membrane continues as the membrane of the nymphae or small lips, which, as an extension of the vagina, slightly project beyond its entrance. The mucous membrane of the vagina contains no mucous glands, and the canal of the vagina is made slippery by the secretions of the uterine glands.

The mucous membrane of the vagina, both on the anterior and posterior walls, has many folds, which, as in the case of the uterus, are necessary in order to enable the vagina to distend. In addition, there are on the membrane ridges forming a sort of friction apparatus, and serving to intensify the voluptuous sensation during intercourse. How elastic the vagina is may be gauged from the large quantity of gauze and cotton wool required to fill it. This enormous elasticity is, of course, manifested most clearly during child-birth.

The middle, muscular layer of the vagina is richly supplied with blood-vessels, which swell during sexual intercourse, causing erection, so to speak, of the vagina. These congested vessels make it possible for the walls of the vagina to fit on to the penis, or, so to speak, slightly grasp it, so that the sensitive terminal nerves of the penis are brought into close contact with the similar terminal nerves

66

of the vagina. At its entrance the vagina is not so elastic, and its diameter at this point is smaller than further up. It is assumed that Nature has designed the vagina in this way in order to prevent the semen injected into the vagina from flowing out.

The length of the vagina ranges between 2 to 6 inches, depending a great deal on the position of the uterus. If the uterus is situated low, then the vaginal canal is considerably shorter than if it is situated high. Cases of a too narrow vagina, which is alleged to render intercourse impossible, are frequently mentioned. But in such cases there are usually other obstacles than narrowness, since in view of the elasticity of the vagina, there is hardly an erect penis that cannot penetrate a normal vagina with comparative ease. However, although a congenitally too narrow vagina is improbable, this condition may be acquired, for instance, by such manipulations as corrosive douches to prevent conception. The vagina may thus become inflamed, and may be narrowed by scars after healing. Also, occasionally stenosis or atresia (shrinking and adhesions) may form after infections of the vagina incurred in childhood, though unknown at the time

The secretion of the mucous membrane of the vagina is a viscous white mucus containing acid. The white color is acquired from cells shed by the vagina. The secretion may frequently increase to a highly inconvenient flow known as white flux or leukorrhea.

The small orifice of the urethra, which is shorter and wider than in the case of the male, is a separate aperture above the entrance of the vagina. It is important to know this, as, remarkably enough, some laymen have regarded this orifice as the opening of the uterus, or even as the narrowed entrance of the vagina, particularly in virgins. In the latter case the error seemed to be confirmed by the fact that the vaginal canal in a virgin is closed by a membrane, known as the hymen.

Formerly it was thought, even in scientific circles, that the hymen is peculiar to humans. But today we know that a similar obstacle exists in nearly all female animals, but that it bursts shortly before sexual maturity is reached. This explains the object assigned by Nature to the hymen—it is probably designed to prevent sexual intercourse before sexual maturity. On the other hand, the remnants of the hymen, which persist even after defloration, may serve to prevent the seminal fluid from flowing out of the vagina.

The shape of the human hymen varies a great deal. Sometimes it is a small, crescent-shaped flap, leaving a similarly crescent-shaped orifice for the passage of the menstrual discharge. Or it may be a disc perforated like a sieve, or having only a single orifice in the center. In a great many cases it lies across the entrance of the vagina like a bridge, or it has the form of a flap with fringed edges. Usually the hymen is a thin membrane, but sometimes it may be up to ⅔ inch thick. In the latter case we are confronted with what is called a fleshy hymen, and operative intervention is necessary before the first intercourse.

The clitoris is situated at the point where the two small lips meet above the entrance of the vagina. It is usually about ¾ inch long, but only the tip, the so-called glans, projects, while the body of the clitoris is hidden. The word clitoris is of Greek origin, and means "key." The ancient anatomists mean to convey that the clitoris is the key to woman's sexuality.

The clitoris in some races, as in Negresses, is sometimes noted to be larger than in Caucasian women. This is not a constant finding, and may be associated with hypertrophy (enlargement) from excessive erotic self-manipulation (a form of female masturbation). In some female apes it is so long that it is difficult to distinguish them from males.

The clitoris serves to arouse voluptuous sensations in the woman, and is even more abundantly supplied with sensitive terminal nerves than the male glans. Also, like the penis, it has cavernous bodies which fill with blood when the adjacent mucous membrane is subjected to excitation. This causes the volume of the clitoris to increase to about one inch, and through this "erection" it comes into closer contact with the male member during the sexual act.

Between the vaginal canal and the small lips there is a pair of important glands, known as Bartholin's glands, whose function will be described further on. To the right and left of the small lips are the large lips (labia majora) which are formed by two raised folds of skin, which contain adipose tissue. Their average height is ¾

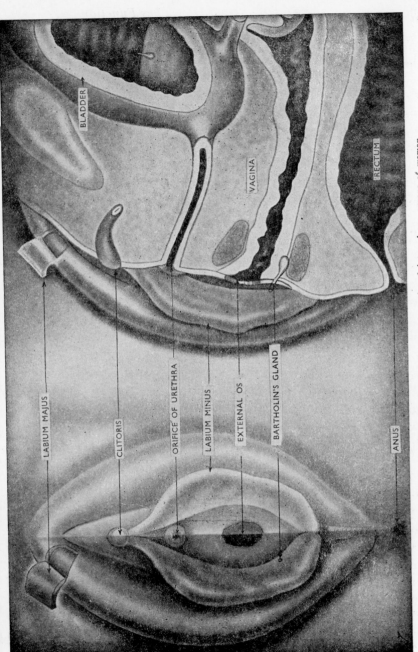

LABIUM MAJUS

CLITORIS

ORIFICE OF URETHRA

LABIUM MINUS

EXTERNAL OS

BARTHOLIN'S GLAND

ANUS

BLADDER

VAGINA

RECTUM

Fig. 33—External view.

Fig. 34—Internal view.

Stylized illustration showing connection between external and internal sex organs of woman.

inch. In virgins the large lips lie close together, in older women they are more and more parted, especially after childbirth.

In the upward direction the large lips merge into a triangular fatty mound, which is covered with hair. Graaf, the anatomist, who discovered the follicle named after him, was of the opinion that the object of this mound, which is called *mons veneris*, is to prevent the pubic bones of the partners from knocking against each other during sexual intercourse.

The functions of the genital organs described here during the sexual acts are as follows:

The organs that participate in the voluptuous sensation are the clitoris, the small lips, the "vault" of the vagina, and, interestingly enough, the orifice of the urethra. All these organs are supplied with cavernous bodies of different sizes. The best developed of these are the so-called *bulbi cavernosi* which are situated at the entrance of the vagina. These, and all the other organs referred to here, become congested with blood under sexual excitement, and become erected like the male member. As sexual excitement abates, the blood accumulated in these organs is drained back. This usually occurs after orgasm, when the return flow of the blood is a spontaneous process, though it takes longer than in the man after ejaculation. If, however, the woman fails to attain orgasm during the sexual act or during some other, similar sexual excitement, then the blood flows back from these organs very slowly, and this, if regularly repeated, may affect the health of the woman.

The contractions of certain muscles enter very importantly into the sexual act. There is, first of all, the muscular ring situated at the entrance of the vagina, and known as *constrictor cunni*. In some women this ring contracts during sexual excitement. It seizes the male member, so to speak, and draws it deep into the vagina. Then the ring relaxes and contracts again, and these rhythmic movements continue until the end of the sexual act, intensifying the voluptuous sensations of both the man and the woman. However, these muscular movements are rather rare in civilized woman, and the *constrictor cunni* appears to be in course of retrogression.

The same applies to the clitoris, which represents the female

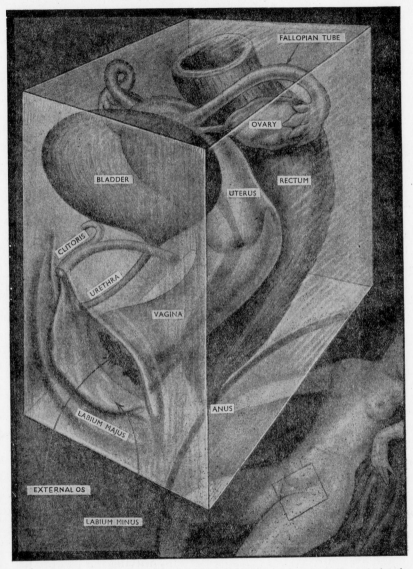

FIG. 35—Anatomical composition showing the clitoris and how it extends inside, and also the position of the other female organs. The vagina is represented as a tube; but it should be noted that this is only for a clearer understanding of the illustration. Normally the walls of the vagina lie close together, particularly in the case of a virgin.

equivalent of the male member. Its structure is approximately the same. It is supplied with well developed cavernous cells, and its glans correspond in every way to the glans of the male member. However, the clitoris has no duct to carry off secretions, whereas, as we know, the penis is pierced by the urethra.

The center of feminine voluptuous sensation, after sexual maturity, should really be the lining membrane of the posterior part of the vagina, whose erotic sensitiveness develops at an increasing rate after puberty. The cervix or neck of the uterus, which projects into the vagina, is also assumed to play an important part, through the contractions of its muscles, in producing voluptuous sensations. Indeed, some scientists go so far as to assert that the neck of the uterus is the center of the greatest sexual excitability in woman. This excitability, these authors hold, increases to the point of orgasm through the impact of the seminal fluid against the cervix. However, this is an improbable theory, because the woman frequently attains orgasm even if the man has no ejaculation. This is a universally recognized fact, and it is met with the argument that in such cases the male member penetrates so deeply into the vagina that it comes into contact with the neck of the uterus, thereby replacing the impact of semen. But this argument also fails, because orgasm has been observed in women whose uteri have been removed. The fact therefore remains that orgasm is usually aroused in the posterior part of the vagina.

Nevertheless, it must be admitted that the neck of the uterus has some part in bringing about orgasm. During sexual excitement this organ also becomes congested with blood, and is therefore just as erectible as the vagina, clitoris, etc. The muscular contractions of the uterus during the sexual act are also transferred to the cervix, and many women feel this movement quite distinctly.

As regards the so-called ejaculation of the woman during intercourse, if comparison to the male ejaculation is postulated, the most that can be said is that there may be a considerable increase in the flow of mucus secreted by the uterus and endocervical lining glands, with perhaps some relaxing or widening of the cervical canal. The overall effect may be considered by improving the pathway of the

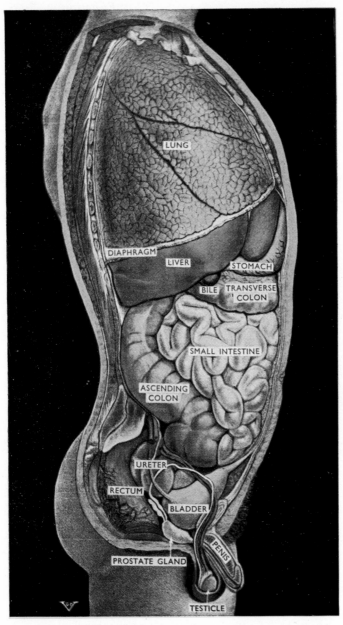

FIG. C-11—Full length picture of interior of male body, including the genital organs.

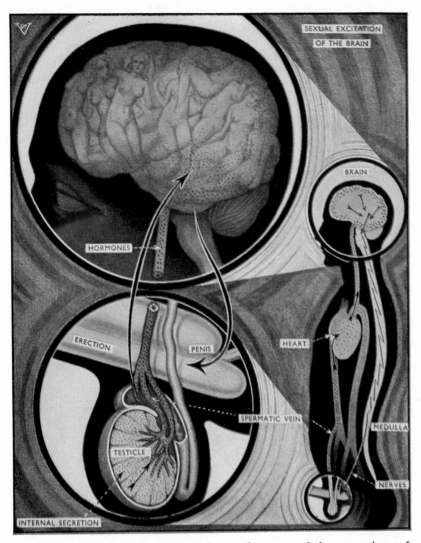

FIG. C-12—Sexual excitement and erection caused by secretion of testicle.

The latter produces, in addition to semen, sexual hormones, which are collected by spermatic vein and, when these hormones reach the brain, they eroticize it; i.e., fill it with erotic images. The sexual excitation of brain is transmitted unconsciously to medulla, and from this to the nerves of the genital organs, causing erection of the member, which further increases sexual excitement.

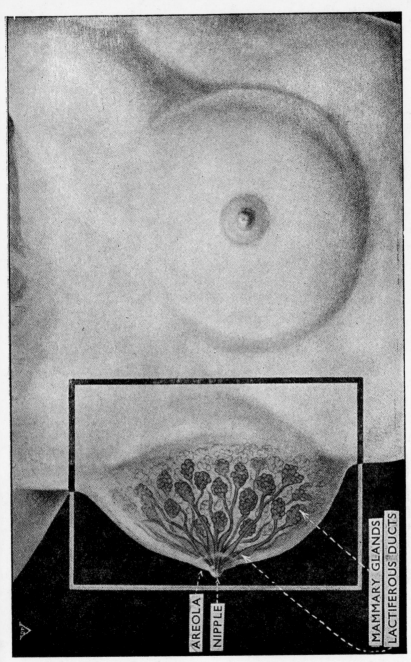

AREOLA

NIPPLE

MAMMARY GLANDS

LACTIFEROUS DUCTS

Fig. 36—Picture of life-like and transparent breast—like "bunches of grapes," together with the lactiferous tubules carrying the milk to the nipple.

spermatozoa to the uterine cavity. In addition, there is the secretion of Bartholin's glands, whose function has not yet been completely cleared up, though it is thought that their secretion serves to lubricate the vagina. However, certain authors disagree with this view, and hold that these glands play the same role in women as in female animals, where they only function when the animal is in rut, secreting odorous substances to attract the male. This theory is contradicted by the observation that in the human female Bartholin's glands only function during, and not before, the sexual act, as in animals. The truth, however, seems to lie midway between the two theories. For if sexual excitement lasts some time before the introduction of the male member, then the glands start to function before the act, while in the contrary case they only start to secrete during the act. The lubrication of the vagina in the latter case occurs partly through the secretions of the male member, and partly through the mucus of the uterus.

A summarized survey of the above shows that science as yet knows very little about what might be termed as female ejaculation, which may be due to the delicate nature of the subject. Both the uterus and Bartholin's glands, as well as other organs, secrete certain lubricating fluids, but these can certainly not be regarded as the equivalent of masculine ejaculation. In the present stage of development, when the human female does not secrete odorous substances to excite the male, all these fluids serve merely as lubricants.

Finally, we come to the mammary glands or breasts, which are closely connected with the functions of the sexual glands. Most mammals, and particularly those that produce a number of issue, have a number of mammae. That human beings originally had the same disposition is proved by the fact that even today there are women who have more than two breasts but the accessory breasts or supernumerary nipples, as they are called, are usually quite small and rudimentary. These may vary from one to several in number, and occur in a line down one or both sides of the front of the body trunk, similar to the rows of breasts in lower animals such as dogs or rabbits.

The mammary gland consists of from fifteen to twenty tiny canals

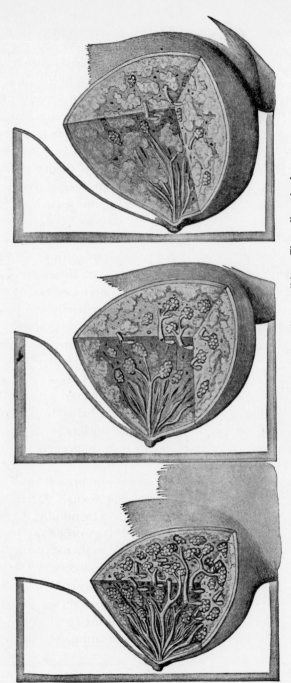

Three pictures of sectional breasts showing various conditions. Three dimensional.

Fig. 37—Section of breast showing the lactic glands and their ducts centering in the nipple.

Fig. 38—Slightly excessive fat between the lactic glands.

Fig. 39—A considerable amount of fat and few glands, so that despite the great volume of the breasts little milk is produced.

situated under the skin, centering in the nipples. The ends of these canals lie in the dark colored court surrounding the nipple. At the beginning of puberty adipose or fatty tissue is accumulated between the canals, so that the female breasts finally rise in hemispherical form. However, the breasts only reach their full development during pregnancy.

CHAPTER 6

IMPREGNATION

LET us now take a glimpse at the microscopic world of the events connected with fecundation which, thanks to the advance of science and the development of the microscope, has been fairly well explored.

The female ovum is only almost microscopic, in that it is only just visible with the naked eye. The ovum, as we know, is the female germinal cell. It matures in the ovary each month, and is then ejected.

In order to understand the properties of this female germinal cell, we must imagine it as a spherical body containing countless elements, some of which represent the qualities not only of the individual, her parents and grandparents, but also of more distant ancestors and of the race as a whole. These elements are known as chromosomes.

There is a striking difference between the size of the ovum and that of the male germinal cell or spermatozoon, which is so tiny that several thousands of them could find room in a single ovum. The explanation of this great difference probably lies in the fact that the ovum contains a reserve of nourishment which aids the process of development after fecundation, i.e., after the spermatozoon has penetrated the ovum, until the latter attaches itself to the mucous membrane of the uterus and starts to receive nourishment direct from the blood.

Although the spermatozoa are very small as compared with the ova, there is a colossal number of them. Whereas only a single ovum is shed every twenty-eight days, the testes eject about 500 million spermatozoa at a single emission of semen, so that the male genital apparatus produces thousands of spermatozoa daily.

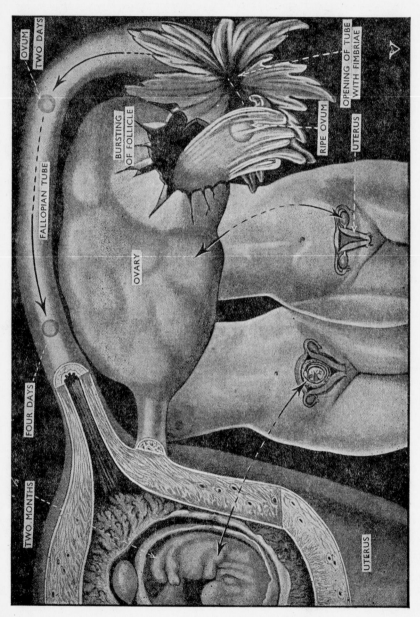

FIG. 40—Female figure on right, showing uterus before im-　　FIG. 43—Female figure on left, showing after two months of
pregnation.　　　　　　　　　　　　　　　　　　　　　　　　pregnancy.

Each month an ovum matures. When the follicle bursts, the ovum is shed, collected by the funnel and conveyed into the

Approximately in the middle between two menstruations a mature ovum leaves one of the ovaries and drops into the abdomen. But it lies there only for an instant. As we know, the ovum is incapable of movement, and its transportation is carried out by the oviduct, which seizes the ovum with its fringed extremity, the so-called funnel, and carries it into the duct. The duct has countless folds, in which the ovum is, so to speak, lost. The cells on the surface of the membrane lining the oviduct are covered with thin hair-like undulating processes called cilia, whose movement pushes the ovum forward towards the uterus, and this movement is further assisted by the rhythmic contractions of the muscles of the oviduct. The ovum thus reaches the uterus, and if it is not fertilized it dissolves there, and is ejected with the menstrual flow that commences about ten days after this.

It is of considerable importance to know how long the ovum takes to cover this journey from the ovary into the uterus, and how long it is capable of fecundation. This question will be discussed elsewhere in the present work, and we will now turn to the spermatozoon, whose task it is to find the ovum and fertilize it.

As soon as the semen has been injected into the posterior of the vagina, the spermatozoa commence their independent activity, as they now possess a considerable motility. When the spermatozoa have reached the uterus, they move on continuously in search of the ovum. This mass movement of the spermatozoa is like a desperate race, as only a single spermatozoon is destined to unite with the ovum, while all the rest must perish.

But the journey that the spermatozoa must cover, according to microscopic standards, is enormous, for the route is about 5 inches long, and this is thousands of times longer than the "travellers." In addition, the mucous membrane of the uterus is not smooth; it has many folds and irregularities which in relation to the spermatozoon represent the same thing as a range of mountains to a human. A further obstacle to the progress of the spermatozoa are the cilia (hairs) in the oviduct, whose "stroke" is in the outward direction. Thus it is impossible to determine the precise time required by the spermatozoon to reach the ovum, as the former's progress depends

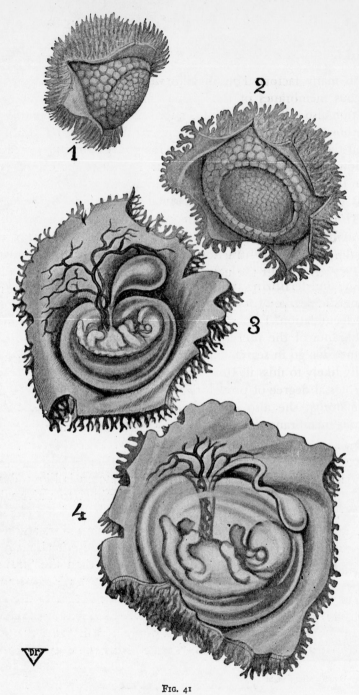

FIG. 41

1 and 2—Evolution a few days after fecundation.
3 and 4—Embryos in the first months of pregnancy.

on so many factors. For, in addition to the configuration of the mucous membranes of the vagina and the uterus, their chemical reaction also enters into the question, and there is the further problem how far the ovum has progressed in the oviduct at the time when the spermatozoa set out on their journey.

However, it may be assumed that fecundation may take place from three to ten hours after the sexual act.

At the same time, the spermatozoa may retain their vigor, and therefore their capacity to fertilize an ovum, for a long time, so that impregnation may occur up to two days after the sexual act.

Considering that at a single emission of semen about 500 million spermatozoa are injected into the vagina, all of which are intent on finding and fertilizing the one female ovum, the process represents a fantastic degree of foresight on the part of nature in order to ensure fecundation. For however full of folds and ridges the mucous membranes of the uterus and the oviduct may be, if 500 million spermatozoa go in search of a single ovum at least some of them are hardly likely to miss it. But nature is not content merely to provide the colossal degree of probability represented by the number of the spermatozoa; she also ensures a certain chemical reaction of the mucous membrane that facilitates the journey of the male germinal

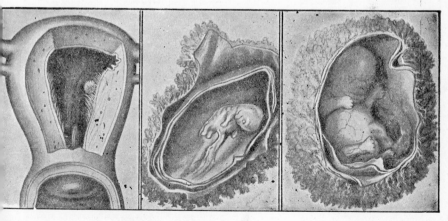

FIG. 42—Ovum after eight days.   FIG. 43—Abortive embryo of six weeks.   FIG. 44—Abortive foetus of two months.

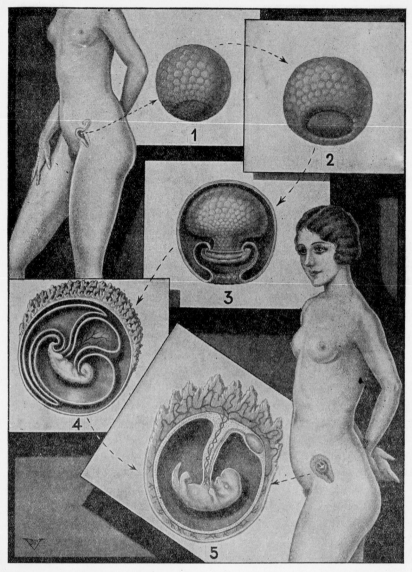

Thirteen grouped illustrations, showing the step-by-step growth of the embryo into a child and its actual position in the mother's body in four progressive figures of women; showing the changes in the female body to provide for the child.

Fig. 45—This shows the gradual evolution of the embryo from the first days of pregnancy; (1) First few days; (2) Gastrula— the first form of the embryo—begins to form; (3) Second week, the embryo starts to evolve; (4) Third week, embryo is clearly distinguishable; (5) Embryo in fourth week.

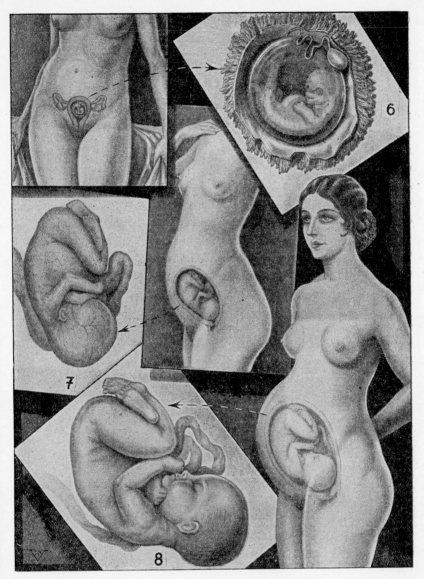

FIG. 46—(6) After approximately five weeks, the head, limbs, eyes and mouth already distinguishable; (7) In fourth month the foetus in every way resembles a human being; (8) After eight months, a few days before delivery, the breasts are now fully prepared for lactation.

cells in the direction of the ovum. It is even assumed that the ovum itself has a certain radiation designed to attract the spermatozoa.

As soon as the first spermatozoa have reached the ovum, they surround it and try to penetrate with their heads the outer membrane. At first they all fail, but then the ovum forms a projection at one point on its surface as its receptive zone, and very soon thereafter one spermatozoon—perhaps the strongest and most vigorous—succeeds in piercing the membrane at that point and penetrating into the ovum. The tail of the spermatozoon now becomes detached from its head and is thrown off, its task—that of enabling the spermatozoon to move forward—being ended.

Once a spermatozoon has penetrated the ovum, its "entrance" closes, so that no other spermatozoon may penetrate. The efforts of the remaining spermatozoa in this direction fail, and they all perish, being dissolved by the mucous membrane of the oviduct.

The mysterious union of two germinal cells has thus been accomplished, an event in this microscopic world that defies human

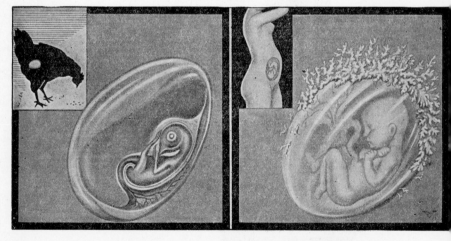

Picture story comparison between birth of chicken and birth of human child.

FIG. 47—Twelve days old embryo of chicken. The egg contains all the necessary nutritive substances.

FIG. 48—In contrast with birds, reptiles and amphibians, in humans and other mammals the development of the embryo depends on nourishment received through the blood, which is conveyed via the umbilical cord and the placenta. Foetus of five months.

understanding no less than the great law of nature that impels two human beings to unite.

And while the advance of medical science affords us this glimpse of the great event in the microscopic organic world, modern psychology, a new science that is daily gaining in importance, reveals to us the mysteries of "love" and its connection with psychological as well as with purely sensual sources.

The microscopic spermatozoon carries with it the physical and mental qualities of the individual's ancestors, endowing the new being with them, the new being which will use them to its own

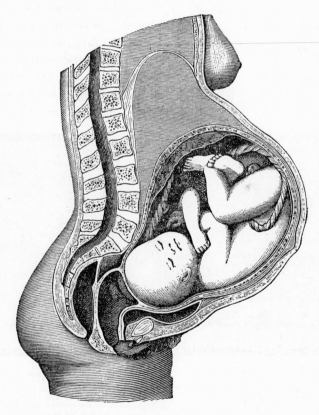

Fig. 49—Child shown in mother's body sectioned, at end of pregnancy—beginning of parturition.

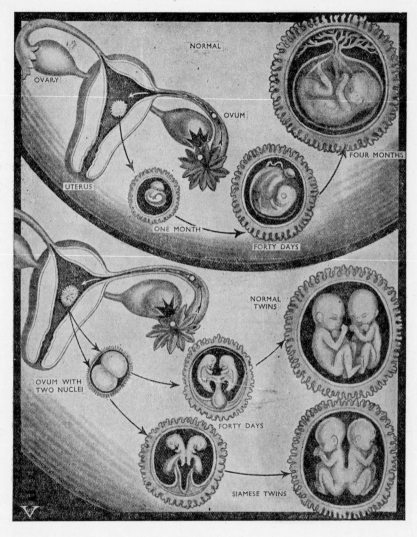

FIG. 50—(Upper) Pictures showing the course of normal pregnancy with one child.
FIG. 51—(Lower) Pictures showing the course of Siamese twin pregnancy.

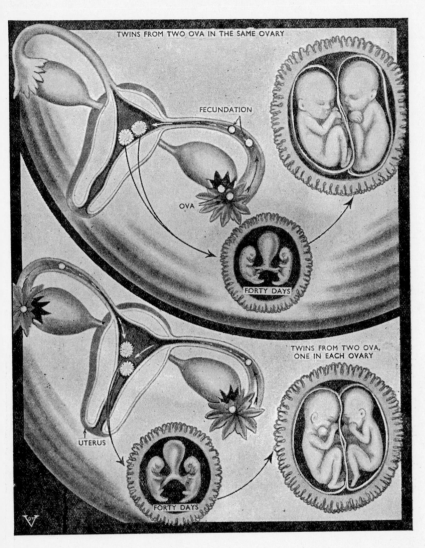

FIG. 52—(Upper) Pictures showing the course of twins in pregnancy. In this case they may be of different sexes, as they come from different ova.

FIG. 53—(Lower) Pictures showing another course of twins in pregnancy. Another possibility occurs when the two ovaries each shed an ovum at the same time.

advantage or ruin, and hand them on to future generations. In the same way, the ovum also carries the hereditary qualities of past generations. Both the spermatozoon and the ovum carry these qualities in the so-called chromosomes, which form the "core" of each.

As the male and female germinal cells mature, the chromosomes they each contain are reduced to half their original number. At the the moment of union between the male semen and the ovum the remaining chromosomes merge, so that the fertilized ovum contains the full number of chromosomes.

When the spermatozoa of the man and the ovum of the woman have united to a neutral entity, growth begins. Cell-divisions arise through the "furrowing" of the original fertilized cell, each division gradually developing into one organ or another. Up to a certain stage of growth the embryo or foetus possesses the genital apparatus of both sexes, and it is impossible to determine whether it is masculine or feminine, then sexual differentiation takes place.

As we have already mentioned, the ovum perishes if it reaches the uterus from the oviduct without having been fertilized. In that case the ovum, together with the greater part of the mucous mem-

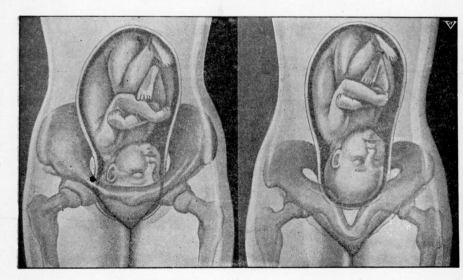

FIG. 54—Showing normal pelvis; child's head passing through easily.

FIG. 55—Showing abnormal pelvis; child's head cannot pass through.

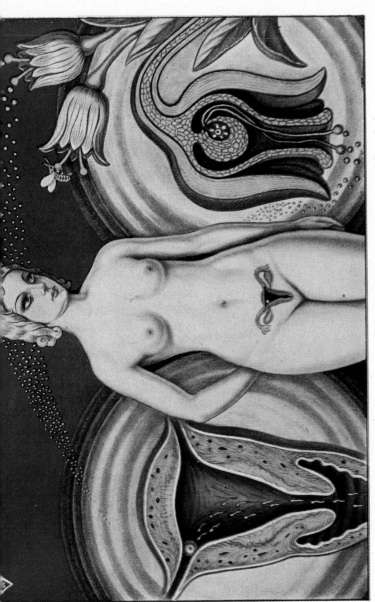

FIG. C-13—Cross-section pictures of mating of male sperm and female ovum.

The process of fecundation in human beings is very similar to that of the animal and plant world. The spermatozoa move towards the ovum in order to fertilize it. The pistil of a flower, representing the penis, sends off the pollen (masculine cells), which the peristyle of the flower receives.

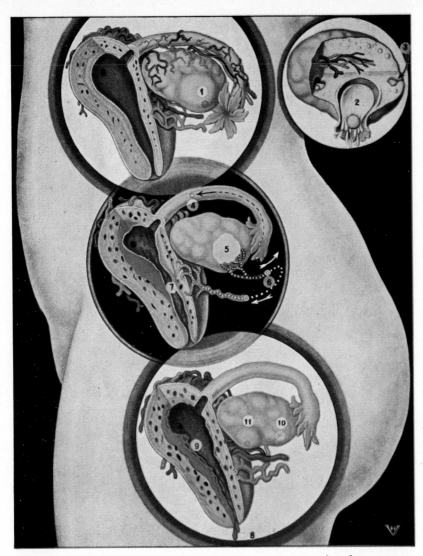

FIG. C-14—Four step-by-step pictures of uterus and associated sex organs in relation to menstruation.

Top circle shows uterus, oviduct and ovary. Uterus is in repose, during the time between menstruations. Ovary contains an almost mature ovum (1). In the small circle, upper right, a few days later, bursting of follicle and shedding of ovum (2). In middle circle, ovum (4) traveling towards uterus through oviduct. The yellow body (3 and 5) sends hormones (yellow globules 6) "ordering" the uterus to prepare by filling the mucous membrane with blood (7) to receive the ovum if fertilized. Lower circle, as the ovum (8) has not been fertilized, it perishes; the congested mucous membrane disintegrates and menstruation (9) starts. The yellow body (10) degenerates and a fresh ovum matures (11).

brane of the uterus, is ejected. This process is known as menstruation. Thus menstruation is, in a sense, equal to an abortion. Upon the conclusion of the process of menstruation the mucous membrane of the uterus gradually re-forms ,and prepares itself once more to receive a fertilized ovum. If within the next twenty-eight days no impregnation takes place, then menstruation is repeated, and this periodical destruction and regeneration of the mucous membrane of the uterus continues until impregnation does take place. Menstruation then ceases, and is usually not resumed until the child is weaned from the breast.

Theoretically, there is a possibility that a woman should have no menstruation throughout her life, as fecundation can take place before the first menstruation. In that case there follows pregnancy, child-birth, and lactation; and during or immediately after lactation there may be a fresh impregnation, and the cycle is repeated. If each birth and subsequent period of lactation is followed by a fresh impregnation, then menstruation is unlikely at any time. Finally, with the climacteric comes barrenness and then, of course, there is no menstruation in any case.

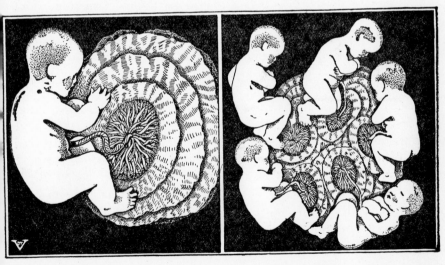

FIG. 56—How the child before birth receives blood through the placenta.

FIG. 57—How quintuplets are linked in the mother's body. Five or more children may be linked with a single placenta, through the most frequent number is two.

CHAPTER 7

MENSTRUATION

NORMAL regular menses are a blessing and usually a sign of healthy female organs functioning properly. It matters not whether the menstrual cycle, from the first day of bleeding of one menses or "period" to the first day of the next is 21, 25, 28, 30, or 35 days, etc. as long as the number of days of the cycle remains relatively constant plus or minus one or two days. The duration of flow is also relatively constant—usually 3 to 4, 4 to 5, 5 to 6, or 6 to 7 days, with heavier flow at the onset, and lesser to a mere stain on the last day. The average cycle in the healthy American woman is 26 to 30 days and average flow duration is 4 to 6 days, though variations from this, as above noted, are by no means abnormal if regular.

The old popular belief that menstruation is a periodic release or purging of poisonous accumulations from a woman's body has been known now for many years to be untrue. In brief, menstruation is merely a periodic discarding of the endometrium (lining of the uterus) when the woman has not become pregnant. Following the menses a new lining develops in preparation for the reception and nourishment of the ovum periodically extruded from the follicle of the ovary. Ovulation usually occurs about 14 days before the next menses. (See the chapters on Impregnation and Natural Birth Control.) If the ovum is not impregnated by a male sperm cell, then the menses will recur. The function of menstruation is controlled by the action of the hormones estrin (or estrogen) and progestin (or progesterone) produced by the ovary, and these are in turn influenced by the gonadotropic hormones from the pituitary, the master gland of the body.

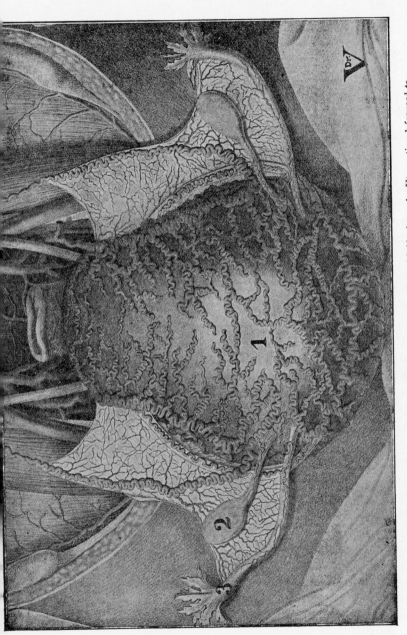

FIG. 58—Female organs showing how richly the uterus is supplied with blood vessels. Uterus tipped forward to show posterior part. (1) Uterus; (2) Ovary; (3) Fallopian tubes.

(a) Various Causes of Irregularities

Heavy or profuse menstrual bleeding, i.e., more than the "usual," with blood clots (there are no blood clots in the normal menstrual flow), bleeding longer than the "usual" number of days, or any bleeding or spotting between the regular menstrual periods, is abnormal. Profuse or prolonged flow is called by the physician *Menorrhagia,* and intermenstrual bleeding, *metrorrhagia.* Too frequent regular or irregular menses is called *polymenorrhea.* Scanty menses is called *hypomenorrhea.* Absence of menses during the normal child-bearing age is called *amenorrhea.*

Menses are apt to be irregular or profuse with various constitutional diseases such as the acute infectious illnesses, but should become normal again once the primary disease has been overcome. Abnormal bleeding occurs also with such chronic diseases as hypertension (high blood pressure), various types of anemias, and other blood diseases which produce bleeding tendencies. The vaginal bleeding is a *symptom,* not a disease.

There may be irregular or abnormal vaginal bleeding associated with such chronic diseases as diabetes, tuberculosis, or syphilis; but in these cases *amenorrhea* for variable times is more likely. (One might mention that the most common cause of amenorrhea, like the most common tumor, in the healthy young woman, is pregnancy.)

There is variable amenorrhea following childbirth, particularly if the woman nurses her child, with menstruation being suppressed by hormone influence associated with lactation. Lack of menses following childbirth however does not mean that the woman is immune from pregnancy. It is not unusual for a new type of menstrual cycle and duration of flow to be established following pregnancy and childbirth.

Menstrual abnormalities and intermenstrual bleeding are the most common signs of disease of the female genital tract itself. Polyps—small benign finger-like growths—of the cervix or endometrium are common causes of menorrhagia and metrorrhagia. Chronic infection and inflammation of the cervix (often called "erosion" by physicians), polyps, and cancer of the cervix or uterus commonly result in light bleeding or spotting between periods. Bleeding following coitus is a significant sign which should always be investigated by a qualified physician.

Often after a supposedly complete spontaneous abortion (loss of pregnancy before five months) or miscarriage (loss of pregnancy after five months) there may be persistent variable bleeding indicating that some of the products of conception have been retained. Here there is risk of hemorrhage and dangerous infection developing, so a physician's care is necessary for proper treatment, at least to determine whether an operation may be necessary to complete emptying of the uterus. Formerly, death from such neglected infections, particularly following illegally induced abortions, was common, and is still not a rarity.

Other common causes of abnormal bleeding from the female genital tract due to disease therein are: (1) endometritis—chronic inflammation of the endometrium, (2) myomas or "fibroids"— common benign tumors of the muscle wall of the uterus which may grow to huge size, (3) acute and chronic inflammation of the tubes and ovaries and ligaments supporting the uterus (called pelvic inflammatory disease, salpingitis, oophoritis, or adnexitis by physicians), commonly occurring after an infected abortion or untreated gonorrheal infection, (4) ectopic pregnancy—meaning usually a pregnancy in a tube, and almost invariably requiring surgical removal—here the bleeding is apt to be a "period" from a few days to two or three weeks "late," and accompanied sometimes by acute pain and signs of shock. Such a situation always requires immediate expert medical attention to make the proper diagnosis, (5) threatened abortion—here the individual may have missed two or three or more menses then suddenly begin variable bleeding with or without lower abdominal cramps, backache, and passage of blood clots. Here again the woman should take to her bed and call her physician, (6) subinvolution, or lack of return of the female organs to the normal size and state following pregnancy, and (7) tuberculosis and other chronic infectious diseases of the female genital tract. One must be forgiven for repeating that any abnormal bleeding or spotting from the vagina (hence likely from the cervix or uterus) *must* be investigated immediately by a qualified physician, preferably a gynecologist (a physician specializing in diseases of the female genital tract) in order to *rule out cancer* of these organs; even then abnormal bleeding may be a *late* sign of this disease—hence every woman should have a complete pelvic (internal) examination at least once a year, and preferably twice a year after the age of thirty. The fact that one may be single or has not borne children in no way obviates the wisdom of such routine examinations.

Change of environment or climate, such as from temperate to tropical, or severe emotional strain or shock may cause temporary alteration in menstrual cycles or even amenorrhea, but once the individual readjusts to the situation, the menses too should become normal. If not, medical investigation is in order.

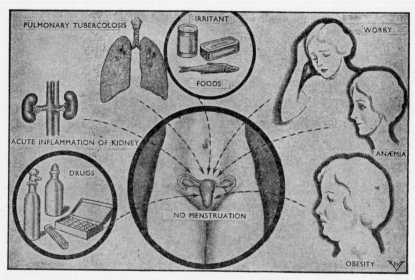

FIG. 59—Eight pictures linked in one plate. Showing *no menstruation* in woman; its 7 causes illustrated.

A common type of abnormal bleeding is called *functional uterine bleeding*, due to lack of balance, too much output, or withdrawal of the hormones controlling the menses. It is common for menses to be irregular in cycle and duration of flow during puberty and early adolescence, but if all is normal, the menses likewise become normal within a reasonable time.

Abnormal functional bleeding during the child-bearing age is often caused by a condition called hyperplasia of the endometrium, meaning overgrowth of the lining of the uterus, due to too much female sex hormone output. This condition can be proven, however, only by currettage (scraping out the lining of the uterus), and examination of the tissue obtained under a microscope. Here repeated currettages may be necessary. Hormone treatment (male sex hormone) is useful in some such cases in judicious hands.

The time of greatest concern over irregular or functional bleeding is at the time of the menopause, when the menses may become very irregular, or profuse, with varying periods of amenorrhea, due to uneven withdrawal (decrease in production by the ovaries) of the hormones estrogen and progesterone which regulate the menses and reproductive mechanisms. Such bleeding can *not* be called

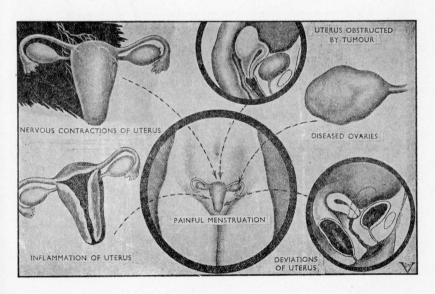

FIG. 60—Six pictures in one plate. Showing *painful menstruation;* its 5 causes illustrated

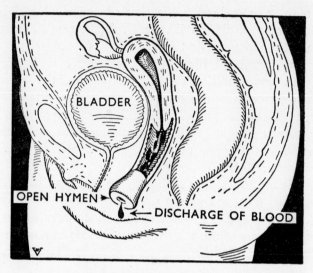

FIG. 61—Normal menstruation without pain.

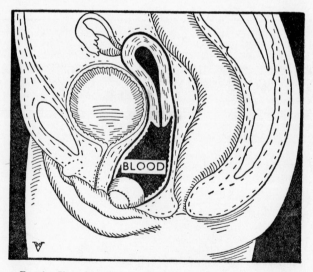

FIG. 62—Unperforated hymen. Menstrual blood **remains in vagina.**

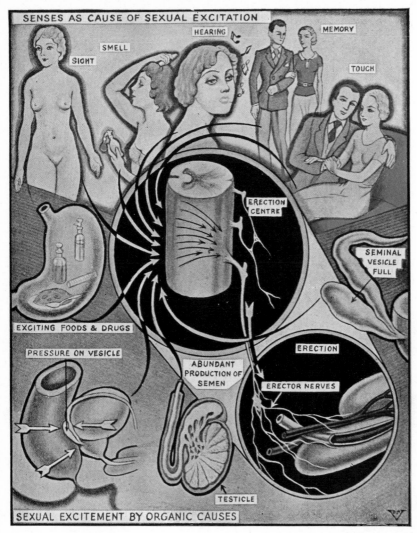

FIG. C-15—Picture story of various causes for sexual excitation and erection.

How they act on the erection center of the medulla, which issues the "order" for an erection through the erector nerves.

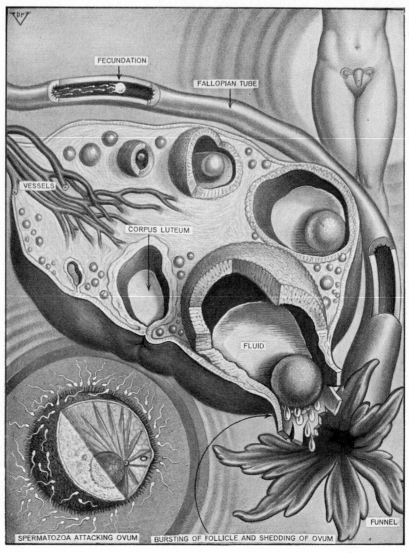

FIG. C-16—Larger than life-size picture of interior of ovary, in woman's process of impregnation.

Schematic representation of maturing of the ovum and its emergence from ovary. Several ova are shown in different stages of development.

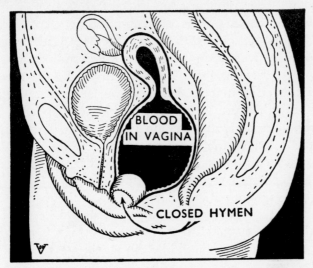

Fig. 63—Dangerous accumulation of blood in vagina with closed hymen.

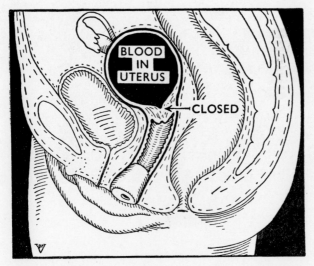

Fig. 64—Menstrual blood retained in uterus owing to obstruction.

functional unless any other possible disease of the female organs such as tumors, infections, or particularly cancer are eliminated by careful examination, observation, and when necessary biopsy (i.e., removal of tissue from the lining of the uterus and from the cervix for microscopic examination). Too often in present day therapy one is tempted to seek treatment by various "hormone shots" and "injections" by busy physicians who may be prone to give such treatment without adequate study and examination of the patient, sometimes missing the cause of the bleeding completely. In skilled hands, however, after dangerous conditions have been eliminated, such therapy may be very beneficial in certain cases.

Suffice it to say that no irregular bleeding in the menopausal age, or for that matter in any other age group, should be taken lightly without thorough examination. Furthermore, any bleeding occurring *after* the menopause should be suspected as due to cancer until proven otherwise.

In some instances absence of menstruation may be due to deficient development of the ovaries. In such cases a doctor will have to decide whether hormone preparations should be administered to encourage the growth of the ovaries.

(b)   *Painful Menstruation (Dysmenorrhea). Pain Before, After, or During Menstruation*

Some women during the critical days suffer more or less intense pain, which usually passes after a certain amount of blood has been discharged.

There are various causes. In a small number of cases the pain is of a nervous character. Apart from that, however, painful menstruation may be caused by displacements of the uterus or the ovaries, or tumors situated in the pelvis exercising pressure on the uterus. The explanation is "overcrowding" in the pelvis which appears as soon as the uterus fills with blood during the menstrual period, swells, and requires more space. This also explains why the pain abates after a certain time, and finally ceases altogether when the uterus has reverted to its normal size, thus eliminating the cause of the pain, namely, "overcrowding."

However, the cause of painful menstruation is frequently a congenital narrowness of the posterior opening of the uterus, or of the cervical canal, which leads to congestion during the menses, thereby producing pain. This phenomenon is particularly frequent in infantile individuals, i.e., women whose sexual organs are insufficiently developed. The complaint is accompanied by headaches, even migraine, gastric troubles and vomiting.

Edometritis (pelvic inflammatory disease) is also an important cause of dysmenorrhea.

Treatment.—The pain can be reduced by any hot object applied locally, such as hot compresses, electric cushions, hot sandbags or linseed poulticies. These should be placed on the lower abdomen. Hot baths also reduce the pain, particularly before menstruation. If the pain is particularly intense, a bath of increasing temperature may be taken. This should last from twenty to thirty minutes.

The elimination of the actual cause of the complaint can, of course, only be undertaken between menses by competent medical care. For this purpose it is necessary to improve the general health. Anemia, acidity, etc., must be eliminated.

In order to improve blood circulation, systematic exercises are recommended.

In some women the menstrual pain disappears as soon as ovarial activity is improved in the direction of normalcy by favorable physiological conditions. Thus, for instance, it has been observed that the menstrual pain sometimes disappears as soon as the individual concerned marries, i.e., as soon as she engages in regular sexual intercourse with normal orgasm. In other cases the pain ceases after the birth of the first child.

BOOK II

Hormones and Vitamins

CHAPTER 8

GLANDS ARE "MOTORS" OF THE LIFE PROCESS

THERE are certain organs in the human (and animal) organism that are comparable to a chemical laboratory. These organs produce chemical substances that play an immensely important role in the life of the body and partly also in the life of the mind. They are called glands.

What is a gland and what does the interior of such a chemical laboratory look like? If we examine a gland under the microscope we only see a number of cells ranged close to each other. But these are the scene of mysterious processes, as a result of which a fluid is produced which in the case of some glands at first appears in the form of tiny drops. These then unite into a larger drop, which leaves the cell. This fluid is the secretion of the gland that may sometimes produce miraculous effects.

Thus a gland is a set of cells which produces one, and sometimes several substances. In some glands the secreting cells form a duct and at the end of this, a bulb. The secretion flows into the duct and is thus carried out of the gland. In other glands there are tiny ducts between the cells, which carry the secretion to a reservoir or exit tube. According to the task of the secretion, the exit tube leads either to the surface of the body or, for example, into the intestine. For instance, the task of the perspiration (sweat) glands is to remove certain poisons from the body and also to promote cooling (by the evaporation of moisture) ; they must therefore carry their secretions to the surface of the skin. On the other hand, the peptic glands must produce substances capable of digesting food, that is to say, breaking it up chemically; therefore they must carry their secretions into the interior of the alimentary canal.

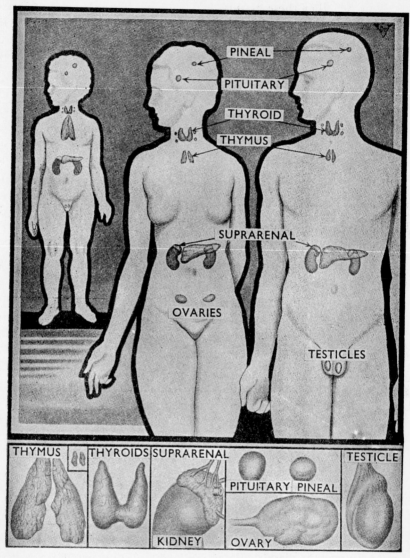

Fig. 65— Pictures of Man, Woman and Child, indicating the comparative development of their endocrine glands. The thymus, which is largest in infancy, becomes completely atrophied by the time adult age is reached.

Fig. 66—Separate pictures of seven different glands.

Now, whether these glands carry their secretions to the surface of the skin or into the alimentary canal, they both produce *external or exocrine secretions,* as in both cases the secretions are carried out to the surface, either of the skin or of the mucous membrane of the alimentary canal, by a discharge tube.

There are other glands, in which there is no discharge tube. The substances secreted by such glands are conveyed direct to the blood, so that they do not reach either the external or the internal surface of the body. If we examine such a gland under the microscope, we see an entirely different picture—the cells form no tubules, there are no bulbs, no reservoir tubes, and, above all, no discharge tube. Instead, the closely set cells are interwoven with very fine blood-vessels. The substances secreted by the cells are immediately taken up by these capillary blood-vessels.

Glands of this type are called *endocrine glands.* Their task is very different from that of the exocrine glands. Their secretions circulate in the bloodstream, carrying messages to distant organs. These secretions are called *hormones.* Thus hormones are substances produced by the endocrine glands for the purpose of influencing the activity of other organs, or of the body as a whole. The life of the organism is regulated and coordinated with the aid of hormones.

There are still other glands which have both an exocrine and an endocrine activity. Under the microscope we first see the exocrine structure, but scattered in the form of small islands we also discover the endocrine parts, which have no discharge tube. The pancreas is a gland of this type.

We only obtain a true idea of the importance of the endocrine glands when, for some reason or another, they cease to function or intensify their function. In such cases severe troubles arise in the organism, which may sometimes even endanger the life of the individual concerned.

In the following chapters we will describe the function of the most important glands. By way of introduction, we may say at this stage that the functions of the glands are not only physical; they also influence, and to a considerable extent determine, the entire personality of the individual. It depends on our glands whether we are cold or temperamental, energetic or lethargic, choleric or phlegmatic, and so on. If science had succeeded in securing control of the glandular functions, it would be possible to change the personality of an individual completely; as it is, we are in a position to regulate the activity of a gland in many cases for the purpose of curing disease.

CHAPTER 9

Activities of the Human Hormone Laboratory

The Thyroid and Suprarenal Glands

The thyroid gland, which is an endocrine gland weighing about one ounce, is situated near the so-called thyroid cartilage in the neck.

There are certain regions in the world, mostly mountainous regions, such as the Alps, Andes, Himalayas, etc., where a large percentage of the population is afflicted with peculiar swelling in the neck, the so-called goiter. This disease is caused by the excessive growth of the thyroid gland. However, it would be a mistake to assume that the function of an overgrown thyroid gland is also intensified. On the contrary. Goiter consists in overdeveloped connective tissue, the actual secreting gland being "crowded out." Indeed, there are cases of goiter in which *the thyroid gland possesses hardly any or no glandular tissue.*

The thyroid gland of such people functions very weakly or not at all, secreting no hormone to convey to the blood. What are persons thus afflicted like in appearance, and what are their physical and psychological characteristics?

Where the thyroid gland fails in childhood, growth stops, and the subject becomes a dwarf. His body temperature is low, his heart beats more slowly, his face bears an apathetic expression, his eyes reflect no intelligence. He is a mentally deficient dwarf, a so-called *cretin.*

If the thyroid gland fails in adult life, the subject's skin becomes pale and puffed. This is due to the presence of water under the skin, while the skin itself remains dry. The hair becomes rough and falls out. Also, here again the body temperature falls, the pulse becomes slower. The subject is apathetic, indifferent, the brain functions more slowly, and mental deficiency develops.

The most common and biologically most important feature of all cases of deficient thyroidal function is the slowing down of the metabolic processes, i.e., the conversion of food into bodily tissue, energy, etc.

If a cretin or an adult suffering from goiter is given a thyroid preparation derived from any mammal (but mostly from cattle) for a long time, a miraculous change occurs. The dwarf starts to grow. The puffiness and the silly expression vanish, the eyes reflect intelligence, the heart beats faster, the brain starts to perceive; the body cells become normally active, consuming more oxygen and producing more carbonic acid, and the metabolic activity of all the cells is intensified. Similar results may be observed in the adult suffering from goiter.

How is this miracle brought about? What does the thyroid gland contain, the lack of which makes a physical and mental wreck of a person, and the administration of which restores him to normal?

The most important active agent of the thyroid gland was first isolated (in 1914) by Kendall. Later, the chemical formula was ascertained, and finally, the substance in question was produced synthetically. Thus today the chemist can produce in his retort the magic substance of the thyroid gland *which governs the pace of physical and mental life,* just as well as the gland itself. The substance is known to science as Thyroxin, and it contains a considerable proportion of iodine.

Accordingly, the cretinism that is so prevalent in mountainous regions is now attributed to the lack of iodine in the soil and in the drinking water.

The amount of Thyroxin required to ensure the normal activity of the organism is amazingly small. Even one or two Gamma, that is to say, one or two thousandths of a milligram will produce certain effects. The total number of Thyroxin in the normal organism is not more than twelve milligrams.

Up till now we have discussed cases in which a *deficiency* of the active thyroidal agent has produced pathological changes. But a surplus of this element is also harmful. For certain reasons that have not yet been completely cleared up, the thyroid gland of some people starts to function with excessive intensity. In the majority of these cases there is a slight swelling of the thyroid gland. This swelling differs very considerably from the swelling that accompanies goiter. It is softer and, above all, it never exceeds a certain size. Also, it consists not of connective tissue but of *functioning thyroidal tissue.* Another striking characteristic in patients is the bulging of the eyes. These two characteristics are expressed in the English name of the disease, which is *exophthalmic goiter.*

The symptoms of this disease are the reverse of those observed in cases of thyroidal deficiency, i.e., acceleration of all the vital processes. Metabolism is intensified, growth in children speeded up, the heart beats faster, the nervous system is sur-excited. The patient is restless and suffers from insomnia. His hands tremble. Owing to the intensified metabolism he may lose a great deal of flesh. In some cases severe psychological disturbances have been observed which in extreme cases may lead to mental derangement.

Embedded in the tissue of the thyroid gland there are four tiny bodies, weighing about one thirtieth of an ounce each. These are the *parathyroid glands.* These, too, are endocrine glands. Their importance was first recognized when the parathyroid glands were unintentionally removed, together with the thyroid gland, in animal experiments, or together with part of that gland in early operations for exophthalmic goiter. The consequence was severe muscular convulsions that finally caused death. If, however, these animals or human beings were given injections of parathyroid extract, the convulsions ceased, and they survived. Thus the parathyroid glands also produce a hormone.

What is their function and why is it that their removal causes convulsions? It has been found that the convulsions in such cases are due to a reduction of the calcium content of the blood. Normally, every six cubic inches of blood contain about 10 milligrams of calcium. Upon removal of the parathyroid glands this falls to four or five milligrams. Calcium being the natural "quietener" of the nervous system, a reduction of this substance in the blood causes pathological excitement in certain nerves, thereby producing convulsion in the muscles with which these nerves are connected. The hormone of the parathyroid gland must see to it that the amount of calcium in the blood is not reduced, the parathyroid glands being the regulators of calcium metabolism.

While a deficiency of this hormone causes convulsions, an excess of calcium in the blood means that the bones are deprived of this substance to a corresponding extent. Thus excessive activity of the parathyroid gland leads to diseases of the bones.

Of similar importance are the effects produced on both body and mind by the *suprarenal glands*, though this occurs in a different direction. The suprarenal glands are small glands situated like tiny caps on the tips of each kidney. Peculiarly enough, the suprarenal glands are composed of two entirely different glands. In the lower

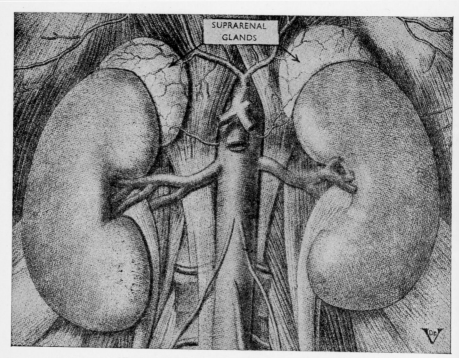

FIG. 67—The Suprarenal glands and the Kidneys.

animals these two different glands are separated from each other. One of these glands, the so-called *cortex* (or "rind") of the suprarenal gland covers the other, the *medullary* (or "marrow") part of the suprarenal gland. The structures of the two glands, as well as their functions, differ from each other very considerably.

We will first consider the cortex of the suprarenal gland. We have seen that the complete absence of the thyroid glands produces a variety of diseases, but only shortens life, and does not directly cause death (except where the parathyroid glands are also removed). In the case of the suprarenal cortex the position is different. Its absence or degeneration produces general debility and, within a short time, death. A partial degeneration of this organ usually causes death, though the process is then slower.

Dr. Addison, an English scientist, first described (in 1855) a disease characterized by a loss of weight, general debility and fatigue, which sooner or later led to the sufferer's death. Another feature of Addison's disease, as it is called, is the fact that the patient's skin changes to a dirty brown. It was subsequently found that this disease is sometimes due to a tuberculous affection of the suprarenal glands. This disease, formerly held to be incurable, can now be mastered, though not quickly cured, by constant treatment with an extract of the active element in the suprarenal cortex.

Thus this organ produces a hormone which governs the output of muscular energy, and probably also of other energy, so that this hormone may be described as the hormone of *vital energy*.

Another effect of the suprarenal cortex relates to the metabolism of fat in the body. Failure of this gland leads to the disappearance of the fat reserves of the body, and the sufferer becomes emaciated. Metabolism in general is also seriously affected, and sensitiveness to poison and other harmful influences is intensified.

It is now assumed that the suprarenal cortex produces several hormones, but all the action of these various hormones has as yet not been determined. One of them was recently isolated, its structure investigated, and attempts to produce it synthetically in the laboratory have been successful. This hormone is the so-called *Corticosteron*, and it is capable of prolonging the lives of animals deprived of their suprarenal glands, and also human beings suffering from Addison's disease.

There is an increasing connection between the suprarenal cortex and the *sexual organs*. This connection becomes manifest particularly where the functioning of the suprarenal cortex is abnormally intense. If this happens before puberty, then it leads to a premature appearance of that stage of sexual development. This may happen at a very early age, even in babies in arms, and the condition is called pubertas praecox, i.e., premature puberty. Children of two or three years of age may have fully developed sex organs and a growth of hair on their bodies. Still more interesting is the fact that the premature puberty arising in this manner produces masculine characteristics even in female children, such as a growth of hair on the face and body. Masculine characteristics may also be observed in adult women in whom the suprarenal cortex started to over-function after, or long after puberty. The distribution of fat loses its feminine character, the voice becomes harsh, there is a growth of hair on the face and the body, and the feminine sexual functions are also affected.

Science has not yet succeeded in clearing up the precise causes of these phenomena. Recently, a hormone—*Adrenosteron*—has been produced from the suprarenal cortex, which as regards its action and chemical structure is strongly reminiscent of the masculine sexual hormone. (See following chapters.)

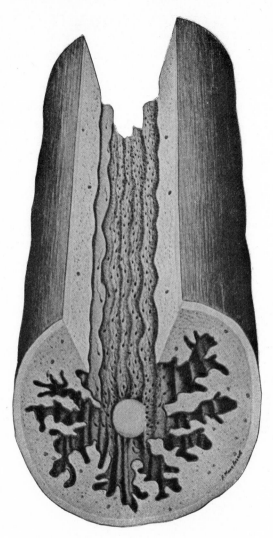

FIG. C-17—Cross-sectional picture shows ovum on its way to the uterus.
Male sperm attacking female ovum.

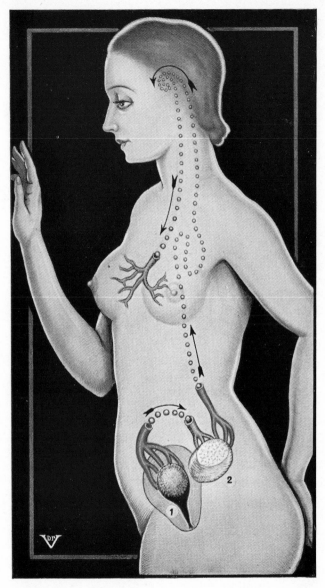

Fɪɢ. C-18—Picture of woman's body, with interior view
at beginning of pregnancy.

Uterus with foetus. Yellow body of the ovary conveying hormones to the blood, and "ordering" the breasts
to prepare for lactation.

CHAPTER 10

ADRENALINE AND INSULIN—BOONS TO HEALTH AND LIFE

THE medulla of the suprarenal gland is a separate gland with an independent function. The hormone which it secretes is called adrenaline or epinephrine, and is one of the longest known hormones. The investigation that led to the isolation, and finally to the synthetic production of this hormone, began as early as the end of the last century. The chemical structure of adrenaline is comparatively simple.

In order to understand the action of adrenaline, we must know something about the so-called *vegatative nervous system.*

As we know, the movements of the body are of two kinds, those that are controlled by the brain, or the so-called *animal nervous system*, such as walking, bending, etc.; and those movements that are not controlled by the brain or the will, such as the action of the heart, the movement of the intestines, breathing, metabolism, etc. The latter movements are all controlled by a different nervous system, known as the vegatative nervous system.

Adrenaline governs this nervous system, and its action is therefore as varied as the realm of the vegatative nervous system. Adrenaline accelerates heart action, increases blood pressure, accelerates respiration, improves the supply of blood to the muscles, increases the sugar content of the blood, etc. However, the true importance of the various actions of adrenaline can only be appreciated if we consider them not separately, but in conjunction. For instance, the action of this hormone on the blood-vessels is such that because of it the blood flows decreases in the intestines and increases in the muscles. The biological sense of this is, so to speak, a great preparedness of the muscles for action. In other words, the muscles are charged with their nourishment, i.e., blood, so that they should be ready for attack or defense. The same applies to the increase of blood sugar, the acceleration of heart action and respiration, and the increase of blood pressure. The investigations of the American scientist, Professor Cannon, have shown that in certain forms of excitement, such as anger, fear, pain, etc., an increased amount of adrenaline is immediately supplied to the blood. The object of this increased supply is to provoke increased "tension," a readiness for attack and defense, in the organism. Under present conditions of civilized life this increased tension is of little practical value, and in order to grasp its great biological significance, we must remember the dangerous conditions under which primitive man lived. It was then of paramount importance that, in case of danger, or when preparing for attack, the organism should be tensed up, everything being so arranged that the muscles should act with lightning rapidity, while the great activity of the digestive organs could for the moment be eliminated by re-transferring the blood supply from the intestines to the bloodvessels. Adrenaline is thus the hormone of vital tension, just as thyroxin is that of the pace of life, and corticosteron that of vital energy.

The accelerated pulse, increased blood pressure and pallor of an excited person, is therefore brought about by adrenaline. As we have said, blood sugar is also increased by adrenaline, and this is not without danger to sufferers from diabetes. For instance, it is a known fact that after the great Wall Street crash some years ago, a large number of diabetic people were obliged to consult a doctor. Many of these were up till then unaware of the disease, and only discovered it when it had been aggravated through excitement. The same mechanism which assisted primitive man in attacking or defending himself from his enemy, today aggravates the diabetes of stock exchange operators after excitements in the course of their business.

The amounts of adrenaline that produce the effects referred to are astonishingly small. Its action can already be traced where it is present in a dilution of one in three hundred millions. Owing to its terrific potency, adrenaline is an important medicine. For instance, its action on the heart is so powerful, that an injection of one milligram into the heart, even after it had stopped, has saved more than one life.

We know that adrenaline aggravates diabetes by increasing the blood sugar. We will now consider the latter disease, as it is also caused by the irregularity of an endocrine function.

After many false starts, medical science finally established that diabetes is caused by a disease, or inadequate functioning, of certain parts of the pancreas. This discovery ultimately made it possible to prolong the lives of millions of diabetic patients and to make it more tolerable.

The pancreas has long been known as a digestive gland secreting important ferments or substances that digest food and convey it into the alimentary canal. Thus the pancreas is first of all an *exocrine gland*, and as such it possesses a duct. However, in the tissue of the pancreas there are small islands of cells, which are interwoven with blood-vessels. The latter are obviously unconnected with the duct of the gland. These islands were first discovered in 1869, but at that time, and for many years afterwards, no one knew what object they served.

Twenty years later a little progress was made by sheer accident. The German scientist, Minkowsky, observed that the urine of a dog whose pancreas had been removed for experimental reasons, contained considerable amounts of sugar. The dog also showed all the other symptoms of diabetes, and in this way it was proved that diabetes is connected with the pancreas.

But it was not until 1922 that the Canadian investigators, Drs. Banting and Best, succeeded in isolating the active agent of the pancreas islands, i.e., *insulin*. As the administration of insulin led to the elimination of all the diabetic symptoms, it was definitely proved that diabetes was due to the inadequate insulin production of the endocrine portion of the pancreas, and with this proof the cure for diabetes was found!

What is diabetes, and what is the action of insulin? It is well known that the urine of a diabetic subject contains sugar. Less well known is the fact that this is due to an increased supply of blood sugar, so that the latter phenomenon is of the greatest importance. Why does the blood sugar increase? Because the sugar ingested with the food does not, as in a healthy person, reach the "sugar depots" of the organism (liver, muscles) but remains in the blood and is finally discharged, unused and unexploited, with the urine. In addition, the reserve of sugar already accumulated is also thrown out into the blood and similarly discharged. This process of senseless waste goes on, while the organism, in desperation, is now producing sugar from protein. The consequence is that the organism suffers on account of the excess of sugar in the blood, but still more on account of the scarcity of sugar in the cells. This gives rise to various troubles. Wounds heal very slowly, the resistance of the organism is reduced, poisonous substances are produced owing to deficient metabolism, and, finally, death supervenes in consequence of internal poisoning.

The reason is that the patient is incapable of utilizing sugar. Amid the abundance of sugar that circulates in the blood, the cells are starved of sugar!

The administration of insulin changes the situation immediately. No sugar is discharged in the urine, and the excess of sugar also vanishes from the blood. The "sugar depots" are once more filled and the individual cells are once more capable of utilizing the sugar. Order is thus restored in the organism.

We invariably find that "too much" is harmful. That is, of course, also the case with the insulin. Until the correct dosage was worked out, there were cases in which an overdose of insulin endangered the life of the patient. The blood sugar dropped below normal, upsetting the activity of the nervous system, and there were convulsions, loss of consciousness, etc. All these symptoms, which, by the way, may also arise without insulin, simply through the over-activity of the pancreas islands, can be eliminated by means of an injection of sugar, or merely by eating sugar, but also by means of an injection of adrenaline, which increases blood sugar.

CHAPTER 11

The Sex Hormones

THE pancreas is an example of a gland which exerts both an exocrine and an endocrine activity. A similar dual activity is characteristic of the germinal glands. There are two of these organs in each sex, the respective structures being different. The germinal glands of the man, the *testes*, are outside the abdomen, in a cutaneous sac called the scrotum. The germinal glands of the woman, the *ovaries*, are situated within the abdomen, and are both invisible and inaccessible from the outside. It is an interesting fact that, during embryonic development, the testes are also in the abdomen, and only descend into the scrotum shortly before birth. However, it may happen that, owing to some impediment, one or both testes fail to reach the scrotum, and are held up somewhere in the abdomen. This condition is known as *cryptorchidism*. It leads to various irregularities in sexual development and activity.

The dual activity of the germinal glands consists in the production of germinal cells, i.e., reproductive cells, on the one hand, and hormones on the other. The reproductive cells constitute the exocrine or external secretion, the hormones the endocrine or internal secretion.

The male germinal cells or spermatozoa are, as we know, microscopically small cells, which move with the aid of a long tail or flagellum. The spermatozoa are formed in tiny convoluted tubules in the interior of the testes. The tubules unite into a single duct, through which the sperms, which are suspended in a fluid, are conveyed into the urethra. During sexual intercourse the spermatozoa are injected into the vagina, whence they proceed into the uterus of the woman.

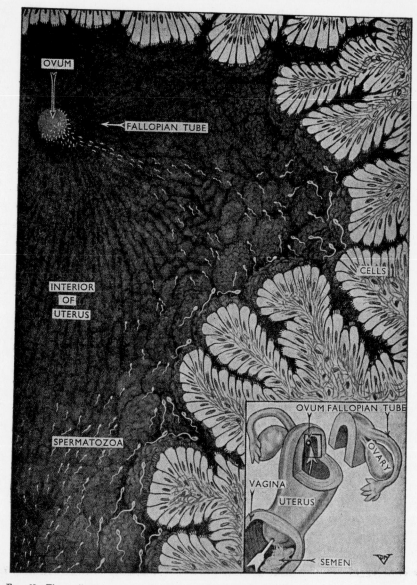

FIG. 68—The perilous journey of male sperms through the interior of the uterus. Cross-section of interior of the uterus shows the hills and dales formed by the mucous membrane of the uterus, which must be overcome by the spermatozoa.

FIG. 69—Lower right picture shows direction taken by semen (see white arrow).

As in the case of the pancreas, there are tiny islands of cells scattered among the seminiferous tubules, which have no connection whatever with the seminal duct through which the spermatozoa leave the testes. These islands produce the male sexual hormone, which is conveyed direct to the bloodstream.

In the case of the woman the position is somewhat different, though essentially the same. The female germinal cells, the ova, are produced not in tubules, but close to the surface of the ovary. As the spherical cell grows and matures, it forms a membranous envelope or follicle, which encloses the ovum. When the ovum has reached complete maturity, the follicle bursts and the ovum is released. It then falls into the funnel of the oviduct, through which it travels towards the uterus, and may be fertilized at some point of its journey.

The female sexual hormone is formed in the follicle, and is therefore called follicular hormone, or estrogenic hormone. It passes through the walls of the follicle direct into the blood. When the follicle has burst, discharging the ovum, a new organ, the so-called yellow body (corpus luteum) is formed in its place. This forms a further hormone, the so-called luteal hormone, which we will discuss in detail further on.

What is the task of the sexual hormones? A striking negative illustration is provided by the consequences of castration. Castration is an age-old practice, and consists in removing the testes of male animals before they reach sexual maturity. The most obvious consequence of this operation is, that the reproductive capacity of the animal is destroyed, as, in the absence of the testes, no spermatozoa can be formed. But the object of castration is something very different. After this operation many changes occur in the appearance and behavior of the animals concerned. The wild bull becomes a quiet, docile and patient ox, willing to work; its horns grow differently, and its body develops on different lines. The same applies to horses, etc. In these cases the object of castration is to make the animals tame and fit for work. In the case of cocks, pigs, etc., castration is practiced because it facilitates fattening.

In former times castration was also carried out on men. Such men —eunuchs—served in the harems of the East, and at the papal court, where they were employed as singers on account of their high-pitched voices. Eunuchs are usually obese, without any hair growth on the face and body.

All these experiences clearly indicate the enormous importance of the testes from the point of view of physical and mental development. But the actual role of these organs remained a secret for a long time, and was only revealed in 1849 through the researches of Berthold, which also laid the foundations of the theory of endocrine secretions.

Berthold removed the testes of cocks, whereupon the comb of these birds degenerated, which, of course, was an expected consequence. But Berthold went further, and regrafted the testes in another part of the cock's body, e.g., its back. He found that the comb resumed its former size and shape. It was thus proved that the change in the appearance of the bird had nothing to do with the loss of reproductive capacity, for, of course, the testes transplanted on the cock's back could not produce any reproductive cells, and its comb nevertheless resumed its masculine form.

Since then a large number of similar experiments have been carried out, and the result has always been the same. Hence we know for certain that the germinal glands produce hormones which exercise a decisive influence on the body as well as on the mind and character.

The physical and mental characteristics that are susceptible to the action of the sexual hormones include, first of all, the genital organs themselves, which during puberty develop under the influence of the sex hormones. If the germinal glands are removed, the genital organs, both in the male and the female, remain at the infantile stage of development. Then there is the growth of hair on the body, which is different in the two sexes, its development in different directions commencing with puberty. After castration the masculine hair growth on the face and body ceases. The same applies to the voice. These various sexual characteristics are divided into two groups, the primary and the secondary. The primary sexual characteristics relate to the structure of the genital organs themselves, while the secondary characteristics have no direct connection with sexual activity. The feminine form of the pelvis serves the purpose

Six illustrations showing the amazing influence of endocrine secretions of the testes on a cock.

FIG. 70—Normal.　　FIG. 71—Castrated.　　FIG. 72—Castrated cock after hormone injections.

121

of reproduction, and should therefore also be regarded as a primary sexual characteristic, in the same way as the breasts or mammae, which serve to feed the new-born child. The secondary sexual characteristics, in addition to the above, include the more powerful osseous and muscular system in the man, and the specifically feminine distribution of the fat deposits of the body, its more delicate form, and the more delicate skin in the woman.

In the psychological sphere the sexual characteristics include the different directions of the sexual instinct in men and women, and also the maternal instinct, but, of course, the entire psychological make-up of the sexes differs very considerably.

Much of this is due to the internal secretions of the germinal glands, i.e., the sexual hormones.

The famous experiments of Prof. Steinach offered a deep insight into this question. The Viennese scientist castrated male and female animals, and the castrated animals acquired a neutral, i.e., sexless, appearance. Steinach then went further and grafted into the neutralized males female germinal glands, and into the neutralized females male germinal glands. The males thus treated acquired female characteristics, behaved towards males like normal females, even developed mammary glands and suckled and nursed the young. The converse happened in the case of females into which male germinal glands had been transplanted.

Steinach's experiment is sometimes carried out by Nature. There have been cases in which a hitherto normal man or woman suddenly developed the characteristics of the opposite sex. Women grow a beard, develop a masculine voice, the mammae (breasts) degenerate, and even the genital organs change. The converse occurs in men. Such phenomena may arise owing to the over-functioning of the suprarenal glands, but also in other circumstances. In the case of women who were "changing into men," pathological growths whose structure appeared to be similar to that of testes have been discovered in the ovaries. In the case of men, the testes were found to have acquired new growths with the structure of ovaries. In both cases the removal of the new growth has resulted in a reversion to normal.

The sex hormones have played an important role in the so-called rejuvenating experiments. As we know, the activity of the germinal glands diminishes at a certain age. In the case of women this usually occurs rather suddenly in the late forties, causing the so-called climacteric complaints. In the case of men the activity of the germinal gland decreases somewhat later, and more gradually, so that the irregularities arising therefrom are hardly noticeable. As signs of age usually appear after the cessation of germinal activity, it was at one time assumed that there is a causal connection between the process of ageing and the cessation of hormone production by the germinal glands, i.e., that most of the phenomena of age were due to the absence of sexual hormones.

The French scientist, Brown-Séquard, in the year 1889, attempted to rejuvenate himself by means of extract from the testes of a bull. This was the first attempt of the kind, and Brown-Séquard reported to the Paris Academy of Science favorable results which, in the light of present knowledge, can only be attributed to auto-suggestion.

Scientifically better founded were the experiments of Prof. Steinach, who tied up the seminal duct, thereby causing the sperm producing portion of the testes to degenerate, and the hormone producing portion to thrive better. Another method was essayed by Prof. Voronoff, who transplanted the germinal glands of apes into men.

However, all these attempts at rejuvenation only produced temporary results, the reason being that the thriving of the hormone producing portion of the testes after tying up the seminal duct, is limited in time, and must eventually degenerate, while the transplanted animal glands also only remain active for a short period. Another reason is that the process of ageing is not solely due to the cessation of germinal activity.

We must refer at this state to the chemical nature of the sexual hormones. Science has succeeded, not only in isolating the hormone through which a man becomes masculine and a woman feminine, but also in producing it synthetically in the laboratory. The astonishing discovery was made that the masculine and feminine sexual hormones are very similar, with only a slight difference between their molecules. The masculine hormone is called *testosteron*. There are two kinds of feminine sexual hormones, the follicular hormone called *estrogen*, and the hormone produced by the yellow body, called *progesterone*.

CHAPTER 12

Your Mysterious Glands

Inside the skull, as a sort of appendix to the base of the brain, there is a peculiar gland, known as the pituitary body.

The pituitary is composed of two entirely different parts, the anterior and posterior lobes. Both, but particularly the anterior lobe, produce a number of hormones that are of considerable importance in the domestic economy of the body. Indeed, as we shall see, the anterior lobe may be regarded as the central organ of the entire system of internal secretions, just as the brain is the center of the nervous system.

The connection of the anterior pituitary lobe with growth has perhaps been known longest. We have already mentioned impeded growth in connection with the action of the thyroid gland. Growth may similarly be impeded by the defective action of the pituitary. However, the appearance of the "pituitary dwarfs" is different from that of cretins, or those whose growth has been impeded by rickets. These two types of dwarfs look like distorted replicas of the human frame, lacking the harmony and balance of the normal organism, whereas the pituitary dwarf is only a miniature man, with approximately normal proportions. These are the dwarfs we sometimes see at variety theatres. What is the cause of these differences between the various kinds of dwarfs? We must assume that in the case of cretins there is a lack of harmony between the individual processes of growth and development. For instance, a cretin may stop growing in height, and continue for a time to grow in width. There are further distortions due to other processes, such as a puffy skin and a stupid expression. In other dwarfs the arms and legs stop growing, while the trunk and head attain almost normal dimensions. In contrast with these, the pituitary dwarf stops growing uniformly as regards all parts of the body, without having a distorted appearance.

The opposite of the pituitary dwarf is the pituitary giant, a person who develops more rapidly than is normal from early childhood. He is bigger, stronger and in all other respects better developed than other children of the same age, and far taller than others in adult life. Such abnormal growth is due to the over-activity of the anterior pituitary lobe. The pituitary giants are reminiscent of the giants of the fairy tales, with the difference that the latter are represented to be strong, mighty men, whereas the former are mostly the victims of disease. Their fame is usually of short duration. Serious irregularities appear in the entire organism, showing that their gigantic stature is due to pathological causes. The organism, so to speak, exhausts itself in the process of growth, and the result is general debility. The poor giants are not long-lived.

It should be noted, however, that not all abnormally big people are pituitary giants. Sometimes excessive growth is due to as yet unexplored constitutional peculiarities, and not to any irregularity in the action of the pituitary. Such giants may be quite healthy, and may even be endowed with special physical qualities.

There is a further type of pituitary giant, besides the one referred to above. The subject is suffering from *acromegaly*, i.e., an enlargement of the ends of certain bones, as the fingers, toes, nose, chin. This happens when the over-activity of the pituitary commences after normal growth is at an end. This stage is reached when the cartilaginous rings that are to be found at the end of each bone in a young person's body has, at a certain age, hardened or become ossified. Lengthwise growth of the bones is then impossible, and the bones grow in the other direction. Acromegaly may lead to the complete distortion of a normal human face in a few years.

Our knowledge concerning the connection between the pituitary and growth is due to the work of the American scientist, Evans, who succeeded in isolating the hormone of growth. Indeed, we can already look back on some successful clinical results in the treatment of children suffering from impeded growth with this hormone, and although certain difficulties still exist, there is reason to hope that we shall in time be in a position to regulate growth at will.

However, the function of the anterior pituitary lobe is not by any means exhausted by its connection with growth. There are cases in which puberty is retarded or entirely prevented by the defective action of the pituitary, and this may occur not only in pituitary dwarfs, but also in persons of normal growth. This is called pituitary *infantilism*. The connection between this condition and the pituitary has been revealed particularly by the work of Ascheim-Zondek, who proved that an infantile animal could be made sexually mature in a few days by injections of pituitary hormone. The question then arose whether the hormone acts on the sexual organs and the secondary sexual characteristics direct, or whether its action is only indirect. The answer is that it is direct, as it has been found that an injection of pituitary hormone will not bring about puberty where the germinal glands have been removed. Thus the pituitary hormone influences the germinal glands themselves, stimulating them to normal activity, and it is only through this activity and the consequent production of sexual hormones that puberty can occur. On the other hand, without pituitary hormone the germinal glands do not act at all, and animals whose pituitary has been removed can never attain sexual maturity. *Thus the activity of the germinal glands is regulated by the pituitary hormone.* But the latter is not sexually specific, that is to say, the same pituitary hormone can impel the activity of either the testes or the ovaries.

The ovaries only produce ova and female sexual hormones under the influence of the pituitary, just as the testes only produce spermatozoa and male sexual hormones under the action of the same hormone. The hormone is called *pituitary gonadothropic* hormone (i.e., a hormone whose action is directed upon the gonads or genital glands).

We have here an example of one endocrine gland governing the activity of another. But the pituitary provides several more examples of this kind, for the pituitary also governs the action of the thyroid, parathyroid, suprarenal and other glands. If the pituitary is removed, all these glands degenerate. There is a disease known as Simmond's Disease, in which the endocrine glands degenerate, causing all kinds of severe complaints, owing to a deficiency of the pituitary.

It is clear, therefore, that the anterior lobe of the pituitary is the central organ of the endocrine gland system, whose activity it governs by means of various hormones (gonadothropic, thyerothropic, para-thyreothropic, adrenothropic and other hormones).

But even that does not exhaust the activity of this tiny gland, which weighs *less than one thirtieth of an ounce.* It also produces hormones that influence metabolism, and a special hormone which starts the secretion of milk in the breasts of a nursing mother.

The connection between the pituitary and the metabolism of adipose tissue in the body have not been completely cleared up. We know that a deficiency of the anterior pituitary lobe may in certain circumstances lead to emaciation, as in the case of Simmond's Disease. On the other hand, there is also a type of pituitary deficiency that produces the contrary result, i.e., obesity. The latter complaint is associated with under-development of the genital organs, and is scientifically known as *dystrophia adiposogenitalis.* Some investigators are of the opinion that the under-development of the genital apparatus is due to deficient activity of the anterior pituitary lobe, while the obesity is caused by a simultaneous defect in the posterior lobe. Other authors, however, hold that the obesity is due to a pathological condition of the metabolic center in the brain, which is situated close to the pituitary, and that this disease is therefore not of endocrine origin.

At all events, we are now in a position to assume with certainty that there is a close connection between these adjacent brain centers and the pituitary, particularly the posterior lobe. The centers in question and the pituitary mutually react upon each other. The pituitary and the vegetative brain centers between them govern a number of important vital processes.

We now come to the posterior pituitary lobe and the intermediate lobe which exists in some animals, and is merged with the posterior lobe in others. The hormones of these lobes regulate, among other things, the metabolism of water and salts. If they become diseased, the so-called *diabetes insipidus* may develop. The patient is tormented by unquenchable thirst and is obliged to drink enormous quantities of water, sometimes up to ten gallons per day. The water is, naturally, discharged in the form of urine. By injecting the hormone, the thirst can be eliminated.

The regulation of water metabolism also occurs through the collaboration of the pituitary and the adjacent brain centers. A further posterior pituitary hormone, called *pitressin*, regulates blood pressure, while a third, called *pitocin,* causes the uterine muscles to contract, thus playing a decisive part in the commencement of labor in child-birth. This hormone is extensively used by obstetricians where labor pains are too mild, and is capable of accelerating an unnecessarily protracted birth.

But the activity of the pituitary body is, in all probability, still not exhausted. There is every reason to believe that the activity of this gland also influences the mental and emotional life, and that it probably plays a part in regard to the character and intellectual qualities of the individual. This presents an extensive field for further research.

As we have seen, despite an extensive knowledge of certain individual pituitary processes, the total activity of the pituitary has not been revealed so far. This applies with even greater force in the case of another endocrine gland, the *epiphysis* or *pineal* gland, which, like the pituitary, is inside the skull and grown on to the top part of the brain. The name pineal derives from the similarity of the gland to a pine cone. As regards the activity of this gland very little is known. However, there is a certain type of premature sexual maturity, characterized by an extraordinarily rapid physical and psychological sexual development, and in such case the pineal gland has been found to be diseased. It is therefore assumed that the hormone of this gland prevents sexual maturity until the age of puberty and its defectiveness causes premature puberty. Some authors further assume that the hormone of the pineal gland accelerates growth.

The thymus gland is also one of the relatively unexplored glands. This gland is situated in the chest, above the heart. Remarkably enough, it is comparatively largest at birth. It then gradually degenerates and when puberty is reached there is only a vestige of it left, and its place is taken by adipose tissue.

This fact alone shows that the active period of the thymus gland falls in earliest childhood. Experiments further indicate that the thymus accelerates growth and the hardening of the bones. It is interesting to note that the thymus persists after puberty where the germinal glands have been removed by castration.

However, despite the above indications, we know very little definitely concerning the function of the thymus gland.

CHAPTER 13

GLANDS IN TELEGRAPHIC COMMUNICATION

Synergism, Antagonism and Hierarchy of the Endocrine Glands

We have seen that a certain vital process may be simultaneously influenced by several glands. This is called synergism, i.e., simultaneous activity. For instance, bodily growth is promoted by the thyroid and pituitary glands, and probably also by the thymus gland. These glands support and complement each other's action. Similarly, sexual development is accelerated by the pituitary and also by the suprarenal cortex, and, in all probability, the thyroid gland also collaborates. Thus normal development of the sexual organs and functions depends on the collaboration of these glands with the germinal glands.

No less important is the phenomenon that is contrary to synergism, and consists in the antagonism or counteraction of glands. Thus we know that sexual development is accelerated by some glands, mainly the pituitary, and impeded by the pineal gland. The sexual hormones impede the activity of the thyroid gland.

Thus the normal course of the vital processes depends on the correct collaboration of a number of mutually counteracting or supporting glands. The connection between the various sets of glands can be very complicated, and has not yet been fully ascertained. Thus we know that the thyroid gland accelerates sexual development, while the sexual hormones impede the action of the thyroid. There is the further fact that in the case of women it has frequently been observed that the thyroid becomes slightly swollen after the first sexual intercourse. Also, in some women this slight swelling appears during every menstruation.

Another kind of collaboration between the endocrine glands is called hierarchy, which consists in the fact that, as we have seen, all the endocrine glands are subordinated to the pituitary.

A particularly edifying and interesting example of the collaboration of various hormones is provided by the menstrual cycle of women, and its connection with fecundation and pregnancy. This subject is dealt with in detail in the Section on Natural Birth Control, and we have seen that the pituitary, by means of a "hormone telegram," causes follicular hormone to be produced, and by another such "telegram" brings about the birth of the ovum. Finally, it sends a third message, which leads to the formation of a new gland, the yellow body, in place of the follicle.

The yellow body, in turn, now takes command of the uterus, eliminating the influence of the pituitary on the uteral muscles and at the same time, preparing the uterus to receive the fertilized ovum.

If the ovum is not fertilized, the yellow body decays after fourteen days, and the pituitary resumes command over the uteral muscles. It sends a "hormone telegram" ordering them to perform powerful contractions for the purpose of ejecting the superfluous, disintegrated mucous membrane. The latter, mixed with a great deal of blood, reaches the outside world through the vagina in the process of menstruation.

If, however, impregnation takes place, then the yellow body persists and protects the embryo. There is, of course, no menstruation, though occasionally cases are seen where regular menses (decreasing in quantity of flow, however) occur for several months after pregnancy has been established. Premature decay of the yellow body may lead to abortion, and there are women who have a tendency to abortion owing to irregularity in corpus luteum formation. In such cases the administration of corpus luteum hormone, the so-called *progesteron*, may save the embryo and ensure the continuance of pregnancy.

However, the yellow body is not the only gland that is active during pregnancy. The pituitary also produces a vast quantity of hormones, the excess of which is discharged in the urine. By establishing the presence of these hormones, and particularly of the gonadothropic hormones, in the urine, pregnancy can be diagnosed at a very early stage. That is the basis of the famous *Ascheim-Zondek pregnancy test*. This consists in injecting the urine into sexually immature female mice, and if this produces sexual maturity in the animals, this fact proves that the urine contains large amounts of gonadothropic hormone, such as can only occur during pregnancy.

In the case of menstruation we witness an interesting interplay between sexual hormones, on the precise coordination of which regularity depends. A similar, though far more simple example of such interplay is presented by the secretion of mother's milk. As we know, the size of the breasts is considerably increased during pregnancy, but actual secretion of milk only starts after child-birth. The growth of the breasts is caused by follicular hormone (oestradiol), which is produced in large quantities during pregnancy. The growth

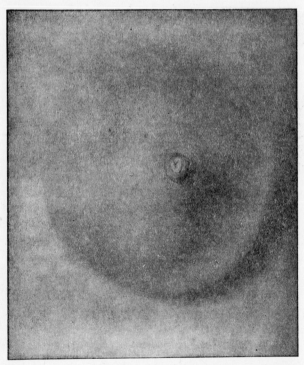

Fig. 73—Breast of a virgin.

of the breasts can be accelerated by means of sufficiently large doses of follicular hormone in a non-pregnant woman or a virgin, and even in a man.

But follicular hormone alone will not lead to secretion of milk. This is effected by a pituitary hormone, the so-called lactation hormone, which the pituitary conveys to the bloodstream after the birth. However, this hormone can only become effective if the breasts have previously been prepared by the follicular hormone.

Investigators have succeeded in bringing about lactation in virgin female animals, and even in males, by means of a preliminary treatment with follicular hormone, followed by the administration of pituitary lactation hormone.

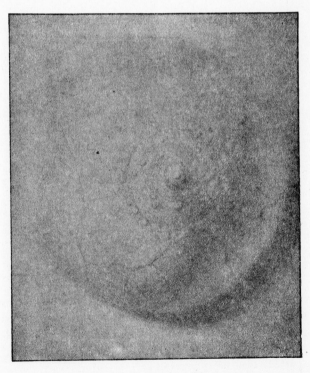

Fig. 74—Breast of a woman who has had children.

CHAPTER 14

REDUCING AND PUTTING ON WEIGHT

WE have seen that there are several hormones capable of changing bodily weight in one direction or the other. This is due to the fact that the hormones exercise an enormous influence on metabolism; that is to say, the burning up, conversion, utilization and depositing of the nourishment in the organism. Thus, for instance, the thyroid hormone accelerates the burning of food in the body. However, if too much of the food is burned up, nothing can be stored up and even the existing reserves are consumed, so that weight is lost. Too much thyroid hormone therefore reduces bodily weight below the normal. This may occur even through a slight over-activity of the thyroid gland, which is insufficient to produce exophthalmic goiter.

The converse is the case if the thyroid does not function adequately. Then too little of the food is burned up, more is stored up in the body, with the result that the person so affected becomes obese. Here again, a slight under-activity of the thyroid is sufficient to produce the phenomenon in question.

But the pituitary also exercises a considerable influence on bodily weight. Firstly, because it influences the activity of the thyroid; and secondly, because the pituitary also affects metabolism otherwise than through the thyroid. For instance, under-activity of the pituitary may lead to loss of weight even when the thyroid functions normally. Further, pituitary irregularity may produce obesity, usually associated with sexual debility. Interestingly enough, obesity of pituitary origin is of a different character than one caused by the thyroid. In the former case the fat accumulates mainly on the chest and the abdomen, and on the upper part of arms and legs. The lower arm and the legs are thin as compared with the upper arms and the thighs, and hands and feet are small. The face is also fat, though the features remain clear-cut. In the case of obesity of thyroidal origin, the distribution of fat over the body is approximately uniform, with a thick deposit of fat on the neck, and vaguely outlined features.

Over-activity of the suprarenal cortex may also lead to obesity. In such cases there is an abundant growth of hair on the body and, in women, certain masculine characteristics develop. Under-activity of the suprarenal cortex causes loss of weight accompanied by general debility, in a somewhat similar manner as the corresponding irregularity in the pituitary. In both cases of severe loss of weight there is an inclination to apathy and fatigue, whereas in cases of thyroidal over-activity there is considerable restlessness.

The elimination of the germinal glands also leads to obesity, though not invariably so. In some animals castration is followed by an increase of weight (capons, etc.). In the case of inadequate functioning of the germinal glands in humans, obesity usually starts in the twenties or thirties, regardless of the time when the under-activity of the germinal cells began. In men suffering from under-activity of the testes, there is a somewhat feminine distribution of the fat deposits; in women with inadequately ovarial activity the hips and breasts may be excessively fat.

However, there are cases of obesity and excessive leanness caused not by the over or under-activity of a certain gland, but by faulty interplay of synergic and antagonistic glands. In such cases it is impossible to draw conclusions as to the cause merely from the type of obesity.

At the same time, it would be a mistake to assume that all obesity is due to endocrine irregularities. There is a kind of obesity and leanness which, apparently, has no connection with the glands. We speak of constitutional obesity or leanness, without, however, being able to determine the cause of these conditions. A common feature of all the glandular and constitutional anomalies of bodily weight is the fact that *they are difficult to influence by dietetic measures or exercise and rest.* The constitutionally fat person may think he is starving himself and still remain fat. We must assume that such people do not burn up the greater part of the nourishment they take, like normal people, but store it up. If they take less food, they burn up still less, but their organism tries not to reduce the amount deposited. These people are unable to reduce their weight to any substantial extent without serious consequences to their health. It is the other way round in the case of the constitutionally lean person. He burns up everything and stores up nothing. If he eats more, he burns up still more, but nothing is stored up.

In the case of normal people obesity or excessive leanness is due not to glandular or constitutional factors, but depends on the amount of nourishment they take, and to a considerable extent on exercise. The amount of food and exercise are the external factors in connection with bodily weight. It is well to note here that most cases of obesity are due simply to *too much food consumed* and *too little energy output* (work, exercise) in proportion, rather than to "glandular" trouble, as many lazy people with acquired excessive appetites would prefer to believe.

Let us see how obesity caused by external factors arises. But first we must know something about the question of calories.

The nourishment absorbed is partly used to build up the organism, and partly burned and converted into bodily energy, while the surplus is stored up in reserve. For "building up," only children and young persons require a proportion of the food; adults only require a proportion to make good "wastage." The proportion required for conversion into energy is, however, of the utmost importance at all ages. For life is really nothing more than an "energy process." We need energy to live; to maintain the temperature of the body, heart action, the action of all the other organs, and, of course, for any external activity, such as standing, walking, all kinds of work, etc.

The unit of energy is the calorie. A calorie is the amount of energy required to heat one kilo of water to one degree C. The number of calories a person requires depends on a number of factors, and most of all on the amount of physical work he must perform, but an average adult exerting a moderate amount of physical effort would require between 2,000 and 3,000 calories per day.

The excess of food taken is stored up in the body. However, in this connection a distinction must be drawn between the various kinds of food. Apart from water and salt, minerals and vitamins (which will be discussed further on) the human body needs protein, carbohydrates and fat. The protein is the means for maintaining the body and is irreplaceable for the purpose. The best dose of protein ranges between fifty and seventy grams per day. An excess of protein, in contrast with fats and carbohydrates, cannot be stored in the body. It disintegrates, and produces harmful substances which, usually in the second half of life cause various diseases, such as gout, arteriosclerosis, etc. Carbohydrates are required in far larger amounts, from ten to fifteen times more than protein. The most suitable quantity of fat is the same as that of protein.

Thus a man performing normal work needs between 2,000 and 3,000 calories per day, protein and fat providing about 6 or 7 per cent each, and carbohydrates 85 per cent.

Below we give the caloric value and chemical composition of some staple foods.

100 grams (3½ oz.)	lard	gives 885 calories;	0·2 g. protein;	95 g. fat;	0 g. carbohydrate
” ”	butter	” 741 ”	0·7 g. ”	80 g. ”	0·5 g. ”
” ”	bacon	” 782 ”	1·9 g. ”	86 g. ”	0 g. ”
” ”	pork	” 361 ”	16 g. ”	32 g. ”	0·2 g. ”
” ”	beef	” 171 ”	17 g. ”	10 g. ”	0·5 g. ”
” ”	veal	” 86 ”	19 g. ”	0·8 g. ”	0·2 g. ”
” ”	goose	” 488 ”	16 g. ”	45 g. ”	0·6 g. ”
” ”	chicken	” 111 ”	18 g. ”	9 g. ”	1·2 g. ”
” ”	milk	” 61 ”	3 g. ”	3·5 g. ”	4·0 g. ”
” ”	bread	” 180 ”	7 g. ”	0 g. ”	36 g. ”
” ”	lentils, beans, peas, average	” 320 ”	23 g. ”	1·8 g. ”	50 g. ”
” ”	potatoes	” 94 ”	2·1 g. ”	0·1 g. ”	21 g. ”
” ”	fresh vegetables, average	” 30 ”	3 g. ”	0·3 g. ”	5 g. ”
” ”	fruit, average	” 40 ”	0·5 g. ”	0 g. ”	8 g. ”

Bodily weight can be reduced either by taking less food (reducing calories) or by increased exercise (sport, work) and consequent greater use of calories.

Some people are able to reduce by taking less water; these are people who retain abnormally large amounts of water in their bodies.

The reason is probably some irregularity in the pituitary. Reduction of salt intake, such as during pregnancy, aids in preventing excess weight gain, as it is well known that excess salt hold excess fluid in the tissues. This applies also in other conditions, such as heart disease, hypertension and kidney disease.

In cases of constitutional obesity adequate and lasting reduction of weight is not possible by means of diet and sport. In such cases hormone treatment (thyroid, pituitary, or sexual hormone) may be tried, though it is not certain to prove successful in all cases, and in any event should be done only under the careful observation of a physician.

CHAPTER 15

DISCOVERY OF VITAMINS

IN former times the men who went down to the sea in ships had to brave not only the normal risks of a seafaring life, but also a mysterious disease that began with the bleeding of the gums, and produced exhaustion, muscular weakness and apathy. The disease, known as scurvy, frequently affected the heart and finally lead to death.

Some peoples knew the remedy for scurvy. It is said, for instance, that the Vikings combatted it by eating onions. Some Indian tribes used pine extract. But the great majority of civilized sailors were ignorant of these remedies, and were at the mercy of the disease. Thus Captain Cook, the famous English sailor, performed a great service to humanity when he began to treat the disease with lemon juice. Careful observations were also made on the European continent, until the correct means of preventing and curing scurvy were found. A Hungarian army surgeon, during an epidemic of scurvy among the troops, discovered that the disease could be cured with fresh vegetables, and orange or lemon juice. Finally it was established that scurvy was caused by the absence of fresh vegetables and fruit from the diet.

More than a century passed before it was discovered that another disease, which had also been known for a long time, was similarly due to the absence of certain substances from the diet. This disease is beri-beri, which was very prevalent in the Orient. Beri-beri involves inflammation of certain nerves, with consequent muscular paralysis, and it frequently proved fatal.

Beri-beri mostly afflicted people who lived exclusively, or almost exclusively, on rice. Towards the end of last century, it was discovered that the disease was not due to under-feeding, because when soldiers suffering from beri-beri were put on a different diet of the same caloric value, they were cured. In view of the ignorance on dietetics that prevailed at that time, this was regarded as an inexplicable phenomenon.

Then a Dutch physician stationed in Java carried out an experiment on the inmates of a prison. He found that those of the convicts who ate polished rice, i.e., with the husk removed, contracted beri-beri, while those who ate unpolished rice remained unaffected. Further, when the convicts suffering from beri-beri were given unpolished rice, they were cured. After a great deal of puzzlement as to the causes of these phenomenon, it was established that beri-beri was due to a deficiency of something in the diet, and that that something was contained in the husk of rice.

However, the matter was only cleared up completely by scientific investigation. At the beginning of the century it was still thought that, in addition to water, four elements were necessary for the bodily development and maintenance of man and beast, namely, protein, fats, carbohydrates and salts. In the course of experiments, these substances were administered to animals in the pure state, and it was found, to the investigators' amazement, that although the animals were given all the necessary foods in adequate quantities, they developed various diseases, which soon killed them.

It was an English scientist, Professor Hopkins, who first grasped the situation. He concluded that there are vitally necessary, though as yet unidentified substances, without which no animal can live, even though its diet included chemically pure protein, carbohydrate, fat and salt. Hopkins called these unidentified substances "accessory factors." These are what we now know under the name of vitamins. The diseases caused by a lack of vitamins in the diet are known as vitamin deficiency diseases.

Today we know a great deal about vitamins, and have even succeeded in producing them in the laboratory, but a great deal more remains to be known.

Vitamins are effective in minute quantities, and in this respect there is a close resemblance between vitamins and hormones, the absence of which, like that of vitamins, leads to disease. The great difference between the two substances is the fact that whereas hormones are produced by the body itself, vitamins must be supplied from outside sources.

Here is a brief description of the various known vitamins:

Vitamin A. In the year 1904, and again in 1917, a peculiar eye disease was discovered. The conjunctive tunica—the lining of the lids—became dry and brittle, the tear ducts ceased to function, and the cornea became hard. The eye lost its power of resistance, bacteria invaded it unhindered, and if left untreated the patient became blind. An interesting early form of this disease is "night blindness." The person thus afflicted can see quite normally by day, but becomes completely blind at dusk. This disease was found in a number of Viennese children in 1921.

Both forms of the disease are vitamin deficiency diseases, and arise when Vitamin A, which is contained in milk and sea fish, is lacking from the diet. The richest source of Vitamin A is cod and halibut liver oil, which cure the above disease with immediate effect. But the liver of mammals (calves, etc.) also contains Vitamin A in large quantities.

However the absence of Vitamin A from the diet, or even its deficiency, also produces other consequences, such as retarded growth in children, and greater susceptibility to infection.

Although the precise action of Vitamin A is still a mystery, we have succeeded in discovering its precise chemical structure, and in producing it synthetically. In the course of scientific investigation, it was found that many plants contain a substance that is similar to Vitamin A. Carrots and beetroots are particularly rich in this substance, which is known as *carotin*, and from which the human organism itself can manufacture Vitamin A. Hence it does not matter whether the ready-made Vitamin A is taken or one of the above mentioned vegetables, since, as we have seen, the body itself can produce Vitamin A from them.

What quantity of Vitamin A or *carotin* is necessary to maintain health or, in case of a Vitamin A deficiency disease, to restore health? The minimum dose for curing the above mentioned eye disease is

0.5 milligrams of Vitamin A, or 1.5 milligrams of *carotin* per day. The best dose, i.e., the one that is adequate to keep the organism in good health, is from one to two milligrams of Vitamin A or 3 to 6 milligrams of *carotin* per day.

Cod liver oil contains from 5 to 250 milligrams of Vitamin A per lb., animal liver 50 in summer and about 12 in winter, egg yolk from 5 to 25. Carrots contain 40 mg. *carotin* per lb., corresponding to 10 mg. of Vitamin A. The active agents contained in spinach correspond to 12-30 mg. Vitamin A per lb. Vitamin A is soluble in fats.

Vitamin D. It was hotly debated for a long time whether rickets was a vitamin deficiency disease or not. This disease essentially consists in a defective calcium metabolism of the bones. The skull of an infant suffering from rickets is almost as soft as paper; later, there is an irregular and inferior development of the teeth, the limbs become misshapen, and the chest also develops irregularly. The spine may also be affected, and its distortion (hump) is frequently due to rickets. But there may be milder consequences, such as malformation of the chest and legs.

As early as sixty years ago, liver oil was administered to rickety children, purely on the basis of practical experience, with an admixture of phosphorus. Later it was gradually discovered that the phosphorus was superfluous, and that the curative effect was due solely to the liver oil. Some investigators later concluded from this that rickets was a vitamin deficiency disease, due to lack of certain foods (milk, butter, cream, etc.). Other investigators held that the disease was due to lack of light and, in fact, rickety children were in some cases cured by means of ultra-violet rays. There was a contradiction here, as both the administration of liver oil and the application of ultra-violet rays led to cures of rickets. However, the contradiction proved to be only apparent when American scientists established that it is not necessary to give artificial sunlight treatment to the patient himself, so long as his food is exposed to artificial sunlight. It followed from this that liver oil contained an anti-rickets substance, but this could also be produced in other foods, which did not contain it in adequate amounts, by exposing those foods to artificial sunlight. Finally, this conclusion proved to be correct, and the substance in question was named Vitamin D, which was later produced synthetically.

Thus it was found that liver oil contains two different vitamins, A and D. The substance in various foods which could be changed into Vitamin D by irradiation with ultra-violet rays was named *ergosterin*.

What quantities of Vitamin D are necessary to ensure normal development? The answer is, millionths of one gram, the so-called gammas. A child should receive 0.000002 grams of Vitamin D per day. This quantity is contained in 0.5-5.0 grams of liver oil, or in 2-4 pints of milk untreated with artificial sunlight, or 1-2 cubic centimetres of irradiated milk, or in 1.0-50 grams of butter, or 10 grams of egg yolk.

In order to prevent rickets, children must have plenty of sunshine and foods containing Vitamin D.

CHAPTER 16

The Sexual and Other Vitamins

In the case of the vitamin deficiency diseases discussed so far, the diseases were known long before the discovery of vitamins, and it was also guessed that they were connected with some dietetic deficiency. Also, the remedies were discovered on the trial and error principle. In the case of Vitamin E, which we will discuss in this chapter, the process was the reverse. It was only when, in the course of investigations relating to other vitamins, Vitamin E was accidentally discovered, that certain pathological conditions were connected with a deficiency of this vitamin.

Some years ago an American investigator observed that rats kept on a certain diet were afflicted with certain disease. *The males became sterile or impotent.* The production of spermatozoa gradually ceased and the testes degenerated. In the females there were at first no corresponding symptoms. The genital cycle, the maturing of ova, remained normal, normal impregnation was also possible, and for a time, the embryo developed normally. *Then, suddenly, it died.* It was eventually discovered that these phenomena were due to deficiency of a substance contained in the greatest quantities in the germ of wheat.

Vitamin E is soluble in fat, and therefore belongs to the same group as Vitamin A and D. An increasing number of observations indicate that abortions in otherwise healthy women are partially due to a deficiency of Vitamin E, and such cases have been considered successfully treated with Vitamin E preparations. Even in animals (cows) a certain type of abortion has been proved to be due to a deficiency of Vitamin E, and has been cured with the aid of that vitamin. It is probable that impaired potency in men may in some

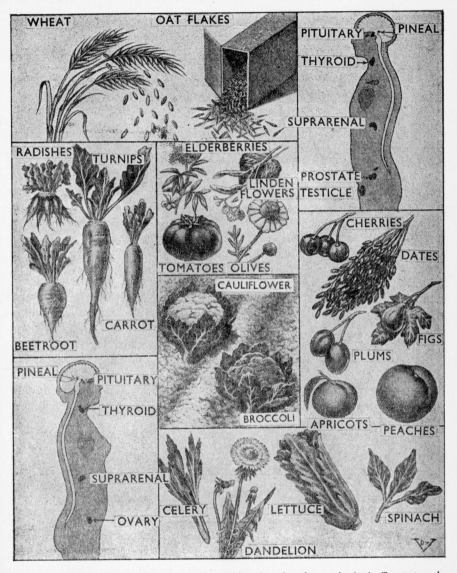

FIG. 75—The male and the female body, showing position of man's and woman's glands. Twenty-two pictures in one plate, showing foods that promote improvement of sexual debility and strengthen the endocrine glands (testes, ovaries, etc.).

cases be due to this deficiency. More recent and careful tests of Vitamin E preparations, both in threatened abortion cases and in male and female sterility, have produced only inconclusive results.

A great deal remains to be discovered in connection with Vitamin E. As a matter of curiosity we mention here that the queen bee cannot develop into such until she is provided with a sufficiency of Vitamin E. The bees see to this, although they have no knowledge of vitamins.

Vitamin B. The vitamins discussed so far are all soluble in fats. Vitamin B, or rather the Vitamins B, are soluble in water. The disease—beri-beri—which is caused by a deficiency of Vitamin B, has already been mentioned. Beri-beri has two forms: "dry" beri-beri, in which muscles are paralyzed and the skin rendered insensitive as a result of inflammation of the nerves; and "wet" beri-beri, in which the body retains large quantities of water, so that swellings appear in the face, limbs and trunk. In many cases this Vitamin B deficiency disease is fatal.

Vitamin B occurs in large quantities in yeast, as well as in rice husk. Up to a few years ago it was thought that Vitamin B is a single substance, but scientific research has now proved that there is a Vitamin B group, which includes several vitamins of this type, which vary both in character and action from each other. The vitamin which prevents the inflammation of the nerves which is a symptom of beri-beri, has been named Vitamin B_1, or thiamin, and can be produced in the laboratory. Another vitamin of the B group is B_2 or Vitamin G, a deficiency of which affects growth. There are further members of this group, designated by numbers 3-7.

The disease called pellagra, which is prevalent particularly in regions where corn is a staple food of the people (Spain, Italy, Roumania, and in some parts of the southern United States), has been attributed to a deficiency of certain group B vitamins. Deficiency of nicotinic acid is considered the principal reason for development of pellagra. The disease first attacks the exposed parts of the body (hands, face, feet), the skin of which turns a brownish black. These symptoms are associated with intestinal and nervous troubles. It is not certain whether pellagra is caused solely by vitamin deficiency or whether other factors are also involved in addition to such lack.

It is interesting to note that the B group includes several vitamins, a deficiency of which causes skin diseases in the animals experimented with. B_6, in particular, appears to have some connection with skin diseases. We will deal with this subject further in the following pages.

Vitamin C. We have already mentioned the disease—scurvy—which is due to a deficiency of Vitamin C. Scurvy last occurred in Europe during and after World War I, particularly where tinned fruit and vegetables were used, as the Vitamin C is destroyed by the process of preservation.

A characteristic feature of scurvy is bleeding from various parts of the body. The bleeding starts in the gums, which then become spongy, so that the teeth eventually fall out. But bleeding also occurs under the skin in the region of the joints, causing acute pain. The disease, if neglected, is fatal. However, administration of substances containing Vitamin C, like lemon and orange juice, works wonders. The bleeding stops, the pain ceases, and the patient quickly recovers. Scurvy also occurs in infants fed for a long time on boiled cow's milk, as the Vitamin C which the milk contains is destroyed by boiling.

Vitamin C has in recent years been isolated in its pure state from paprika, also known as capsicum. The chemical composition of the vitamin has also been discovered, and synthetic production is now common. The chemical name of Vitamin C is *ascorbic acid*. It is an interesting fact that the human organism requires more of Vitamin C than of the other vitamins. The amount required daily by the average person is 30 milligrams. Recently there has been developed good evidence that a subclinical Vitamin C deficiency is often greatly responsible for abortions and early miscarriages in women, due to a hemorrhagic tendency in the uterine cavity about the fetus.

We have seen that Vitamin B has some connection with affections of the skin. The same applies to other vitamins, some of which have been utilized for beauty treatments, either in the form of vitamin ointments or as preparations to be taken internally. The vitamins so used include Vitamin A, which preserves the mucous membranes, and also protects the skin. It has been found that injuries and burns heal very quickly after an application of cod liver oil, and ointments on this principle are extensively used in cases of skin disorders.

There is an unpleasant skin disease of childhood which manifests itself in the form of moist scabs. It has been found that this disease can be favorably influenced by the administration of Vitamin D.

Deficiency of Vitamin B_6 caused inflammation of the skin in animals experimented with, but we have little data concerning the effect on humans.

In this brief survey of the consequences of vitamin deficiency we have only dealt with definite diseases, in order to illustrate the subject more strikingly. But there are other, less pronounced pathological conditions caused by vitamin deficiency, though not total deficiency. In such cases there are no characteristic disease symptoms, only such phenomena as retarded growth, inadequate development of the teeth, susceptibility to colds, infections, etc., and also digestive troubles.

It will be seen what an enormous influence these minute amounts of vitamins exercise on the organism. Unfortunately, we are still far from having a complete knowledge of the full scope of vitamins.

BOOK III

Natural Birth Control

CHAPTER 17

AN AGE-OLD DREAM OF SEX LIFE

Some years ago, Dr. Willy endeavored to answer the question whether there was a time between menstruations when a woman was immune against conception. He discussed the problem in accordance with the *then* state of scientific research, and was forced to the conclusion that there probably were such days of immunity, but that nothing of practical value could be said on the subject, since science was unable to determine the precise time of ovulation.

But in view of the present rapid pace of scientific progress, new discoveries have arisen that destroy old theories, and at the same time open up new horizons.

In the year 1929 a report reached Europe from Japan through the pages of a medical journal to the effect that a Japanese gynecologist named Ogino had succeeded in establishing the precise time of ovulation during a menstrual cycle. A few months later, Professor Hermann Knaus, then of Prague University, published his discovery, the preliminary research for which he had begun in 1924 in London under Professor A. J. Clerk, and later continued in Cambridge in association with Professor W. A. Dixon, Dr. F. H. A. Marshall and Dr. J. Hammond. Without any knowledge of Ogino's discovery, Professor Knaus had also succeeded in determining the precise day of ovulation during a menstrual cycle.

And the results of the work of the Japanese scientist, working at a distance of many thousands of miles from Europe, and with different methods, were essentially the same as those obtained by Professor Knaus. The time of ovulation fixed in both cases was essentially the same.

Now, the practical significance of the discovery of these two scientists is immense—for if we are able to determine the precise day of ovulation, then we are also able to determine on what days during the menstrual cycle the sexual act can result in impregnation.

That brings us a step nearer to the age-old dream of humanity, the dream of being masters and not slaves of sexuality. So long as sexual activity could at any time result in undesired pregnancy, undesired for health, economic or social reasons, we were slaves of sexuality, because we could never detach the greatest gift of nature, love, from fear and anxiety.

It is sometimes argued that sexual pleasure is nature's reward for self-sacrificing care that parents give to their children, and those who reject this responsibility should not partake of the reward.

But this argument is basically wrong. In contrast to animals, humans have no rutting time, i.e., no specific mating season. The woman produces throughout the year ova capable of being fertilized, that is to say, about 350 or 400 ova in the whole course of her sexual maturity of thirty to thirty-five years. If the above argument were correct, then an adult woman could only engage in the sexual act some 360 times in her life, i.e., an average of once per month. But to carry this theory to its logical conclusion, a woman should never have sexual intercourse except for the purpose of impregnation, so that she could only do so about twenty times in her whole life as a maximum, as no woman can bear more than twenty children.

It is abundantly clear from this how absurd the reward theory is. The truth is that civilized man is entitled to be the master of his sexuality, and such mastery involves no conflict with nature.

However, it might also be argued that in view of the present highly developed methods of birth control the discovery of Ogino and Knaus is of no great value. There are several reliable means of preventing conception. It is possible today to prevent pregnancy with reasonable certainty by some mechanical, i.e., artificial means, if intelligently used.

Those who advance this argument apparently ignore the fact that vast numbers of people only employ a method of contraception that is simple and without cost and that this is injurious to health—the so-called coitus interruptus, and the employment of rubber sheaths and chemicals. But even diaphragms, unless they are made of the very best materials, may be harmful to the health of the woman.

In the following chapter we will consider the influence of this method on the health of both the man and the woman; for not until the consequences of the present unnatural methods of birth control are clear to him, will the reader be able to appreciate the true value of the discovery of Ogino and Knaus.

We use the term "unnatural" in connection with present methods of birth control deliberately, and we may add that artificiality in this matter is not only unnatural in itself, but also contrary to nature in that it may seriously affect—and sometimes even renders impossible—the pleasurable conclusion of the sexual act.

Thus we will first consider to what extent this natural method of birth control is efficient and harmless, then we will follow Professor Knaus' scientific "voyage of discovery," the individual stages of which must be more interesting to the intelligent reader than any novel. And finally, we will indicate to the reader the practical conclusions to be drawn from Professor Knaus' scientific work, and instruct the reader as to how the woman's days of immunity can be calculated. At the same time, *we shall not omit to point out the defects of this natural method of birth control,* though we may say at once that in our view the discovery of Knaus may be applied with some safety in the majority of cases of normal women with regular menstrual cycles. There are very few normal women in regard to whom the precise day of ovulation cannot be easily determined by the lay person, and then only owing to some pathological factor.

We would add here that the theoretical part of Professor Knaus' work was completed in the year 1929, but the professor's scientific conscience caused him to wait for a further five years before publishing his results. During those five years he put his theory to practical *Birth Control.* But both the German and the English versions were tests, and it was only when these tests had completely succeeded, when Professor Knaus found that no healthy woman who had followed his advice had become pregnant, that he published his book on natural birth control. The book was first published in 1934. In 1936 it also appeared in the English language under the title, *Periodic Fertility and Sterility in Woman. A Natural Method of* published in Vienna.

CHAPTER 18

EFFECT OF UNNATURAL BIRTH CONTROL ON HEALTH

We must first deal with coitus interruptus, which is the most widespread, and at the same time the most harmful method of birth control.

As regards its widespread employment, it is sufficient to mention that the greatest authority on the neuroses of our age, Professor Sigmund Freud, in a lecture delivered to an audience of doctors, advised them to ask their patients first of all whether they practice coitus interruptus, and only to proceed further in their search for the cause of a sexual neurosis when they have made sure that this is not the case. Freud is convinced that 75 per cent of all cases of sexual neurosis are to be ascribed to the practice of coitus interruptus.

What is coitus interruptus? In coitus interruptus the man withdraws his member from the vagina shortly before ejaculation, so that the semen does not go into the vagina and impregnation cannot take place.

That is to say, those who practice coitus interruptus think so, but actually, it is impossible to be certain of this. Firstly, a few drops of semen may escape into the vagina before the ejaculation without the man being aware of it. And secondly, if the first sexual act is followed by another within a short time, the man may introduce into the vagina a few spermatozoa adhering to his member from the first coitus.

It will be seen, therefore, that this method is not even absolutely reliable, and cases in which impregnation occurs are all the more tragic, because a method detrimental to health and sexual enjoyment has been employed without the desired result being achieved.

It is argued—unfortunately, in some cases by medical men—that

154

if coitus interruptus were in fact injurious to health, half of civilized humanity would be ill. However, this argument is completely wrong from one viewpoint, if only for the reason that it is not claimed that coitus interruptus causes an acute illness, in which the connection between cause and effect can be immediately ascertained. Coitus interruptus cumulatively may undermine the health of both the man and the woman in the course of years, and one may say that many men are suffering from some degree of impotence and from some disease of the prostate. As regards the women, fully 50 per cent are sexually insensible, apart from other troubles in the internal genital organs that are directly or indirectly caused by the practice of coitus interruptus.

But even if we disregard the physical injuries that may arise, it is easy to see that the caution demanded of the man in withdrawing his member from the vagina shortly before ejaculation involves an effort of concentration that seriously interferes with sexual pleasure. The same applies to the woman to an even greater extent. She constantly watches the man, lest he should miss the moment of withdrawal, and instead of concentrating on the joy of the union, her thoughts are distracted by anxiety. It goes without saying that in these circumstances even the healthiest woman will hardly be able to attain orgasm. Thus coitus interruptus may easily produce complete impotence in the woman. But apart from the loss of pleasure, coitus interruptus may cause physical injury, particularly to the man, to whom this practice involves a severe physical shock. According to some scientists, coitus interruptus also affects the erection center in the spinal column, and this means a disturbance of the man's potency. But potency may be far more seriously affected through the evil effect that coitus interruptus exercises on the prostate. It is a well-known fact that the disease known as prostatitis, which consists in inflammation and enlargement of the prostate, is only too frequently caused by the practice of coitus interruptus. The connection is all the more striking because prostatitis often improves as soon as coitus interruptus is given up.

The position as regards the woman is similar. According to some of the best known gynecologists, consequences, such as the prolonged

pelvic congestion (swelling or distention with blood) following unsatisfactory or prematurely terminated coitus, may produce distress-
ing physical and emotional discomfort.

Probably the foregoing mentioned consequences are partly due to
the imperfect course of orgasm.

It should also be noted that the impact of the semen against the
entrance of the uterus, and the awareness of the twitching of the
male member during ejaculaion in the vagina, is very apt to intensify
the orgasm of the woman. But all this is missed in coitus interruptus.

Similarly injurious consequences arise where a rubber sheath is
used. Here again, the semen is injected not into the vagina, but into
the sheath, so that all we have said concerning the absence of semen
from the female genital organs in the case of coitus interruptus also
applies here.

Many men, perhaps most, only put on the rubber sheath shortly
before the sexual act. In the case of refined men this fumbling with
their own genital organs necessarily produces disillusionment, and
affects the excitement induced through the preliminaries. In addition, there are times when their use fails to serve the purpose, if the
sheaths are made from inferior materials.

As regards diaphragms, the harmful effect on the health of the
parties is less serious. The diaphragm is usually inserted long before
the sexual act—the woman can learn to insert it herself—so that there
is not the same disturbing effect as in the case of manipulation with
the sheath immediately before the sexual act.

As regards other contraceptives, there are the so-called safety
sponges, and we need only say in regard to them that "safety
sponges" is a wrong designation, since their safety coefficient is extremely low.

The same may be said about the certain chemical contraceptives
that the woman may introduce into the vagina before the sexual act.
Apart from other disadvantages, some of these preparations exercise
an irritant effect both on the mucous membrane of the vagina and
on the male member. In the case of the woman this may produce the
so-called white flux (leukorrhea).

Douching with chemicals after the sexual act is a form of contraception largely employed by poorer women, owing to its cheapness. But this method is also unreliable and sometimes harmful, particularly when the preparation is injected at high pressure, when it may cause inflammation in the pelvic organs.

Another adverse effect of douching lies in the psychological domain. A period of rest, during which the excitement abates, is a necessary part of perfect orgasm, and this period is longer in the case of the woman than in the case of the man. If the woman has to jump out of bed immediately after the sexual act in order to douche herself, this period of rest is interrupted, and the harmony of the sexual act is thereby ruined. On the other hand, if the woman delays douching too long, the spermatozoa may in the meanwhile penetrate into the uterus.

Finally, there are objections to the employment of chemical preparations from the eugenic point of view. For even when applied at the right time, the chemicals do not kill all the spermatozoa, but leave a few which, while still capable of fertilizing the ovum, are considerably weakened, so that the resulting embryo may either die before birth or if born develop into a physically and/or mentally inferior creature. Whether this assumption is correct, it is impossible to say, but some scientists postulate that in families where chemical contraceptives are employed abortions and miscarriages are comparatively frequent.

To sum up, it will be seen from the foregoing that the most widespread methods of birth control have included coitus interruptus and the use of chemical preparations, and also that these methods are the most injurious to health. Sheaths and diaphragms are less injurious to health, but these are not used to the same extent.

We may conclude this chapter with the words of Professor Sellheim, President of the International Congress for Gynecology:

"Everything that interferes with the natural course of sexual life, everything artificial, is injurious to health."

CHAPTER 19

New Discoveries in Birth Control Made at Cambridge, England

In order to fix those days of the menstrual cycle on which the woman is immune from fecundation, science had to find exact answers to three questions.

First question: On what days will the spermatozoa find in the female organism an ovum capable of being fertilized? If the sexual act took place on the days before the ovum has matured, or after it had perished, then no impregnation can take place.

But is it really possible to determine scientifically on what day of the menstrual cycle the ovum is born? Is this process governed by any strict rule?

Second question: How long after it is shed from the ovary is the ovum capable of being fertilized? In other words, once the exact day on which the ovum is born has been established, how long thereafter must the woman abstain from sexual intercourse before the ovum loses its capacity of being fertilized?

Third question: How long do spermatozoa in the female organism remain capable of fertilizing the ovum? For it may happen that the sexual act takes place before the birth of the ovum, and if the spermatozoa in the female genital organs remain capable of fertilizing an ovum for a long time, they can wait there for the ovum to be shed, and then fertilize it.

It will be seen that the problem is rather complicated, the more so as the microscopically small spermatozoa and the barely visible ovum defy observation within the female genital organs, X-rays or the microscope being useless for the purpose.

There have been cases in which a surgeon was able, during an operation on a woman, to make certain observations concerning the day of ovulation, and the fertilizing properties of ova and spermatozoa. But apart from the fact that these cases have been very rare, the value of the observations made in connection with them must be regarded as extremely doubtful, since operations are only carried out on sick women, and it would be impossible to draw valid conclusions from a sick organism in respect of healthy organisms.

However, in the absence of direct observation of general validity, there were three ways in which the problem could be investigated. Firstly, experiments with animals, secondly, experiments with healthy women (naturally without operative means), and thirdly, logical deduction.

We know that menstruation in a healthy woman takes place twelve or thirteen times in a year.

In animals there is no menstruation. Instead, there is the so-called rutting time, the season when the sexual organs of the female (and also the male) secrete certain odorous substances by which the animals are excited to sexual intercourse. At other seasons, when these odorous substances are not secreted, the female does not allow the sexual act, and the male usually does not attempt it. What is the meaning of this process and what is Nature's intention in bringing it about?

As the sexual act in the animal world, where love in the human sense does not exist, is designed solely for the purpose of procreation, rutting time, i.e., the secretion of the odorous substances, can only mean that the sexual act can only lead to impregnation *at that time*, and at no other. Which means that an ovum capable of being fertilized is present in the genital organs of the female animal at that time, and probably at no other.

Now, breeders and scientists have had female animals served on different days of the rutting period, in order to observe on which days the mating leads to impregnation.

The first experiments were made on dogs. It was found that the rutting time of bitches occurs every six or eight months. Rutting begins with the swelling of the external genital organ. This is followed by a discharge of blood from the genital organs lasting from six to eight days, then, from the eighth until the fourteenth day, by rutting proper. During these six days the sexual urge of the bitch is strongest, and although an odorous substance is secreted during the *first* eight days, and the bitch will allow herself to be served, she can only be impregnated from the ninth until the twelfth day.

By means of artificially induced mating, it has been established that the bitch cannot be impregnated during the period between two rutting times, and as the bitch cannot be in rut more than twice in a year, this means that she can only be impregnated on *six days in the year*.

The rutting time of the sow lasts approximately twenty-one days, but she can only be impregnated on three days.

The cow is in rut in cycles of approximately twenty-one days, but the period during which she is capable of being impregnated is confined to twenty-one hours, so that this most useful of domestic animals is barren for more than nineteen days out of the twenty-one.

The mare is in rut for from six to eight days at average intervals of four weeks during the spring and early summer. But the period of fertility is confined to a few days. Professor Hammond of Cambridge was able to prove that if a mare was served during the first two days of her rutting time no impregnation could follow. On the third and fourth days the animal is still sterile to the extent of 50 per cent and full fertility does not come until the sixth and seventh days of the rutting period. Thus a mare is completely sterile for twenty-four days out of twenty-eight and completely fertile only on two of the remaining four days.

All these examples from the world of mammals go to prove that animals are only fertile for a very short time during the rutting period, and only for a very few days during the whole year. And the results quoted above have been determined with absolute certainty by scientists and breeders, so that there can be no doubt whatever as to their accuracy.

But why is it that animals can only be impregnated during their rutting time? As fertile spermatozoa have been found to be present in the male animal throughout the whole of the rutting period, the cause of this phenomenon can only lie in the female animal, and it must be this, that the fertile germinal cells of the male only find a fertile ovum in the female on certain days. We are therefore in a position to say that *the fertile ovum is born during those few days of the rutting period, and that it perishes or becomes sterile after a short time.*

Although the animal experiments referred to above are convinc-ing enough, it will be useful to describe one more such experiment, a brilliant effort of Professor Hammond, which gave Professor Knaus the strongest impulse in his own investigations. Professor Hammond's experiment was based on the following considerations:

In certain mammals the ovum only detaches itself from the ovary (or is only born) after mating. In these animals, the excitement induced by the sexual act affects the ovaries in such a manner that they eject the mature ovum, and no ovulation can take place without previous mating, as it is the muscular contractions accompany-ing the mating that ultimately lead to the birth of the ovum. Cats and rabbits, whose fertility is proverbial, are among the animals in which ovulation occurs in this manner. Some present-day American sterility specialists feel that this type of ovulation can occur at least occasionally in the young woman not yet adjusted to a regular mari-tal and sexual life.

The great fertility of these and similar animals is due to the fact that every sexual act results in impregnation. As often as the female accepts the approaches of the male, all the mature ova are subse-quently ejected from the ovaries, and the spermatozoa present in the abdomen of the female wait there until the ova are born, and then fertilize them.

Professor Hammond examined some hundreds of female rabbits after mating, and found that the ova are shed about ten hours after mating. As the spermatozoa require six hours to reach the abdominal cavity through the vagina and the uterus, they accordingly have to wait about four hours for the birth of the ova. But as soon as the ova are shed by the ovaries, they are fertilized by the waiting spermatozoa.

Now Professor Hammond wanted to ascertain how long the ovum of a rabbit remains fertile. He evolved the brilliant idea of subjecting male rabbits to the so-called Steinach operation. This operation consists in tying up the seminal duct, so that the semen cannot leave the seminal reservoir. The object operated on nevertheless has normal erection and is capable of performing the sexual act, but is not capable of impregnating the female, as the semen cannot leave the genital organs, and therefore cannot reach the female genital organs.

Professor Hammond caused several female rabbits to be served by male rabbits thus operated on. As a result, the ova in the female animals were shed some ten hours later, but they were not awaited by spermatozoa, since none had reached their genital organs. Now, the same females were mated with normal males, each after a different interval of time. Professor Hammond then found that where the second mating took place within two or three hours of the first, impregnation followed, while if the second mating occurred six hours after the first, the ova were already sterile. *It was easy to conclude from this that the ova of rabbits are only fertile for a few hours after they are born.*

The female ape is the only animal which, according to the observations of many scientists, has a regular menstrual cycle of between twenty-seven and thirty days. In contrast with other animals, which have a distinct rutting time, and usually do not allow the sexual act at any other time, the female ape consents to mating at any time during the menstrual cycle, without, however, being impregnated by each act. It follows from this that the female ape also has fertile and sterile days.

An American scientist, Professor Hartman, investigated this problem on a carefully tended colony of monkeys. He found that out of 420 copulations, which took place on any given day of the menstrual cycle, only 49 resulted in impregnation. But all the forty-nine cases of copulation took place between the eleventh and sixteenth days of the menstrual cycle. It will be seen from this that there is a sharp division between the fertile and sterile days of the female ape, so that we are entitled to speak of a period of complete immunity to impregnation in that animal.

Many further examples could be quoted from the animal world

in which it has been proved that the female is only fertile for a few days or hours; but no single case is known to science in which mammals are *always* fertile outside their rutting time.

Having established beyond doubt that the period of fertility in the higher mamals is thus confined, it is logical to ask why this should not also be the case with regard to the human female?

And the answer is that the fertility of the human female, who in the zoological sense is also a mammal, is similarly confined to certain periods. To anyone acquainted with the maturing processes of human ova, this is in no way surprising. For the human ova passes through a double maturing process, one in the ovary, and another after fertilization, and if the interval between the first maturing process and fertilization is too long, the ovum degenerates. It never reaches full maturity, and any subsequent attempt by the spermatozoa must fail, since the ovum is by then sterile.

What happens to the unfertilized ovum? It proceeds through the oviduct towards the uterus, being moved along by the feelers with which the mucous membrane of the walls of the oviduct are studded. These "feelers" are in constant agitation, somewhat like a field of corn in the wind, with a rapid forward stroke, towards the uterus, and a slow backward stroke. During its slow progress in the oviduct, the ovum acquires an albuminous covering composed of several layers. The albumen is derived from the secretions of the oviduct, and the covering not only protects the ovum, but also supplies it with valuable nourishment.

But the albuminous covering has a further role, in that it prevents the spermatozoa from penetrating the ovum, as when the envelope is complete they are incapable of piercing it.

Indeed, ape ova have been found with dead spermatozoa embedded in the envelope, showing that the spermatozoa died in a vain effort to pierce the envelope. This proves that the female ovum can only be fertilized before it has acquired its albuminous envelope. Thus fertilization must take place either before the ovum has reached the oviduct, or soon after, when it has only covered a short journey in it, since, as we have said, the albuminous envelope is acquired in the course of its passage through the oviduct, and if it travels far enough it will have acquired the albuminous envelope that prevents fertilization.

Thus the human ovum is no exception to the rule applying to mammals in general. It, too, can only be fertilized for a short time, a period, as we will show later, not exceeding twenty-four hours.

It might be thought that, in view of this, a woman is only fertile for twenty-four hours during each menstrual cycle, so that no intercourse that takes place outside those twenty-four hours can lead to impregnation. But what if the spermatozoa retain their capacity of fertilizing an ovum for a long time? Assume, for instance, that the twenty-four hours during which a certain woman has a fertile ovum in her body falls on October 10th. If it is true that the spermatozoa retain their fertility for several days or even weeks, then a sexual act that took place, say on October 1st, can still result in impregnation, as the spermatozoa can wait until the ovum is born, in order to fertilize it immediately on its appearance.

We will therefore investigate, in the following chapter, the problem as to how long the spermatozoa lodged in the abdomen or in the genital organs of the female, retain their fertilizing capacity.

CHAPTER 20

MALE SPERMS' ENERGY

We have already discussed the structure of the testes, epididymis and seminal ducts elsewhere in this work. We know that the scrotum is composed of two cutaneous folds which are joined together in the middle to form a sac, and that these folds are in turn composed of several layers of skin. We further know that the scrotum possesses a so-called automatic muscular system, i.e., a muscular system whose activity is independent of the will, so that we are unable to contract the scrotum at will.

The two testes lie in the scrotum. Their structure is highly complicated. Each testicle is divided by thin membranes into about 300 sections, each section containing convoluted tubules. The spermatozoa are produced by the cells constituting the walls of these tubules.

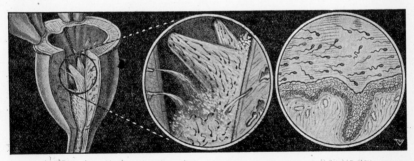

The picture story of how the prostate gland of man gives the spermatozoa the power to move to the membrane of the vagina.

FIG. 76 — The prostate, open. The semen is in the prostatic urethra.

FIG. 77—The prostatic fluid gives the spermatozoa the power to move.

FIG. 78—Spermatozoa moving over the mucous membrane of the vagina.

The complicated process by which the spermatozoa are produced and matured is of no interest here, and it is only necessary for our purpose to recall that the spermatozoon consists of three parts, the head, body and tail. The most important of these is the head, as only the head penetrates and thereby fertilizes the ovum, while the body and tail only serve to enable the spermatozoon to move, and become detached and perish as soon as the head has penetrated the ovum. As we know, the tail performs the same sort of strokes as the tail of a fish, thereby propelling the head forward in the fluids secreted by the male and later in those secreted by the female genital organs.

The spermatozoa, upon leaving the testes, enter into the epididymis, where they must rest, as the effort involved in travelling from the tubules of the testes into the epididymis is rather exhausting to the young germinal cells. Nature has thus made provision for the spermatozoa to conserve their energies for their essential task of fertilization and the epididymis is therefore so constructed that the spermatozoa may rest in it and gather fresh energy. For this purpose the epididymis is equipped with various "installations." The prime object is to make the spermatozoa "lazy" and unwilling to move. The epididymis therefore contains a very small amount of oxygen, so that the cells become "indolent" in the foul air and are unable to waste their energy.

The interior of the vas deferens, which is a continuation of the epididymis, secretes a fluid that is slightly acid, and since acid impedes the movement of spermatozoa, this is the second means provided by nature to force the spermatozoa to "keep quiet" in their reservoir, and to conserve their energy.

Finally, there is a third means for reducing the motility of the spermatozoa and yet maintaining their vitality—the vas deferens lies at the lowest and coolest point of the scrotum, and, of course, a low temperature decelerates all vital processes.

Scientific research has sought to answer the question, how long the spermatozoa can remain in their reservoir in their fertile state. The problem was solved by means of a simple experiment on a rabbit. The entry of further spermatozoa into the epididymis from the testes was prevented by tying up the efferent duct, i.e., the tubules connecting the testes with the epididymis. It was found that the animals thus treated were still fertile up to the fortieth day. But the vas deferens still contained motile spermatozoa after sixty days, though these were no longer fertile. *Thus motility of the spermatozoa is not the same thing as fertility, it is only when they are able to propel themselves rapidly that fertility may be assumed.*

FIG. 79—Various parts of man showing how the spermatozoa are transported in body.

Testicle with its epi-	Seminiferous tubules,	Transverse section of	The vas deferens,
didymis.	enlarged.	a seminiferous tu-	which transports the
		bule, with spermato-	spermatozoa, as at
		zoa in the center.	this stage they are
			not motile.

The next problem to be investigated was, how long and under what conditions spermatozoa can maintain their fertility *outside the body*. Semen was extracted from the vas deferens of a rabbit, and also from the vagina of a female that had just been mated, and it was found that the semen from the vas deferens remained fertile for seven days, while that from the vagina only for four days, and then only if it was kept at a suitable temperature. Remarkably enough, the suitable temperature was found to be from ten to fifteen degrees C., and not body heat, which one would have thought would have been most favorable to the semen. When kept at body heat the semen only remained fertile for about thirteen or fourteen hours! Indeed, even zero was more favorable to the semen than body temperature. This unexpected result recalled earlier observations that had been made by various investigators, including one to the effect that semen maintained its motility in a dead animal longer than in a live one. In the vas deferens of animals that died in the summer the spermatozoa lost their motility much more quickly than in that of animals that died in winter. Also, if the testes of an animal were kept in a refrigerator, the germinal cells remained alive much longer than if kept at body temperature. From all this evidence it was concluded that *the life of spermatozoa is shortest at body temperature.*

But this conclusion presented a contradiction. The question arose, how is it possible for spermatozoa to maintain their fertility for so long in the vas deferens if it is true that body heat reduces the fertility of spermatozoa? In order to solve this problem, it was necessary to investigate the behavior of the testes under certain changes of temperature, and also to determine whether the temperature of the scrotum is the same as that of the rest of the body.

For this purpose the fertility of animals was tested after they had been exposed to high temperatures. Male mice were kept in a hatching oven for some time at a temperature of about 110 degrees, and it was found that their fertility was rapidly reduced. It was observed that during their stay in the hatching oven, the testes of the animals sank low in the scrotum, so that the scrotum was dragging along on the floor. The animals dipped the lower part of their bodies in the dish of water that stood in the hatching oven, thereby instinctively endeavoring to reduce the temperature of the testes.

However, it is not necessary to expose the whole animal to a high temperature in order to reduce its fertility, as the same result may be achieved by heating the testes alone. Nor is it necessary to supply external heat; it is sufficient to wrap the scrotum in waterproof, non-conductive cloth, so that the blood heat does not escape. This experiment was carried out on pigs, goats and sheep, and after fifty days the same damage to fertility was observed as in the mice that had been heated up. It had long been known that both in animals and humans, the testes descend deep into the scrotum in a hot atmosphere, i.e., that they get as far away from the body as possible. The scrotum in such cases becomes thin and flaccid, so that the heat can escape all the more easily. On the other hand, in a cold atmosphere, e.g., in an open air bath, the scrotum contracts, so that the testes are pressed close to the body, and the walls of the scrotum, now become thicker as a result of contraction, protect the testes from becoming too cold. As the skin of the scrotum contains no fat, so that it lacks the normal protective property of other parts of the skin against cold, it was assumed that the temperature within the scrotum would be lower than, for instance, in the abdomen. Tests were made on a number of animals, and it was found that the temperature within the scrotum was, in fact, a few degrees lower. A Dutch scientist established that in the case of humans the temperature in the scrotum is from six to fifteen degrees lower than in the abdomen.

This discovery also provided the answer to another problem, a detailed discussion of which is not out of place here.

As we know, at a certain stage of the development of the normal male embryo the testes descend through the inguinal canal into the scrotum, and the normal male child is born with the testes already in the scrotum. Now, it frequently happens that one or both of the testes remain in the abdomen, and the child is born with a half-empty, or wholly empty scrotum. The testes can be brought down by means of a minor operation, but if this operation is not performed the testes usually remain in the abdomen even after puberty. Formerly it was not known why it was that, although the testes of men thus afflicted are normal, and they are able to perform the sexual act normally, they are nevertheless sterile. Today, as a result of the above mentioned discovery, we know that this is due to the fact that owing to the excessive heat of the abdomen the testes cannot produce fertile spermatozoa.

Professor Knaus produced this condition in rabbits artificially in the course of his experiments, and found that the germinal cells in the hidden testes retained their motility for fourteen days, but that their fertility ceased after seven days. Thus it is clear that abdominal heat is destructive of spermatozoa, and that the male germinal gland requires a lower temperature in order to function normally.

We have mentioned above that spermatozoa that have already reached the vas deferens remain fertile for forty days. Professor

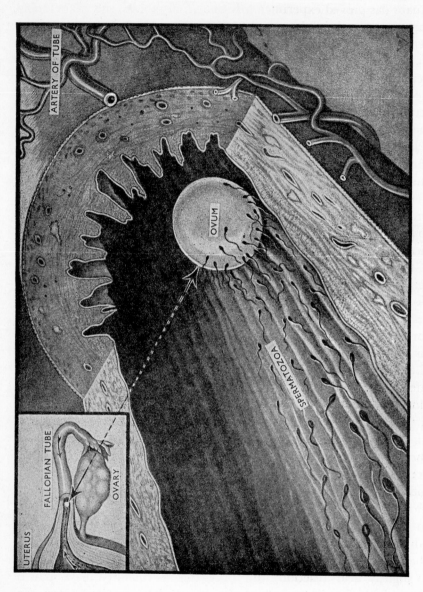

FIG. 80—A section of the fallopian tube considerably enlarged, showing in three dimensions the strange interior. How the spermatozoa hasten to meet the ovum which proceeds toward the uterus.

Knaus has proved experimentally that if, in rabbits, the vas deferens came to be in the abdomen, the fertility of the spermatozoa was only retained for four days, instead of forty.

These experiments clearly show how injurious body heat is to the germinal cells, and they explain not only why nature has found it necessary to locate the germinal glands outside the body (in the scrotum) but also why the reservoir of the spermatozoa—the vas deferens—is located in the lowest and coolest part of the scrotum. Thus· Nature has allotted to the scrotum the task of maintaining the male germinal glands at a lower temperature than the rest of the body, as it is only then that they can function normally. This is in accord with the observations of an investigator to the effect that the fertility of man pursuing a sedentary occupation suffers, because their germinal glands are exposed to high temperatures for a long time, in the same way as in obese persons.

Why Nature has made the germinal cells of man and of some mammals more sensitive to heat than those of some other animals (the bat, birds, etc.) is as yet an unsolved mystery.

Now that we know why the spermatozoa can retain their fertility for so long in their reservoir, the vas deferens, it will not be difficult to comprehend how they must behave under different conditions. To sum up briefly: in the vas deferens the supply of oxygen is very slight, the temperature is lower than in the abdomen, and the secretion is slightly acid, and all these factors reduce the motility of the spermatozoa, hence, as we have said, they can retain their fertility in the vas deferens for forty days. But when they are injected into the vagina, they are faced here, and in the other female genital organs, with different conditions. The abdominal temperature alone reduces their fertility to four days. But this period is substantially shortened by the fact that, on their way through the seminal duct to the urethra, various glands add to the spermatozoa substances which owing to their alkaline reaction lend considerably motility to these germinal cells. The secretion of the vagina normally produces a slightly acid reaction; but once the spermatozoa have passed through the cervix or neck of the uterus, they once more move in an alkaline environment, as the secretions of the uterus and the oviduct are both alkaline. Thus the spermatozoa find the most favorable conditions in these organs (which cause them to be constantly and vigorously "on the move"), but they thereby exhaust their reserve of vitality very rapidly.

In view of these facts, investigators have arrived at the conclusion that *the fertility of spermatozoa in the female genital organs is limited to forty-eight hours,* but according to the latest investigations it is probable that this period may be further reduced to thirty hours. These conclusions accord well with the results of similar investigations in various mammals. Thus, according to the present state of research, *it is a biological law that the fertility of the spermatozoa of warm-blooded animals whose testes are in a scrotum, is limited, when in the female genital organs, to a maximum of forty-eight hours.*

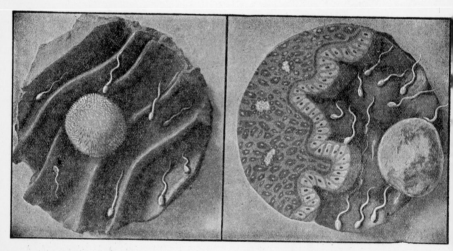

FIG. 81—Vigorous ovum and weak sperm incapable of attacking it.

FIG. 82—Vigorous sperm which do not attack ovum, as it is dead.

Now, when the extremely motile spermatozoa have passed through the neck of the uterus, they are faced with a great many obstacles that they must overcome. They must battle against the current of the secretions, which is directed outwards, and also against the outward stroke of the feelers with which the interior of the oviduct is studded. But even the spermatozoon that has overcome all these resistances, may easily get lost among the "hills and dales" of the oviduct. But that is not all. The spermatozoa in the female genital organs are received as undesired invaders, and the white corpuscles of the blood are mobilized against them. The greater part of the spermatozoa are devoured by these corpuscles. Nature's precaution against this process of destruction is the presence of some hundreds of millions of spermatozoa in each emission of semen, so that one or other of them may in spite of everything reach the ovum. The importance of this enormous excess in the number of spermatozoa may be gathered from the fact that experiments with rabbits have proved that the fertility of these animals is reduced when there are only a million spermatozoa in a cubic centimeter of seminal fluid, and completely ceases when there are only 3,000. After a journey of many hours the quickest and strongest spermatozoon can, if still strong enough to pierce the envelope of the ovum, fertilize it.

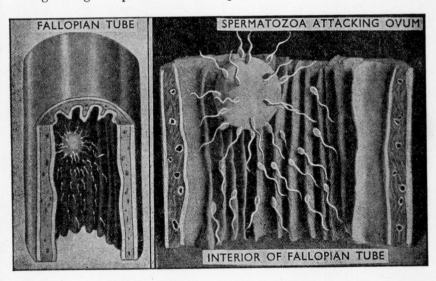

FIGS. 83 and 84—Pictures showing spermatozoa attacking ovum.

Motile spermatozoa had been found in oviducts removed from women in the course of operations, although the last coitus had taken place forty days earlier, and it was concluded from this that spermatozoa may retain their fertility in the female organs for weeks.

We now know that this conclusion is wrong, as motility and fertility are not the same thing. A spermatozoon is only fertile if it is capable of performing *powerful* movements.

To sum up: the human ovum can only be fertilized if it is reached by spermatozoa within a few hours of its birth. For soon after its birth the ovum acquires an albuminous envelope that is impenetrable to spermatozoa. As a result of observation and experiment, it has been found that the male germinal glands cannot bear the abdominal temperature and remain vigorous enough to perform their function. The same applies to their secretion, the spermatozoa. The testes and the epididymis are situated in the scrotum because the temperature in the latter is lower than in the body; it is only here that these organs function properly, and it is only here that spermatozoa reach the female genital organs, the abdominal temperature and the alkaline reaction of the uterus cause them to engage in violent movement, so that they become completely exhausted after a maximum of forty-eight hours and are no longer capable of fertilizing the ovum.

Now, we know that the female ovum is only fertile for twenty-four hours, whereas the spermatozoa, after reaching the female organism, may remain fertile for a maximum of forty-eight hours. It follows from this that a sexual act that takes place about forty-eight hours before the birth of the ovum may still result in pregnancy. Thus, at most, there are not more than seventy-two hours, or three days, during the menstrual cycle when sexual intercourse can result in impregnation, i.e., the twenty-four hours following the birth of the ovum, and the forty-eight hours preceding this event.

However, all this is only of theoretical importance, unless we are able to determine on what day the ovum is born, that is to say, during which seventy-two hours of the menstrual cycle the woman can be impregnated.

This problem, and Professor Knaus' investigations in connection with it, will be dealt with in the following chapter.

CHAPTER 21

"Central Motor" of Feminine Sexual Activity

In the section entitled "Vitamins and Hormones" we have discussed in detail the glands, their secretions, and their influence on the human organism, but we must reiterate part of our explanation here, in order to facilitate comprehension of the present chapter.

We know that there are three kinds of glands: 1. Those that secrete their product onto the surface of the skin or the mucous membranes, such as the perspiration glands, whose secretion comes out on the skin, and the salivary glands, whose secretion emerges through the mucous membrane of the mouth. 2. Glands whose secretions are conveyed direct to the bloodstream and not to the outside world; these secretions are called hormones. 3. Glands whose secretions are partly conveyed to the bloodstream direct and partly to the outside world; these are glands of combined exocrine and endocrine activity.

At this stage we are only interested in the endocrine glands, i.e., those that produce hormones. What are hormones? To use a technical simile, hormones are chemical substances with the aid of which the glands of the body exchange telegrams with each other, thereby informing each other what is happening in the organism. In addition, the hormones are capable, through their chemical reactions, of starting, accelerating and decelerating certain functions in the organism. In other words, the glands govern our bodily functions through the hormones, thereby helping to coordinate them to the benefit of the individual.

The most important endocrine gland is the pituitary. This gland is no larger than a small cherry, and considering that it produces at least sixteen different hormones, it must be regarded as a far more complicated chemical laboratory than any created by human ingenuity. The pituitary sends "instructions" to various parts of the body, of which, however, we will only consider those affecting feminine sexual activity.

The pituitary, first of all, governs the function of the ovaries, which consists in maturing ova. We know that the ovum matures in a tiny cavity, the so-called Graafian follicle. When the ovum is mature, the Graafian follicle, which is also an endocrine gland producing a hormone, notifies the pituitary of this fact. The pituitary then sends out another hormone, which compels the ovary to contract, whereby the Graafian follicle bursts and the ovum is shed. Now the pituitary "orders" a rhythmic movement of the oviducts in the direction of the uterus, through which movement the mature ovum is transported towards the uterus (though, of course, the progress of the ovum is also facilitated by other factors, as we have seen elsewhere in this work). Again, the pituitary impels the oviduct to produce albuminous secretions, from which the ovum acquires for itself an albuminous envelope. This envelope is partly designed to prevent the penetration of undesirable spermatozoa, and partly to supply nourishment to the ovum.

The pituitary, by means of a special hormone, further influences the muscular movements of the uterus, which is of extreme importance during child-birth, when the child is expelled through the contractions of the uteral muscles.

The pituitary also influences the female genital organs in a number of other ways, but what we are concerned with here is that this gland completely governs the activity of the oviducts and the uterus.

When the ovum has reached maturity in the Graafian follicle, the latter bursts, shedding the ovum and leaving a depression like a wound on the ovary. But the cells of this "wound" soon begin to multiply at a rapid rate, until they completely fill the depression. After a time the new structure—which is an endocrine gland—assumes a yellow color, hence it is called *corpus luteum* or "yellow body."

The function of the yellow body is as follows: By means of hormone "telegrams" it notifies the uterus that an ovum is on its way, thereby causing the uterus to prepare for its reception. The uterus obeys, loosening or relaxing its mucous membrane in order to enable the ovum to "dig itself in." The fertilized ovum does so in order to derive nourishment from the mucous membrane, and develop into an embryo.

However, in order to enable the ovum to dig itself in, the uterus must remain motionless, as twitching would prevent the ovum from taking root. Now, we know that the movements of the uterus are governed by the pituitary; the yellow body sees to it that this influence of the pituitary is paralyzed, so that the uterus is kept motionless in order to allow the ovum to settle down.

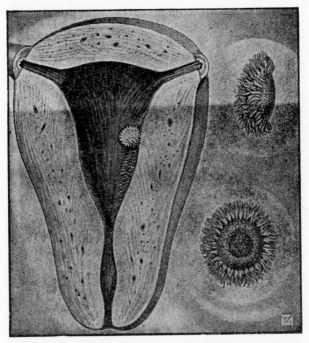

FIG. 85—Fertilized ovum anchored in the mucous membrane of the uterus. On the right, fertilized ova after a few days of development.

Naturally, it would have been extremely difficult to observe all these processes in the genital organs of a woman, and animal experiments—on rabbits—were necessary for the purpose.

The problem that confronted the Cambridge scientists was to determine the influence of the yellow body on the uterus when no that the yellow body would affect the uterus in a different way when there was no mature ovum in it than when there was an ovum embedded in it. A sterilized male rabbit (on which the Steinach operation had been carried out) was therefore made to mate with a female. As we know, in female rabbits the ova are shed as a result of the sexual act. But in this case, the male being sterilized, the ova were not fertilized, so that they set out on their journey towards the uterus unfertilized. Now, we know that unfertilized ova perish in a few hours and never reach the uterus.

But the yellow body is not aware of this tragedy. It sends out its orders in the same way as if fecundation had taken place, that is to say, firstly it paralyzes the action of the pituitary on the uterus, and secondly, it sends hormone "telegrams" to the uterus notifying it that an ovum, or ova, are on the way, so that the uterus may prepare for this reception. Thus the Cambridge scientists "fooled" the yellow body, and with it the uterus and the pituitary.

Now what happens in the uterus as a result of the instructions from the yellow body?

If the uterus is examined in the rabbit a few hours after the mating, no change can be observed. But if this operation is carried out thirty-two hours after the mating, we find that the uterus is beginning to swell, its mucous membrane becomes loose, and its color has changed owing to the richer supply of blood. It may also be observed that the uterus, after this period, is indifferent to excitation, is quieter than usual, and cannot be made to contract even if the pituitary hormone is artificially supplied to it. Not until ten days later does the uterus again become responsive to excitation and to the action of the pituitary hormone. But it is only after the seventeenth day that the uterus behaves as before the mating. If the uterus is examined two days after the mating, a colossal rate of growth in the cells of the mucous membrane may be observed. During the following days the mucous membrane forms a large number of folds, the process increasing in intensity until it reaches its climax after ten days. On the seventeenth day the mucous membrane suddenly breaks up and is ejected. As, at the same time, the uterus once more starts to react to the pituitary hormone, the question arises, What is the cause of this complete change both in the uterus and in its mucous membrane?

It was found that the changes described above immediately disappear as soon as the yellow bodies are removed from the animal. Conversely, these changes in the uterus can be artificially produced by injecting into the animal substances extracted from the yellow bodies. That shows that the change in the uterus is caused by the yellow bodies evolving from the Graafian follicle. Further confirmation of this conclusion will be found in the fact that if we examine yellow bodies under the microscope we find that the first yellow cells appear thirty-two hours after the mating, i.e., at the exact time when the changes in the uterus have been observed.

Thus observation of the rabbit's uterus proved that the changes in that organ are really caused by the yellow bodies. It was further found that the yellow bodies perish about fifteen days after the mating, so that their influence on the uterus ceases. The over-developed mucous membrane then disintegrates and is ejected through the convulsive contractions of that organ. The activity of the yellow bodies, in the case of rabbits, extends to sixteen days, and when its influence stops the apparent pregnancy of the rabbit ceases.

Another experiment that deserves to be recorded consisted in mating the females with normal males, so that impregnation took place. By means of operation on these pregnant animals the action of the yellow bodies on the uterus was studied, and it was found that during the first ten days after mating the influence of the yellow bodies was the same in the pregnant as in the apparently pregnant rabbits. In the case of the latter the preparations of the uterus for the reception of the ovum abate after ten days; in the case of the pregnant animal this activity becomes intensified. Now, why is it that the yellow bodies in the apparently pregnant animal start to degenerate after the tenth day, so that the pituitary gradually resumes control of the uterus, whereas in the pregnant animal the yellow bodies continue their activity? The reason must be that in some manner the yellow bodies must in both cases have become aware of what was happening in the uterus.

Since we know that the fertilized ovum becomes embedded in the uterus on about the tenth day, the connection is clear. Up till this time the ovum is on its travels, and is therefore not connected with the bloodstream, so that it is unable to send a hormone "telegram" to notify the yellow body that it has been fertilized. It can only send off this message when it has become embedded in the uterus, thereby coming into contact with the bloodstream. The message "instructs" the yellow body to continue to exercise its influence on the uterus.

Before we proceed further to examine the functions of the pituitary and the yellow body in the female organism, let us sum up the results of our animal experiments:

1. Thirty-two hours after mating the dominant influence of the pituitary on the ovaries and the uterus is interrupted.

2. Thirty-two hours after mating the yellow body assumes control over the ovaries, at the same time paralyzing the action of the pituitary hormone.

3. If the ovum has not been fertilized, the yellow body exercises its full influence on the uterus, impelling that organ to prepare for the arrival of the ovum. If no fertilizing ovum arrives by the tenth day, the yellow body gradually degenerates and the pituitary just as gradually resumes control of the uterus.

4. But if a fertilized ovum becomes embedded in the uterus, it sends a message through the bloodstream to the yellow body, notifying it of the event, and the yellow body then continues to control the uterus until the embryo matures.

5. When the embryo is mature, the pituitary resumes control of the uterus, impelling the muscles of that organ to violent effort, which manifests itself in the so-called labor pains, and the new creature is born.

Thus we see that the uterus is controlled by the alternate action of the yellow body and the pituitary. Until the formation of the yellow body the pituitary is master; but *the yellow body only forms after the ovum has been shed.*

The meaning of our animal experiments is therefore clear. If we are able to establish that the yellow body is in control of the uterus, then we also know that an ovum has been shed; and if we are able to establish the precise time when the yellow body develops, then we also know *the precise time when the ovum is born.*

CHAPTER 22

EXPERIMENTS ON BEHAVIOR OF FEMALE UTERUS

WHEN the English scientists and Professor Knaus had determined the influence of the pituitary and the yellow bodies on the uterus of the rabbit, Professor Knaus set himself the task of investigating the behavior of the uterus in the human female. In the year 1928 he found an opportunity to make a series of observations by means of X-rays at a women's clinic in Berlin. He found the uterus of a woman would sometimes perform powerful contractions through the action of the uterine muscles, while at other times it would lie almost inert in the abdomen. On the basis of his animal researches, Professor Knaus concluded that when the uterus was at rest, this organ was under the influence of the yellow body, and that the ovum must have left the Graafian follicle.

The question to be answered now was, On what day of the menstrual cycle does the yellow body begin to act? For if that could be determined, then *the precise time of ovulation, or the shedding of the ovum, could also be determined.* Naturally, it would have been impossible to keep a large number of women under X-ray observation day and night for several days, and Professor Knaus overcame the difficulty by constructing a very ingenious apparatus which, when introduced into the uterus, recorded its movements *automatically.* The experiment consisted in introducing this apparatus into the uterus of a woman and observing its recordings for about half an hour. Then the woman received an injection of pituitary hormone, and it was observed whether this caused the uterus to perform stronger contractions or not. The apparatus, of course, showed whether the uterus was on that particular day affected by the injection of pituitary hormone or not, that is to say, whether the uterus was under the control of the pituitary or of the yellow body. The behavior of the uterus was in this manner observed every

181

day in a large number of women. It was found that the uterus reacted to the pituitary hormone until the fourteenth day of the menstrual cycle. It was only on the sixteenth day that a striking change was observed. The apparatus recorded only very slight movements in the uterus, and even when pituitary hormone was injected the movements did not become stronger. That means that the pituitary loses control of the uterus on the sixteenth day. This situation persists until a day before the next menstruation. On the last day of the monthly cycle the uterus again starts to behave in the same way as before the sixteenth day, that is to say the pituitary resumes control of the uterus on that day. The uterus now performs strong contractions, thereby ejecting its disintegrated mucous membrane —and menstruation begins.

In view of the results of the animal experiments, the meaning of all these processes is clear. The human uterus is also under the influence of the yellow body for part of the menstrual cycle. We know that in the case of the rabbit the yellow body starts to function twenty-four hours after ovulation, producing certain changes in the uterus. We must therefore assume that the birth of the ovum in a woman also occurs at a time within twenty-four hours before the uterus ceases to be under the control of the pituitary. But as it was only possible to make one experiment daily with Professor Knaus' apparatus, the change in the human uterus could not be fixed to the precise hour as in the case of rabbits, and a full twenty-four hours has therefore been allowed for the event.

Professor Knaus carried out these investigations on fifty women, and came to the conclusion that *the ovum was always born in these women on the fifteenth day prior to the commencement of menstruation.* The fact that the interval of time until the next menstruation is always the same, is explained by the circumstance that the activity of the yellow body also extends to a certain definite number of days. Professor Knaus established that *the yellow body in a woman is active for fourteen days.*

In other words the interval from the day on which the ovum is born until the next menstruation is always the same for that particular woman.

As the yellow body in a woman always functions for fourteen days, the birth of the ovum must always take place fifteen days prior to menstruation. More recent and large series of studies than those of Dr. Knaus have shown that in individual normal women ovulation may regularly take place from 14 to 18 days prior to the first day of the next menses, depending on the length of the normal menstrual cycle in the individual woman.

Thus if we wish to determine the precise day of ovulation, we must not base our calculation on the day when the previous menstruation began, but *on the day when the next menstruation is due to begin.*

There is only one recurring function of the human body that lasts a definite period of time, that of the yellow body which, as we know, normally lasts neither less nor more than fourteen days. Thus, if we count fourteen days backwards from the first day of the next menstruation, we will know that the yellow body was born on that day, and that ovulation took place twenty-four hours earlier.

These are the only fixed points in connection with the menstrual cycle upon which a calculation of the fertile and sterile days of a woman can be based. However, before we proceed to deal with the practical application of these data, we must first deal in detail with the menstrual cycle itself.

CHAPTER 23

The Menstrual Calendar

UNTIL a few years ago people were content to express the duration of the menstrual cycle in weeks, and spoke of four-weekly or three-weekly cycles. Indeed, as far as can be established from literature, investigators were not greatly interested in the duration of the cycle.

But even those who took the trouble to investigate the matter, did so in women's clinics, where it was easiest to obtain data concerning menstruation. The results always proved to be contradictory, for it did not occur to the scientists concerned that women who go to a clinic do so precisely because they are suffering from some irregularity of the sexual organs, so that the observations made on them could not, in any case, have been applied to healthy women.

It was only when experiments with healthy women were made that the regularity of the menstrual cycle cleary emerged. It was found that ninety percent of women as a rule have a regular monthly cycle lasting twenty-eight days, or a cycle varying from this figure by two or three days in either direction. Experiments were also conducted on selected healthy women, and it was found that in ninety-seven percent of cases the duration of the menstrual cycle was almost always regular. Twenty-two percent of these women menstruated punctually every twenty-eight days, thirty-nine percent every thirty days, and eleven percent every thirty-two days. That makes a total of seventy-two percent, i.e., the porportion of women in whom menstruation was most regular. The remaining twenty-five percent menstruated at shorter or longer intervals, but these intervals recurred quite regularly. Only in three percent of the selected healthy women was there a considerable irregularity.

We will first of all consider the case of the seventy-two percent whose menstruation was most regular. We will deal with the second group next, and with the three percent in a separate chapter.

There is one point that we must emphasize at the outset: It is a characteristic fact that the great majority of women are themselves unaware how long their menstrual cycle lasts. Many women, if asked, say they have a regular twenty-eight-day cycle, but if they are observed for several months it is found that the cycle lasts either twenty-seven or twenty-nine days, or even alternately twenty-seven, twenty-eight or thirty days.

Thus a woman who wishes to take practical advantage of Professor Knaus' discovery, must first of all take the trouble to observe her menstrual cycle for several months, in order to ascertain its exact duration. It is advisable to conduct these observations for at least a year and, in order to be absolutely certain, the results should always be noted down.

In order to enable you to make up your own "menstrual calendar" in a separate notebook or pad, included here is a sample page for you to follow, as suggested by Professor Knaus. There is also shown here a "second example page of menstrual calendar" which will be of aid in keeping your own records.

In the first "menstrual calendar" which you make up for your

FIG. 86   **MENSTRUAL CALENDAR**

1st days of menstrual cycle	Following Days of Menstrual Cycle																																		
	2	3	4	5	6	7	8	9	10	11	12	13	14	15	16	17	18	19	20	21	22	23	24	25	26	27	28	29	30	31	32	33	34	35	36

own use, follow this method: The first column is for the first day of the menstrual cycle. But do not rely on memory, as the memory is frequently deceptive in this connection. It is best to wait until the next menstruation and to start the calendar by entering the date in the first column on the first day. The duration of the actual menstruation is of no importance. The date of the commencement of the following menstruation must also be entered in the first column, below the first entry. Now count the days that have elapsed between the commencement of the first and second menstruations, including the first day of the first menstruation, but *not* the first day of the *second* menstruation.

SECOND EXAMPLE PAGE OF MENSTRUAL CALENDAR

Fig. 87

1st day of menstrual cycle	Following Days of Menstrual Cycle																																		
	2	3	4	5	6	7	8	9	10	11	12	13	14	15	16	17	18	19	20	21	22	23	24	25	26	27	28	29	30	31	32	33	34	35	36
May 1																														x						
May 31																														x						
June 30																														x						
July 30																														x						
Aug. 29																														x						
Sept. 28																														x						
Oct. 28																														x						
Nov. 27																														x						
Dec. 27																														x						
Jan. 26																														x						
Feb. 25																														x						
Mar. 27																														x						
April 26																														x						

Menstruation Recurs Regularly Every Thirty Days.

In the suggested "second example page of menstrual calendar," the date of the commencement of each menstruation is entered in the first column while the thirtieth day is marked each time in the wider column, as thirty days have been found to have elapsed since the previous date. If the result is the same for a whole year, the woman in such a case would know that she has a regular menstrual cycle of thirty days, and therefore a so-called *"simple menstrual cycle,"* that is to say, one which always lasts exactly the same number of days. A "simple menstrual cycle" may also last twenty-seven, twenty-eight, twenty-nine, thirty-one days, etc.; the important thing is that it should always last an equal number of days. But if the duration of the menstrual cycle is, for instance, one month twenty-seven days and the next thirty days, it is no longer a simple, but a so-called *"double menstrual cycle."*

Finally, it may happen that a woman has on one occasion a twenty-seven-day cycle, on the second occasion a twenty-eight-day cycle, and on the third occasion a thirty-day cycle. This is called a *"triple menstrual cycle."*

Now, let us first consider the simple menstrual cycle.

If a woman has observed herself for a year, and found that she has a simple menstrual cycle, she will have no difficulty in calculating the day when her ovulation occurs. She will know from the foregoing that the yellow body is in command of her uterus for fourteen days during each cycle, independently of the duration of the cycle. In the case of a woman with a twenty-seven-day cycle, the yellow body reigns for fourteen days—no more and no less—in precisely the same way as in a woman wth a thirty or thirty-two-day cycle. Now, a woman with a simple menstrual cycle always knows beforehand on what date her next menstruation will begin, so, by counting fourteen days backwards from that date, she will be able to establish on what date the influence of the yellow body on her uterus will begin. As, however, ovulation always takes place twenty-four hours before the yellow body is formed, it is possible to say with certainty that such a woman will ovulate fifteen days before the commencement of her next menstruation.

To help in keeping accurate records, included here is an "ovulation calendar" which you can make up for yourself, in a separate notebook, starting with your next menstrual period. In this sample "ovulation calendar" shown just as an example, the woman has a simple menstrual cycle of thirty days, so that she knows that if, for instance, her menstruation begins on May 1st, it will end on the 30th of that month. Now, if she counts fifteen days backwards from

FIG. 88   OVULATION CALENDAR

1st day of menstrual cycle	Following Days of Menstrual Cycle																																		
	2	3	4	5	6	7	8	9	10	11	12	13	14	15	16	17	18	19	20	21	22	23	24	25	26	27	28	29	30	31	32	33	34	35	36
May 1															o														x						
May 31															o														x						
June 30															o														x						
July 30															o														x						
Aug. 29															o														x						
Sept. 28															o														x						
Oct. 28															o														x						
Nov. 27															o														x						
Dec. 27															o														x						
Jan. 26															o														x						
Feb. 25															o														x						
Mar 27															o														x						
April 26															o														x						

Ovulation Calendar of a Simple Cycle of thirty days.
x—last day of cycle; o—day of ovulation.

May 30th, she will know that her ovulation takes place on May 16th. She is also able to tell in advance that her next menstrual cycle will end on June 29th, and if she again deducts fifteen days (always including the last day of the menstrual cycle) she can establish in advance that her ovulation during that cycle will take place on June 15th.

Thus women with simple menstrual cycles are able to calculate their ovulation dates far ahead.

The matter is somewhat more complicated in the case of women with double or multiple menstrual cycles. To show practical examples, sample charts are included here of the "menstrual calendar" and the "ovulation calendar" of a woman who has a triple menstrual cycle.

This woman first menstruated since beginning the calendar on March 1st, and her next menstruation began on the 28th of that month, so that on this occasion she had a twenty-seven-day cycle. Deducting fifteen days, her ovulation must have taken place on March 13th. The third menstruation began on April 29th, so that this cycle lasted thirty-two days, and going back for fifteen days, we

FIG. 89

MENSTRUAL CALENDAR

1st day of menstrual cycle	Following Days of Menstrual Cycle																																	
	2	3	4	5	6	7	8	9	10	11	12	13	14	15	16	17	18	19	20	21	22	23	24	25	26	27	28	29	30	31	32	33	34	35	36
Mar. 1																										x									
Mar. 28																															x				
April 29																														x					
May 29																														x					
June 28																															x				
July 30																									x										
Aug. 26																									x										
Sept. 22																									x										
Oct. 19																														x					
Nov. 18																														x					
Dec. 18																															x				
Jan. 19																														x					
Feb. 18																																			

Menstrual Calendar of Triple Menstrual Cycle.

FIG. 90

OVULATION CALENDAR

1st day of menstrual cycle	Following Days of Menstrual Cycle.																																	
	2	3	4	5	6	7	8	9	10	11	12	13	14	15	16	17	18	19	20	21	22	23	24	25	26	27	28	29	30	31	32	33	34	35	36
Mar. 1												o														x									
Mar. 28																o															x				
April 29															o											x									
May 29															o											x									
June 28																o														x					
July 30												o														x									
Aug. 26												o														x									
Sept. 22												o														x									
Oct. 19															o															x					
Nov. 18															o															x					
Dec. 18																	o														x				
Jan. 19															o															x					
Feb. 18																																			

Ovulation Calendar of Triple Cycle.
x—last day of cycle.

find that ovulation must have occurred on April 14th. The fourth menstruation began on May 29th, i.e., thirty days after the previous menstruation on April 29th, so that this time her cycle was thirty days and, deducting fifteen days from the last day of her cycle, i.e., from May 28th, her ovulation during this cycle must have occurred on May 14th.

Now, this woman, according to her menstrual calendar, sometimes had a twenty-seven-day cycle, and sometimes a thirty or thirty-two-day cycle. In this case it is not easy to fix the day of ovulation, as the woman cannot know in advance whether her current menstrual cycle will last twenty-seven, thirty or thirty-two days. She only knows that she ovulates fifteen days earlier than the last day of her cycle, but she cannot determine the date of that fifteenth day. See the "ovulation calendar" which explains the case of a mixed cycle of not less than twenty-seven and not more than thirty-two days, in order to get a clearer understanding of this situation.

FIG. 91   **OVULATION CALENDAR**

1st day of menstrual cycle	Following Days of Menstrual Cycle.																																		
	2	3	4	5	6	7	8	9	10	11	12	13	14	15	16	17	18	19	20	21	22	23	24	25	26	27	28	29	30	31	32	33	34	35	36
												O8					O1									X8					XL				

Examples of days when ovulation may take place in the case of a mixed cycle with a menstrual cycle of not less than twenty-seven and not more than thirty-two days.
O_8—Ovulation during shortest cycle. X_8—End of shortest cycle (twenty-seven days).
O_L—Ovulation during longest cycle. X_L—End of longest cycle (thirty-two days).

[ ]—days on which ovulation may take place.

It will be seen that *a woman with a double or multiple menstrual cycle can never determine the exact day of her ovulation.* However, there is no reason for her to despair. She knows that the maximum duration of her cycle is, say, thirty-two days, and also that the minimum duration is twenty-seven days, having kept her menstrual calendar for a whole year. If she wishes to calculate the date of her next ovulation, she will reason it out as follows: My last menstruation began on May 29th. If my next cycle is of the minimum duration, i.e., twenty-seven days, then my next menstruation must begin on June 25th, in which case the ovulation would fall on June 10th. If, however, the next cycle happens to be of the maximum duration, i.e., thirty-two days, then my next menstruation will fall on June 30th, and ovulation on June 15th. And if the cycle is one of thirty days, my next menstruation will fall on June 28th and ovulation on the 13th. I am able to establish from this that whatever the duration of my next cycle is going to be, ovulation cannot take place either before June 10th or after the 15th, therefore *it falls between those two dates.*

It will be seen from the foregoing that a woman with a simple menstrual cycle can calculate the exact day of ovulation, while a woman with a double or multiple menstrual cycle can only calculate the exact period of days during which ovulation must take place, and she can do this with all the greater exactitude, the shorter the difference is between the maximum and minimum duration of her cycle.

As this calculation is of such paramount importance, we give as a further illustration the "ovulation calendar" of a multiple cycle with a minmum of twenty-five and a maximum of thirty-three days, to serve as an example.

Assume that a woman has made up her calendar carefully for a year, and has found that she has a quadruple cycle of twenty-five, twenty-nine, thirty and thirty-three days respectively. Supposing her last menstruation began on September 1st, and she wishes to calculate the date of her next ovulation. She will not be interested in the cycles of twenty-nine and thirty days, since she knows that only the minimum and maximum durations—twenty-five and thirty-three days—are of consequence. She will therefore start with the minimum cycle and reason as follows: As my menstruation began on September 1st and my shortest cycle is twenty-five days, I may have my next menstruation on September 26th, in which case ovulation will take

FIG. 92   OVULATION CALENDAR

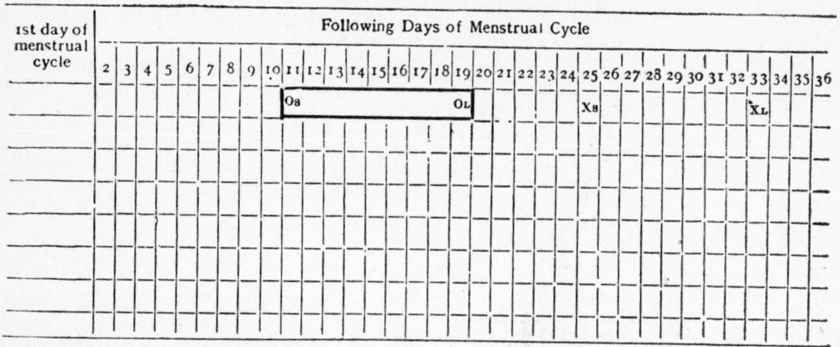

1st day of menstrual cycle	Following Days of Menstrual Cycle																																		
	2	3	4	5	6	7	8	9	10	11	12	13	14	15	16	17	18	19	20	21	22	23	24	25	26	27	28	29	30	31	32	33	34	35	36
										Os								OL							XS								XL			

Example of days during which ovulation can take place in a multiple cycle with a minimum of twenty-five and a maximum of thirty-three days.

Os—Ovulation in shortest cycle.   Xs—End of shortest cycle (twenty-five days).
OL—Ovulation in longest cycle.   XL—End of longest cycle (thirty-three days).

⸻days on which ovulation may take place.

place on September 11th; but if my present cycle lasts thirty-three days, then my next menstruation will begin on October 4th, in which case ovulation will occur on September 19th. Thus it is certain that ovulation will take place sometime between September 11th and 19th.

Now this knowledge is quite sufficient, as we will show in the following chapter, even though the woman does not, and cannot, know the exact day of ovulation.

CHAPTER 24

WOMAN'S STERILE DAYS

WE know that fecundation depends on the presence in the feminine genital organs of a fertile ovum and strongly motile spermatozoa, and we further know that the ovum only remains fertile for a few hours after ovulation. It will now be easy to determine a normal woman's days of immunity, as we are acquainted with all the relevant facts, namely:

1. That spermatozoa only remain fertile for forty-eight hours after the sexual act.

2. That the ovum is born fifteen days before the commencement of the next menstruation.

3. That the ovum only remains fertile for a few hours after it is born.

If we consider the problem from the viewpoint of the spermatozoa, we must argue as follows: As the spermatozoa remain fertile for a maximum of forty-eight hours, a sexual act taking place within forty-eight hours *before* the birth of the ovum can still lead to fecundation, as the spermatozoa may wait in the abdomen until the ovum is born and then fertilize it. In other words, the sexual act may lead to fecundation not only fifteen days before the next menstruation, when the ovum is born, but also sixteen or seventeen days before the next menstruation.

From the viewpoint of the ovum, fecundation can take place only on the fifteenth day before the next menstruation as by the next day the ovum must perish.

The result of the investigations in this matter may therefore be summed up in the following sentence:

193

No woman can be impregnated unless by a sexual act taking place fifteen, sixteen or seventeen days before the next menstruation.

It will be seen that the practical utility of the results obtained by Professor Knaus depends on a woman knowing the exact duration of her menstrual cycle, and that is why we have devoted the whole of the previous chapter to that question.

Women with a simple menstrual cycle have an easy task. They always know when the next menstruation will take place, and all they have to do is to count back fifteen, sixteen and seventeen days from the date concerned. However, in order to save even that little trouble, we give below a table from which the fertile days of such a woman can be determined at a glance. As, however, the author's responsibility in this matter is very great, he has, in agreement with Professor Knaus, established this table on the basis of five-day fertility, adding a day each for safety both before and after the three-day period, though there is no scientific basis for this precaution.

In other words, although according to the latest scientific researches there are only three days in the menstrual cycle of a woman during which she can be impregnated, i.e., the fifteenth, sixteenth and seventeenth days before menstruation, we add the fourteenth and eighteenth days as a measure of precaution. Accordingly, we must vary the above summing up to the following effect:

A sexual act taking place on the fourteenth, fifteenth, sixteenth, seventeenth or eighteenth day before the commencement of the next menstruation, may lead to impregnation.

So that you may make your own table, in a pad or notebook, here is a sample table to act as an example, to enable you to calculate the days of your fertility. In this sample chart, our calculations range from a cycle of twenty-four days. The days of fertility are indicated.

This table shows that, for instance, a woman with a 24-day cycle cannot be impregnated between the 1st and 6th and the 12th and 24th days;

25-day cycle cannot be impregnated between the 1st and 7th and the 13th and 25th days:

26-day cycle cannot be impregnated between the 1st and 8th and the 14th and 26th days.

And so on, the fertile days in the above instance being:

7—11

8—12, and

9—13, respectively.

TABLE FOR CALCULATING FERTILE DAYS IN

MENSTRUAL CYCLE

Duration of Cycle	1	2	3	4	5	6	7	8	9	10	11	12	13	14	15	16	17	18	19	20	21	22	23	24	25	26	27	28	29	30	31	32	33	34	35
24 days									o															x											
25 ,,									o																x										
26 ,,										o																x									
27 ,,											o																x								
28 ,,												o																x							
29 ,,													o																x						
30 ,,														o																x					
31 ,,															o																x				
32 ,,																o																x			
33 ,,																	o																x		
34 ,,																		o																x	

☐—Days of Fertility.

This table shows that, for instance, a woman with a

   24-day cycle cannot be impregnated between the 1st and 6th and the 12th and 24th days;

   25 ,, ,, ,, ,, ,, ,, ,, 1st and 7th and the 13th and 25th days;

   26 ,, ,, ,, ,, ,, ,, ., 1st and 8th and the 14th and 26th days.

   And so on, the fertile days in the above instance being: 7—11,

                                     8—12, and

                                     9—13 respectively.

If you have a double or multiple cycle, you can also keep your own calendar (using this table as a suggestion). It is only necessary for you to make your own "ovulation calendar" with a cross on the ovulation day of your shortest menstrual cycle. Next, on your own calendar mark with a cross the ovulation day of the longest cycle, which can also be determined from the table. Then shade the square between the two ovulations, including the crosses marking the ovulation days. You will then know that on the days falling within the shaded portion you are fertile, as ovulation takes place on one of these days. However, in accordance with the above safety rule, the day following the later ovulation should also be shaded on your calendar.

As a further illustration of an "ovulation calendar" for a woman with a multiple cycle, we include one which shows a minimum cycle of twenty-six days, and a maximum cycle of thirty-two days.

FIG. 94

OVULATION CALENDAR

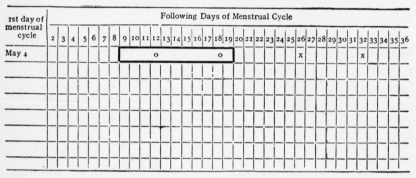

1st day of menstrual cycle	Following Days of Menstrual Cycle																																		
	2	3	4	5	6	7	8	9	10	11	12	13	14	15	16	17	18	19	20	21	22	23	24	25	26	27	28	29	30	31	32	33	34	35	36
May 4											o							o							x						x				

Minimum cycle of 26 days. Maximum cycle of 32 days.

Thus a woman with a minimum cycle of twenty-six and a maximum of thirty-two days can only be impregnated between the ninth and nineteenth days of the menstrual cycle. In the above instance, as the menstruation falls on ·May 4th, the woman will be fertile from May 12th to the 22nd. She is *not* fertile from May 4th till the 11th, and from May 23rd until the end of the menstrual cycle. The first day of the next menstruation will fall between May 29th and June 4th, but she will not know on which day until the menstruation actually commences. She should then note down the first day of menstruation and calculate her fertile days as above.

It will be seen that a woman with a double or multiple cycle must assume that she may be impregnated on a greater number of days than a woman with a simple cycle. Whereas the latter always has five days of fertility, the former will have to calculate the difference between the longest and shortest cycles, plus three days before and one day after the possible days of ovulation. Thus if the minimum cycle is twenty-seven days and the maximum thirty-two, six days plus four days, or a total of ten days must be calculated.

Fortunately, the number of women with multiple cycles is very small, and the difference between the longest and shortest cycles is usually not more than two or three days, so that by applying natural birth control the vast majority of women would only have to abstain from sexual intercourse for from five to eight days during each menstrual cycle.

CHAPTER 25

The Exception That Proves the Rule

NATURALLY enough, Professor Knaus' important discovery has led to a great deal of scientific controversy. That is the fate of every new scientific discovery, and it is fortunate that it should be so, for such discussion is apt to present the discovery in its true light and to separate the important from the unimportant. We will therefore first review the scientific objections raised against the theories of Professor Knaus, then explain the limitations set by the professor himself.

It has been argued that spermatozoa may retain their fertility longer than forty-eight hours. Thus motile spermatozoa have been found in the female organism ten or twelve days after the last sexual intercourse.

Professor Knaus countered this argument with the statement that the motility of spermatozoa does not mean in the least that they are also fertile. We have seen above that the high temperature prevailing within the female organism and the alkaline secretions of the uterus impel the spermatozoa to such violent movement that for the most part they exhaust their "motile energy" in forty-eight hours. But even if a few spermatozoa escape destruction in this way, they certainly become incapable of *powerful* movement, and it is only spermatozoa capable of powerful movement that can penetrate and fertilize the ovum.

It has also been argued that there are some mammals in whom the spermatozoa remain fertile for a long time in the female abdomen. It was pointed out, for instance, that the bat settles down to its winter sleep shortly after its rutting time, and the female retains the spermatozoa in a fertile state throughout the winter.

The answer is that the bat is the only mammal in which the testes of the male are not in a scrotum, but in the abdomen. Thus the spermatozoa of the bat are used to an abdominal temperature from the moment of their formation in the male organism. At the same time, hibernation involves a slowing down of the bodily functions, so that little heat is produced even in the abdomen of the female, and these two reasons are a sufficient explanation of the continued fertility of the spermatozoa after several months.

Thus the objections relating to the fertility of the spermatozoa in the female organism may be rejected.

An objection relating to the ovum was to the effect that if the sexual act is particularly pleasurable to the woman, the resulting muscular contractions may produce contractions in the ovary, so that the Graafian follicle may burst sooner than expected, and ovulation occur earlier. As we mentioned in Chapter 19, some eminent American gynecologists with special knowledge of fertility and sterility problems suspect this sort of phenomena to occur, particularly in certain younger women not accustomed to regular sexual life. There seems to be another explanation as to why occasionally a young woman becomes pregnant by coitus during her "safe period." A change in the menstrual cycle may occur if ovulation happens at such an unusual time. In fact, one or two authorities feel that on the basis of careful basal temperature studies, occasionally a woman may ovulate two or three times in the same month, associated with superexcitation sexually.

Now, it is true that some women menstruate less and more painfully before engaging in sexual activity than women leading normal sexual lives. But that is due to causes unconnected with ovulation. Cases of women in whom the duration of the menstrual cycle has changed after commencing to engage in sexual intercourse, are relatively infrequent.

However, Professor Knaus admits that there are cases in which the duration of the menstrual cycle may change as a result of external circumstances. Thus, pregnancy may produce a temporary or permanent change in the duration of the cycle. It often happens that after a birth or an abortion the cycles are excessively long, but they may revert to their normal duration later. It is therefore understandable that after a birth at least four menstruations must be observed in order to determine the nature of the menstrual cycle, as this is indispensable for a precise calculation of the fertile days. If the duration of the cycles is the same as before pregnancy, then the woman may rely on the previously calculated fertile days again. But if the cycles fluctuate, showing that the ovaries have not yet resumed their normal activity, then the woman must wait until the cycles revert to the former duration, or until a new duration can be ascertained.

It is also easy to understand that the course of the menstrual cycle may be affected by illness involving fever, physical injuries, surgical operations, or a serious psychological upheaval. In such cases the time of ovulation may change in an incalculable manner, so that there is no basis upon which the fertile days can be determined. Here again, the woman must wait until the regular cycle returns.

All those events that seriously affect the vital processes in the body as a whole, also influence the activity of the ovaries. Such events are, e.g., mountaineering, or severe physical strain in connection with sports, or long journeys in a different climate. The effect may be one of two kinds, according to the period in the menstrual cycle when the event occurs. If it falls in the first half of the cycle, ovulation may be delayed, but if it falls in the second half, menstruation may start prematurely, because the activity of the yellow bodies ceases earlier.

It will be gathered from the above that a woman must be particularly careful after childbirth, after an illness, or in case of a change of climate.

We have thus dealt with all the exceptions which Professor Knaus himself recognizes.

However, in order to avoid unpleasant surprises in connection with the practice of natural birth control, women must rigidly observe the conditions laid down here. Above all, a woman must not

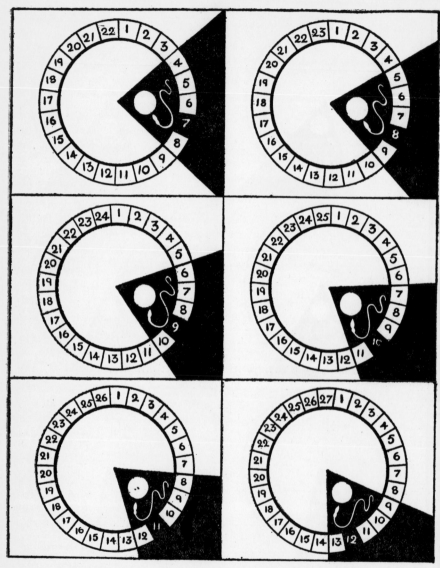

Fig. 95—Six fecundation calendars of six different sex-cycle types of women.
We have devised fecundation calendars for various menstrual cycles. The numbers marked in the black zone indicate the days near ovulation (the actual day being entered in the black space in the circle), on which days fecundation is easy. The days marked in white are those on which fecundation is impossible.

FIG. 96—Six more fecundation calendars for women with menstrual cycles from 22 to 33 days. Our fecundation calendars are valid for women with menstrual cycles from 22 to 33 days. The first, second, third days are the days of menstruation.

begin natural birth control until she has determined the precise duration of her menstrual cycle, and in order to achieve that *she must keep a calendar conscientiously for one year.*

If a woman neglects this precaution, or if she relies on her memory in determining her fertile days, then any errors will be due not to a defect in the natural method of birth control, but to the woman herself.

If a woman is for some reason unable to determine her safe period herself, her notes must be submitted to a doctor, who will mark her safety days in the menstrual cycle. Recent large series of women studied have shown that impregnation can occur on any day of the menstrual cycle, including the days of bleeding, the proof being that these women each had only one instance of coitus in the cycle (cases of short furloughs of soldiers). However, the majority of pregnancies occurred roughly in the 8th to 15th day of the cycle.

CHAPTER 26

SEX OPERATIONS ON WOMEN

THE Japanese scientist, Ogino, began his investigations concerning the fertile days of a woman in the year 1924, and his results were first published in English in 1930 in *The Japan Medical World*.

Ogino established, by means of operations carried out on more than seventy Japanese women, that the ovum was always born between the sixteenth and twelfth days before menstruation. Thus the difference between the results of Ogino and Knaus lies in the fact that according to the latter the birth of the ovum falls on the fifteenth day before the next menstruation. But it must be remembered that Ogino made his observations by means of surgical operations, whereas Professor Knaus obtained his results experimentally. The women operated upon were, naturally, ill, hence Ogino could not fix the day of ovulation so exactly as Knaus, who worked on healthy women.

The scientific dispute between the two scientists as to priority in making this discovery is of no importance here, where we are dealing with its practical application. Suffice it to say that two scientists, who did not know each other or about each other, came to the conclusion independently that there are fertile and immune days in the menstrual cycle. Ogino holds that ovulation may take place at any time in the course of five days. Professor Knaus says that ovulation can only occur on one day, but as an extra precaution he advises that a day each should be added before and the after the day of ovulation, so that the difference between the two scientists is not very great.

It happens very rarely that scientists working independently of each other on different continents, reach the identical result. When it does happen, every unprejudiced observer must admit that human

knowledge has been enriched. In the present case it has been enriched by something whose significance cannot be overestimated.

Because a knowledge of the fertile and immune days of woman
does not only mean that natural birth control is now possible. It
also means that some types of sterility may be combatted with success.

That this idea engaged the mind of man thousands of years ago,
may be gathered from the Old Testament, where the ritual laws
relating to the menstrual cycle are designed to ensure fertility.
First, conjugal intercourse is prohibited within at least twenty-four
hours of the expected menstruation; second, during menstruation,
and however brief the process may be, it must be assumed to last at
least five days; and third, for seven days after the fifth day the woman
must take ritual baths to clean herself, and if the menstruation lasts
longer than five days, then seven days after the last dav. What is the
result of these laws?

Assuming that a woman has a twenty-eight-day cycle, which is the
most frequent, she will ovulate on the fourteenth day of her menstrual cycle (calculated from the beginning). As sexual intercourse
is forbidden during the five days of menstruation and the following
seven days, she can only engage in intercourse on the thirteenth day.
In that case the spermatozoa will be waiting in the abdomen for
the birth of the ovum in order to fertilize it.

Thus the laws laid down in the Third Book of Moses promote
the fulfillment of the commandment of the First to "increase and
multiply," as sexual intercourse on the thirteenth day was almost
always bound to lead to fecundation. This explains the great fertility of Orthodox Jews, who strictly observe the above laws.

It also provides a further example of modern science illuminating
a truth discovered, or perhaps only guessed, by the Ancients.

BOOK IV

The Sexual Impulse

CHAPTER 27

ORGASM

NOT more than one-half of all women experience during the sexual act voluptuous pleasure rising to the intensity of orgasm. This process depends on a combination of various factors, which we consider necessary to describe, as even among the educated classes the subject is but imperfectly understood.

How does a sensual excitement originate in a woman? First, there is a mental impression leading to an emotional libido, which in turn is conveyed to the sexual apparatus. These organs become congested with blood, causing a swelling of the clitoris, which thereby becomes extremely sensitive to touch and friction. When the so-called preliminary phase in sexual union is over, the local and general excitement increases second by second. The Bartholin's glands secrete their typical lubricant fluid in order to facilitate ingress of the male member into the vagina. At the same time, the entrance of the vagina relaxes in order not to impede the entry of the member. The erect clitoris converts every fresh contact with the member into voluptuous sensations. After the entry of the member the entrance of the vagina may tighten owing to the contraction of the vaginal muscles. This contraction may be rendered so complete by the *bulbi cavernosi* or cavernous cells, which are located to the right and left of the vagina, and are at this stage filled with blood, that the member cannot enter. The voluptuous sensation, which is mainly concentrated in the clitoris, may spread to the entrance of the vagina, the body of the vagina, and even to the neck of the uterus, if this is reached by the member. With the intensification of excitement the activity of the glands is also speeded up. At a certain stage consciousness of the external world gradually fades, brain activity being

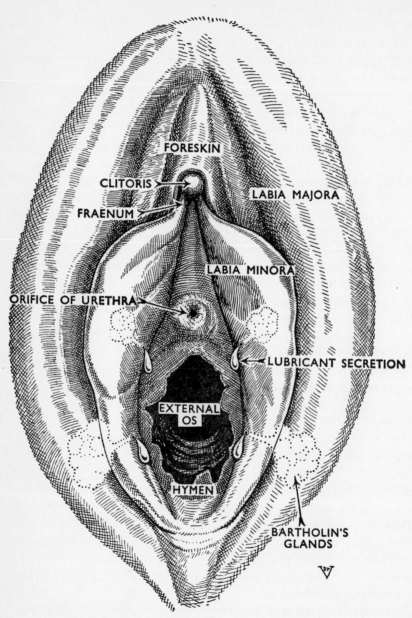

FIG. 97—The female external genitals with the glands in action.

eliminated as a result of the intense excitement, until orgasm, the peak of voluptuous sensation, occurs. At this moment there is a convulsive contraction of all the glands and muscles of the female genital apparatus. The mucous secretion from the glands of the lining of the uterus and cervix increases in amount rapidly to pre- pare a smoother pathway for the spermatozoa. If the man ejaculates simultaneously with the orgasm of the woman, this coincidence rep- resents the ultimate perfection of the sexual act.

Orgasm is followed by a stage of relaxation and peace, and the woman for a time remains in a state of contented well-being.

That, approximately, is the physiological process of the sexual act in a woman, although there are a number of variations that may still be regarded as normal. Thus in some women there is intense glandular activity even when they are only slightly excited, while in others this activity is insignificant. Also, whereas some women only attain a single orgasm, there are others who, within a short time, desire and experience several orgasms.

This difference in the sensitiveness of women depends on a num- ber of circumstances, such as their own sexual make-up and their sensual and emotional relationship with their partner.

It will be seen that during the sexual act important and intensely active phenomena occur in the female genital apparatus, and it would therefore be a mistake to assume that the woman plays an entirely passive role during intercourse. That impression could only arise in the case of women who experience no orgasm.

How is it possible to determine whether a woman does or does not experience orgasm? How can she tell herself, and how can her male partner tell? What are the circumstances in which a woman can be sure that she has had a real orgasm and how can the man observe this?

Before we proceed to answer these questions we must point out that this knowledge can only be obtained from experience. Theories only serve to confuse practical observation, particularly as they are not based on the experience of those most closely concerned, i.e., the women themselves.

The orgasm of the woman in its purest and most intense form—

and there are many forms and intensities—manifests itself quite clearly by four simultaneous muscular movements in the female genital zone. During an intense orgasm in a woman, there are rhythmic contractions of the entrance of the vagina and certain muscles in the region of the clitoris, of the urinary meatus, the sphincter ani (or contracting muscle of the anus), and the muscles of the opening of the uterus. All these muscles contract and relax repeatedly, the rhythm of the movements being sometimes rapid and sometimes slow. The movements are the same involuntary twisting movements of contraction and relaxation as occur in the muscles of the male member and in the sphincter ani of the man at the moment of ejaculation.

During a particularly intense orgasm these four rhythmic movements take place simultaneously. They may be so strong that they can be felt with absolute distinctness. For instance, the contractions of the opening of the uterus may be accompanied by a contraction of the entire uterus, which the woman may feel in the form of a light, wavy movement that goes over to the abdomen. Even the nipples of the breasts may be affected. (Conversely, the nipples may contribute very considerably to the production of orgasm.)

If the simultaneous individual contractions of the groups of muscles in question are very powerful, then the movements of the urethral and anal contracting muscles may be felt separately even if all the muscular movements merge in a general ecstasy of a powerful general movement of the entire genital zone or even of the entire body.

These purely local, though at the same time pervasive movements are inseparably associated with an acceleration of the heart action, which manifests itself in heavy breathing or panting. Like the man, the woman experiences a desire to exhale strongly, as though to relieve herself of all that has accumulated within her and is oppressing her heart. She has the sensation not so much of accelerated as of more powerful heart action—the individual heart beats go parallel with the orgastic movements, and so the whole body is shaken by a number of convulsions that communicate themselves right to the flesh of the thighs, the abdomen, even the neck.

Everyone possessing the least athletic training—i.e., the majority of people—will easily comprehend the need for exhalation during orgasm, as this produces a relaxation of the whole body, particularly of the abdominal muscles and the region of the bladder, which enables the unimpeded continuance of the automatic movements in all the organs. In the case of the man, exhalation relaxes the chest, which in the coital position, when man and woman lie breast to breast, merges him still closer with his female partner at the peak of sexual excitement.

Relaxation through exhalation (everything naturally happens automatically) also favors one of the most important secondary sensations of orgasm, namely, the feeling that one is now relieved of all physical effort, as though the body were now working of itself, and one feels, detachedly, contentedly, the final twitchings of the muscles and the activity of the heart as a transition to a restful state.

As stated, the reaction of the heart does not always consist in acceleration. Instead, one has the sensation that the heart is thundering against one's ribs, as though it were about to burst with the violent effort. This is frequently associated with a sensation, merging into the physical yet still distinctly psychical, that the local and central excitation of the genital zone pervades the whole body, right up to the heart, through a direct physical line, sometimes in an almost painful manner.

This kind of heart activity, into whose physiological explanation we need not enter here, is probably the surest sign—in case of doubt —of orgasm. Having reached the peak it diminishes just as jerkily as it started. The heart does not immediately resume its normal activity, but slows down gradually, and the excitement continues to vibrate through the body in the form of pleasant fatigue.

The movements vibrating through the whole body of the woman produce in her a sensation that must be very similar to the man's sensation during ejaculation, namely, that she is discharging something, that the body is forcing something down towards the genital zone, and thence into the outside world, into the man; the woman has a sensation as though she were giving something of herself to the man, in the purely physical sense of the term.

Duration and intensity of the orgasm vary not only in different women, but also in one and the same woman at different times and in different circumstances. The duration of the rhythmic movements can only be measured in seconds, and in most cases an orgasm accompanied by four or five strong contractions of the muscles and a few fainter movements, would be an intense orgasm in a woman.

It is a well-known fact that there are also considerable differences in the case of the man in this respect without any determinable cause. That an orgasm in a man would be influenced by lack of time, repressions, or particularly intense excitement, is, of course, comprehensible; but even in the absence of such influences ejaculation and orgastic sensation vary in intensity. Nor does this depend on the time elapsing before the ejaculation, or on any deliberate prolongation of this time, which in any case is a matter of habit and experience.

The orgasm of a man is particularly perfect when the semen is ejected rapidly and with considerable force; this is usually preceded by considerable swelling of the male member during erection. There are in this connection many subtle differences both in the case of the man and the woman. The orgasm of the woman may be particularly intense without previous prolonged excitement, and sometimes it may be particularly intensified by tension brought about through prolonged excitation. The same applies to the sense of erection in a woman, which will be dealt with in detail later.

The movements accompanying orgasm in the man, and which are necessary for the ejection of the semen, are very irregular; there may be four or five, or there may be eight or ten clearly distinguishable twisting movements.

On the other hand, in the case of both sexes, but particularly in the woman, the contractions may be so slight that the peak of the voluptuous sensation only lasts a single moment. At the same time, particularly when the secretion of vaginal fluids is unusually intense, the movements may be externally undiscernible, though the woman herself would feel them. The same thing frequently happens in a man; sometimes the woman feels in the vagina the movements of the member caused by ejaculation, while at others she does not know whether the man has "finished." Yet the peak was reached.

A weakening of the orgasm may be brought about by a phenomenon which is usually held to produce the contrary effect, namely, if the secretions of the male and female organs are particularly intense.

The object of the male and female secretions, according to science, is to make the male member slippery and facilitate its introduction into the vagina, to contribute to the intensification of excitement and bring about orgasm. But practical experience shows that excessive moistening diminishes the voluptuous sensations of both the man and the woman. It reduces friction to such an extent that the man sometimes hardly feels the friction of the member against the walls of the vagina. In the case of women it may frequently be observed that considerable moisture of the genital apparatus, which may occur in connection with the menses, under extraordinary excitement, or after protracted preliminaries, considerably impedes the attainment of orgasm, and particularly distinct consciousness of it. The woman has the feeling that the moist, soft muscles cannot attain the tenseness that marks the transition to the contracting movements.

Science has so far failed to establish with certainty the precise position as regards a discharge like ejaculation during the orgasm of the woman. It has already been mentioned that a general exocrine activity in the female genital organs is induced through excitement to varying degrees. This activity is sometimes slight, and only increases in intensity in the course of the coital movements through the intensification of the excitation brought about by the male organ; but whether, in addition to these secretions, there is at the moment of orgasm an ejaculation of any kind similar to that of a man, cannot be determined in practice in view of the arrangement of the female genital apparatus.

The prevailing view in this connection is as follows:

At the moment of the most intense sexual excitement the uterus contracts, and as this organ in normal circumstances also contains a fluid, this is forced into the vagina. However, there are two factors which complicate the question whether there is any such discharge.

Firstly, a large number of women have a catarrhal flux which also appears during sexual intercourse, moistening the entire vaginal region. This is a blue-white, viscous fluid, which differs from the other secretions, and whose precise nature is of no interest here. And secondly—particularly in the case of women who have had children —it frequently happens that the semen flows out of the vagina immediately after the act, thus creating the impression that this fluid comes from the woman.

The solution of the wad of mucus that closes the uterus was for a time considered by medical men as an indispensable condition for the penetration of spermatozoa into the uterus, and as it was assumed that the expulsion of this wad of mucus was effected through the twisting movements of the uterus during orgasm, orgasm in the woman was held to be indispensable for fecundation.

In contrast with this view we now have the fact, recognized by most medical men, that perhaps the majority of women conceive without orgasm.

That the intensity and perfection of orgasm, both in men and women, is considerably influenced by psychical processes, is so obvious that it hardly requires stressing.

For instance, a change of position during the sexual act, particularly if it is being tried for the first time, not only facilitates the attainment of orgasm as such, but it also gives the partners the sensation that their sexual union has never been so perfect. On the other hand, in certain positions, though the man may attain ejaculation, and the woman her orgasm, both will feel that it has not been the real thing. The man will have the sensation that some of the semen has been left behind; while the woman will feel that the tension has not completely relaxed.

However, all this, unless it produces a feeling of unsatisfaction, is of no importance and represents no cause for worry. In this connection the psychical elements frequently cancel or compensate each other. It is mentioned elsewhere in this work that to some men an ejaculation while lying on their backs is not so pleasant as in the normal coital position, i.e., with the front part of the body downward. If, however, a couple for once choose this position, in which the man is lying on his back and the woman is lying or sitting on him, the slight inconvenience experienced by the man during ejaculation will probably be compensated for by other physical and psychical attractions involved in the change.

The intensity and perfection of the orgasm may naturally be affected by any sense of pain appearing at the same moment. Of course, there are certain pains that are inflicted by the lovers for the purpose of intensifying the voluptuous sensation, such as biting, pinching, beating, etc., all of which, up to a point, may constitute a regular component of sexual intercourse even between sexually normal people. But these actions may produce undesired consequences, and should therefore be practiced as carefully as the reactions of the individual partner may indicate.

In addition, it may also happen that protracted friction of the male member against the walls of the vagina produces a slight pain both in the member and in the vagina which, though not preventing the attainment of orgasm, detracts from the relief and pleasure it gives. Further, it happens in a good many cases that a woman or a man require a tensing of the whole body for the attainment of orgasm, and this leads to sudden cramp in the muscles at the moment when orgasm is on the way, thus preventing orgasm. This kind of cramp, particularly in the hips and calves, occurs not infrequently in the case of women who have had children.

Cramp in the calves may also occur during pregnancy, when it may easily be caused by other factors. Cramp during sexual intercourse caused by an over-tensing of the muscles is not dangerous, but the woman must mention to her partner that her failure is due to this harmless cause.

Incidentally, the best way to cure such cramp is to beat the muscles affected with short, sharp blows with the edge of the hand.

Some married couples are ignorant of the fact that orgasm, both in the man and the woman, may be prevented at the last moment by such physical causes as an insufficiently relieved bladder (though this may intensify the sensation of excitement). The failure of a man, particularly in the morning, is frequently due to this cause, and should therefore not be regarded as embarrassing.

CHAPTER 28

SEXUAL LIBIDO IN WOMEN; THE RIGHT MANNER OF AROUSING IT

WE have dealt with the question of orgasm in detail because lack of or inadequate orgasm during sexual intercourse is one of the most important characteristics of a frigid woman.

Having described the mechanism and the principal external signs of orgasm, we will now consider all the physical and psychical factors that render orgasm in a woman possible at all.

The question we have to answer is: How is voluptuousness aroused in the woman during sexual intercourse, and in particular, how does her voluptuous sensation reach the intensity that we call orgasm? A precise knowledge of the normal process with all its casual relations is necessary before we can understand any irregularities or abnormal phenomena.

The sexual sense in man is a tactile sense, a sense of touch. The excitations induced by the contacts with, and caresses of the loved person, are conveyed to the brain by certain terminal nerves in the skin through certain nerve tracks, and are felt in the brain as pleasant sensations. As reflexes of these pleasurable sensations, erotic images arise in the brain and certain sets or groups of muscles are activated, so that these, in turn, carry out erotic contacts, such as caresses and kisses, on the loved person.

Whereas in the case of all other excitations (such as itching) the reflex induced (e.g., scratching) serves to eliminate the excitation itself, sexual excitations have the peculiarity that for a time excitation and reflex strengthen and intensify each other. The intensification of the excitation only ceases after the final reflex, the peak of voluptuous sensation (orgasm) has been attained in the brain

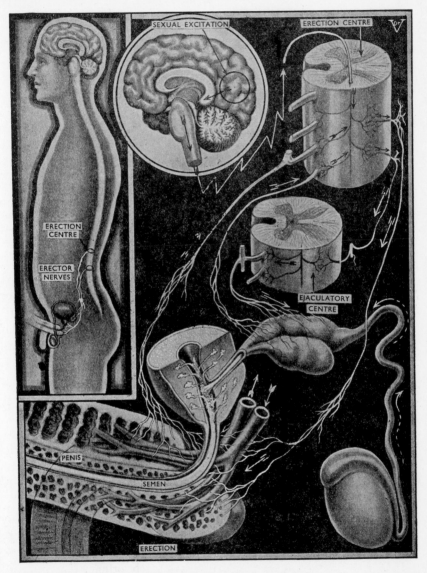

FIG. 98—Picture story of how erection and ejaculation occur. Inset figure of man, transparent, to show erection center and erector nerves inside his body.

of the man and woman; then there is a pleasant relief, a sense of satisfaction and contentment. With that, the sexual excitations are over for the occasion concerned.

In practical life the process would take place somewhat as follows: The wife sees the husband she loves, the man whose individual physical qualities (for instance his hair) produces a sexually exciting effect upon her.

The man (in turn attracted by certain qualities of the woman) approaches her with tender words, and the woman's first reaction to the visually conveyed excitation consists in stroking his hair. This manifestation of tenderness intensifies the man's excitation, impelling him to more definite reflex acts, for instance, taking the woman into his arms and kissing her. Hugging and kissing in turn intensifies the sexual excitation of the woman, so that she actively reciprocates these manifestations of affection, until the man proceeds to increasingly more definite and decisive sexual actions. And this love-play culminates in the sexual act itself. In the course of the sexual act, through contact between the highly sensitive sexual organs, sexual excitement rises rapidly to its peak, and when the woman has experienced the sensation of orgasm, which lasts some little time, her excitement gradually abates, and there follows that happy feeling of relief with which all harmonious sexual intercourse between healthy people should end on both sides.

Now, the various parts of the skin are not uniformly sensitive to sexual excitation, and that is why during the first sexual intercourse, the parties must "explore" each other's bodies before they discover the most sensitive points (which are usually in the vicinity of the genital apparatus).

Fundamentally, therefore, the entire surface of the body is of a sexual character, and there is probably no area that cannot become an erogenous (or sexually excitable) zone in some individuals, no area whose excitation cannot either produce orgasm or facilitate the attainment of orgasm.

But what is happening in the woman during the process exemplified above, including the sexual act itself?

The excitations aroused in the clitoris and in the entrance of the

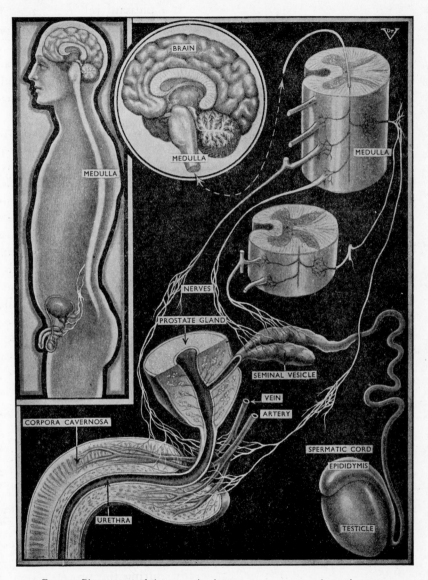

FIG. 99—Picture story of the connection between nerve centers and sexual organs.

vagina, reinforced by mental images and impressions, induce nervous impulses which cause certain muscular movements, and particularly certain phenomena in the vascular system, i.e., the blood vessels. There is a jerky to and fro movement between the posterior part of the vagina and the opening of the uterus, caused by the rhythmic movements of the male member, which hermetically closes the vagina and therefore, during its to and fro movement, exerts a kind of suction which is followed by the female organ. Through the excitation of the nerves the blood vessels of the uterus, the cavernous cells of the vagina and the clitoris are filled with arterial blood, and owing to certain muscular contractions the return flow of this blood is temporarily impeded.

It is only with the attainment of orgasm that these muscular contractions gradually relax and cease to bar the back-flow of the blood. The muscles of the uterus now contract, so that the external and internal os (or mouth) of the uterus form a continuous open canal with the uterus itself, into which the semen can therefore be directly injected. Through this muscular activity the wad of mucus situated in the cervix (or neck) of the uterus is expelled, whereby the acid secretion of the vagina is neutralized, in addition to which the uterus itself secretes a more or less considerable quantity of mucus.

The question now is: on which of these various processes does the sensation of orgasm depend?

Naturally, the ultimate process that brings this sensation to the consciousness of the woman must ultimately take place in the brain. But this conversion of physical into psychical phenomena has so far not been elucidated, and will probably remain a secret forever, and what we wish to discover here is only the physiological process that induces the excitation of the brain during the sexual act.

This question has been the subject of discussion and dispute in medical science for a long time, until finally the following conclusion was reached. Orgasm in a woman is *not* caused by the discharge of secretions of the female genital organs. Thus the female "ejaculation," which, as we have seen, consists of various secretions, is only an accompanying phenomenon of female orgasm, but not its cause, the more so, as these secretions appear *before* the sexual act, with the beginning of sexual desire in the woman, and they serve for the *mechanical* facilitation of the sexual act, that is to say, to make the interior of the vagina slippery, so that the male member can enter easily.

But if the glandular secretions are only accompanying phenomena of orgasm, then the principal cause of orgasm must be the contraction of the uteral muscles. This contraction of the muscles adjacent to or surrounding the uterus and the vagina is effected through a number of uniform peripheral (or external) excitations repeated for a certain time. The source or seat of the excitation is partly in the tip of the clitoris and partly in other portions of the genital apparatus, like the vulva and the vagina. The excitation of the sensory nerves of the clitoris, the nymphae or small lips, and the vagina, which runs to the brain, is intensified through the congestion of the vessels of these organs, which congestion is also known as *internal erection*, that is to say, the stiffening of these internal parts. In physically and mentally entirely normal women (unfortunately the minority today), the posterior part of the vagina is the most sensitive of these three main sources of excitation.

We may therefore say that *the seat of female sexual satisfaction is the posterior part of the vagina.*

Our use of the words "seat" and "satisfaction" is not to be taken in the psychological sense. What we mean is that this part of the vagina is the most important "receiving station" of excitations, the actual seat of voluptuous sensation being, of course, the central nervous system, i.e., the brain. The particular point within the brain where sexual sensations are experienced has so far not been determined; in other words, the precise location of the genital center in the brain has not yet been discovered. It is probably located in the cerebrum or the "large brain," and not in the cerebellum or "small brain," though it is quite possible that there is no special genital center in the brain at all.

However, in view of the fact that the course of sexual excitement is nevertheless ultimately determined by the brain, the size of the clitoris and the other sensitive zones is entirely immaterial as far as the intensity of the sexual sensations is concerned, and that is why orgasm is not equally intense in equal external circumstances, even in one and the same person. The intensity of the orgasm depends, in the first place, on the degree to which the brain has been eroticized (through the action of the glands and psychical influences).

Far more important is the consideration that *the process of voluptuous sensation is specifically different in men and women.* This can best be illustrated by a graphic representation of sexual excitement, a so-called "voluptuous diagram." For the sake of clearness, this diagram is divided into four parts.

Part 1. Gradual inception of excitement evoked by the preliminary excitation of the erogenuous zones, apart from the genital organs themselves, i.e., caresses, kisses, etc.

Part 2. Intensification of excitement at the time of sexual *preparedness*, characterized by simultaneous erection (congestion of the sexual organs) of the male member, the clitoris, the nymphae and the vagina.

Part 3. From the introduction of the male member to the peak of orgasm, that is to say, the actual intercourse in the narrow sense of the term.

Part 4. The abatement of the voluptuous sensation and the subsequent sensations.

Now, the entire process is different in the two sexes, but particularly as regards Parts 3 and 4. The preliminaries and the state of sexual preparedness are practically the same in both cases, though perhaps shorter in duration in the case of the man than in the case of the woman. However, these slight differences in time are of little practical importance. But during Part 3, that is to say, during the sexual act itself, there is a most important difference between the man and the woman. Whereas in the man the ticklish sensation, which is at first uniform, becomes intensified with sudden vehemence, precipitating orgasm, the woman only reaches the peak of sexual excitement gradually, and far more slowly. Thus, on an average, the woman attains orgasm later than the man. On the other hand, the abatement of the voluptuous sensation also proceeds far more slowly in the woman than in the man. During Part 4 the man's voluptuous sensation drops abruptly to the initial stage (i.e., before the sexual act) and even lower; whereas in the case of the woman it diminishes gradually and slowly, in the same manner as it rises before and during the act.

We give four parallel illustrations to explain all stages of sexual excitement, from the beginning to end, in men and women.

In view of these differences in the course of the sexual sensations, it naturally requires a certain skill to *coordinate* the mutual orgasms, which is highly desirable. Since the principal difference lies in Part 3 of the sexual act, the lovers can only attain a simultaneous occurrence of the orgasms if the man draws out the preliminaries until the excitement of the woman is somewhat more intense than his own, and in normal circumstances the man will be easily capable of this. Only when this stage has been reached should the man introduce his member, and his excitement will then reach its climax at approximately the same time as that of the woman.

It will be useful at this point to dispel a common error. Owing to the rapid and abrupt abatement of the voluptuous sensation in the man, the woman, particularly if the sexual act has not been carried out in such a manner that her orgasm should take place simultaneously with that of the man, may easily imagine that the man is depressed. Although this is not the case in normal circumstances, it does happen very frequently that owing to a nervous depression the man is really in low spirits after the sexual act. That was probably what gave rise to the dictum of the famous Roman physician Calenus: *Triste este onme animal post coitum, praeter mulierem gallumque.* (Every animal is depressed after coitus, except the woman and the cock.)

Well, sexual science has clearly and incontrovertibly proved that this dictum of the Roman physician is wrong. Like all healthy women, all healthy men experience a pleasant relief after the sexual act. A man is then in excellent spirits, and full of gratitude to the woman, and therefore actuated by an emotion which will cause him to manifest his tenderness towards her after the sexual act. The fact that the very contrary happens in so many cases, that is to say, that men are very frequently morose after the sexual act, to say nothing of the tactless attitude that seems so humiliating to the woman, is due to the inadequate sexual education of our times. As a conse-

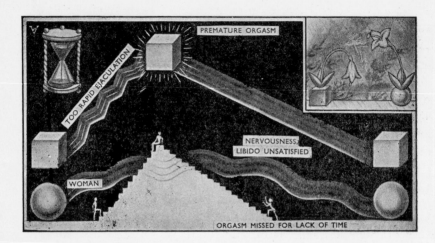

FIG. 100—Schematic representation of the sexual act, showing why in most cases woman fails to attain climax. Where the man has premature orgasm with early ejaculation, in most cases the woman cannot attain orgasm.

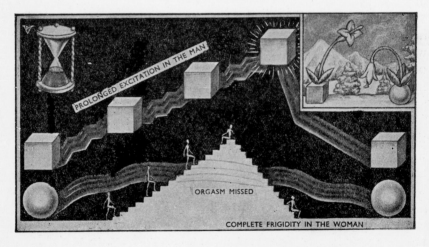

FIG. 101—Representation schematically of picture story of prolonged excitation in the man because of frigidity in the woman.

FIG. 102—Schematic representation of simultaneous orgasm.

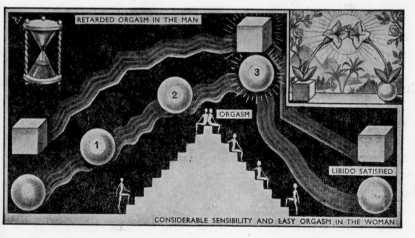

FIG. 103—Schematic picture of several climaxes in woman through control of man.

quence of this many men are burdened with a sense of guilt which, at a time when the normal physical urge does not silence it, operates in the subconscious with especial force. The repentance of past sins after the sexual act is not recognized by the consciousness as what it is, but manifests itself in the form of depression and a feeling of aversion for the woman.

It is hardly necessary to say that intercourse with such a man may aggravate or bring to the surface the frigidity of a woman in whom an inclination in that direction already exists.

Particularly in essays older of date the question of the comparative intensity of feminine sexual enjoyment has frequently been discussed, that is to say, whether the sexual sensations of a woman are more or less intense than those of a man, or equally so. But this question is in itself impossible, since it relates to two things that are incapable of comparison. Nevertheless, it is possible to say that owing to the complicated psychical development of sexuality in a girl, deviations from the normal as regards sexual sensation are more frequent in women than in men.

That is why there are so many women who apparently have no sexual desires whatever (frigidity), and also, on the other hand, so many more women than men who are over-sexed. The latter observation is strikingly confirmed by the fact that whereas a pathologically excessive sexual desire in woman (nymphomania) is fairly frequent, the corresponding state in a man (satyriasis) is an absolute rarity.

With regard to the relationship between the sexual sensations of the woman and fecundation, the following may be said:

It is obvious, that fecundation is easier and likelier if the woman attains orgasm, for the reason that in that case the entire female genital canal, owing to congestion and the muscular movements described above, forms a continuous tube leading right into the uterus, so that the semen of the man can be injected practically into the uterus direct—and this is particularly so if the two orgasms take place at the same moment. Thus the chances of fecundation are increased by the female orgasm, but, at the same time, it is not an indispensable condition of fecundation.

CHAPTER 29

Sex Hunger of Women

The sexual desire of a mature person may be compared with hunger, with one important difference—whereas in the case of hunger for food the first mouthful may give the greatest pleasure, until the enjoyment of eating abates to practically nil at the last mouthful, the exact opposite happens in the case of sexual hunger. The first actions impelled by sexual hunger do not reduce, but, on the contrary, intensify the sexual excitement, so that satisfaction only comes with the final acts of sexual intercourse.

There is some disagreement among authors as to what constitutes the sexual instinct in woman. Some define it as a periodical instinct, composed on the one hand of the urge for copulation, and on the other hand of the urge for procreation, while other authors only recognize the former. According to them the urge for motherhood is not part of the feminine sexual instinct.

We on our part hold that the maternal instinct is up to a certain degree a component of the feminine sexual instinct, but it is biologically wrong to speak of a separate procreative instinct. It is not procreation to which the instinctive sexual desire of woman is directed, but to satisfaction through intercourse, through which fecundation may also occur. If the direct aim of the feminine sexual instinct were really procreation, then sexual desire ought to abate after fecundation. Actually, however, the exact opposite can be observed during the first months of pregnancy. Nevertheless, the vision of future motherhood undoubtedly plays some part in the sexual life of woman, in the sense that it influences in a certain manner the nature and intensity of her libido.

We must now declare our attitude in the keenly debated question whether the sexual instinct of the human male is stronger than that of the female, or whether the reverse is the case, or whether both sexes have a sexual instinct of the same intensity.

Opinion on this subject is greatly divided. Some famous gynecologists hold that the masculine sexual instinct is stronger, while other equally famous gynecologists favor the view that the feminine sexual instinct is equally strong, but that it is somewhat weaker in an adolescent, sexually inexperienced girl than in a boy of the same age. According to this view, the feminine sexual instinct only develops fully through the usual mutual manifestations of affection.

Havelock Ellis, the famous sexologist, represents the view that the sexual instinct of woman is equally strong, but that it "only attains its full development after the commencement of regular sexual intercourse."

As against this, there is the contention of those authors who consider, without any qualifications, that the feminine sexual instinct is no less strong than the masculine. Confirmation of this view may be found particularly in the country, where many of the repressions produced by civilization do not exist, and where it frequently happens that girls await the young men in the latters' bedrooms, and even in their beds.

The scientific dispute indicated here is only possible because the cultural influence on the development of the feminine sexual instinct and its repressions have not been taken sufficiently into account.

The same mistake has been made by those authors who, though recognizing that the sexual instincts of the sexes are equally strong, hold that the woman's instinct is more "constant," while the man is by nature "polygamous." In actual fact, the man is no more inconstant "by nature" than the woman. That sexual disloyalty is so much more frequent among men than among women is simply due to the fact that in our so-called civilization men are almost systematically brought up to this splitting of their personalities in the matter of love.

Thus, the man is no more polygamous by nature than the woman, provided he has found the right partner. So long as the partners complement each other, their relationship will remain monogamous and "deviations" from loyalty will only occur when there is a rift of some sort between the partners.

When a man or a woman has found *the* partner who entirely complements them both physically and psychologicaly, then they will both tend to be absolutely monogamous. If, on the other hand, they are consciously or unconsciously seeking for a complementing partner, then they are already polygamous in a certain sense. If, in a marriage, one party feels the need for a change, that is a sign that he or she has not found a physically and psychologically complementing partner in the marriage, and that there is something wrong with the marriage. And if this desire manifests itself less frequently in the female than in the male partner, that is to say, if women appear to be more monogamous, that is to a considerable extent due to the fact that sexual repressions are developed with greater finality in women, for whom the desire for a "change" holds incomparably greater perils than for men.

At the same time, there is a further reason for the greater frequency with which this desire for a change occurs in husbands than in wives, namely, that what we might call unevenness in the sexual temper of a woman is more frequent, and this is apt to lead to estrangement.

However, let us revert to the original question posed at the beginning of this chapter, with regard to which we can quote some further interesting views.

One of the most interesting is to the effect that it is not as regards intensity that the sexual insincts of men and women differ, but in their character, in their nature. Otto Weininger, the Austrian philosopher, also drew this qualitative distinction, though in a far more radical sense when he wrote: "Woman is nothing but sexuality; man is sexual and something more; woman is only sexual."

But what is the truth with regard to the intensity of feminine sexuality? Undoubtedly the feminine sex hunger or sexual appetite is *apparently* less intense and frequently even seems to be entirely absent. However, although this observation in itself is correct, the view that the feminine sexual instinct only begins to manifest itself after amorous or sexual intercourse with a man, i.e., it must be "awakened," should be treated at least with caution. For even though it is true that in our civilization there really is a greater initial repression in the case of the average woman, that does not mean that this repression or reserve is natural and has its roots in biological factors. It may just as easily be acquired, that is to say, based on social factors.

Protagonists of the "awakening" theory sometimes argue that pain plays such a considerable role in the sexual life of a woman—defloration, pregnancy, parturition, after-effects; in a word, nearly all the feminine sexual processes, except normal intercourse, are accompanied by more or less severe pain. In pathological cases the woman derives from her sexual life nothing but pain (even during normal intercourse). All these arguments are advanced to show why the feminine sexual instinct is so frequently weak and repressed.

But these arguments have no foundation in fact. Firstly, as psychoanalysis has proved, pain in feminine sexual life is not experienced as such, but as *pleasure*. But apart from that, many cases are known in which women, despite all the pain of child-birth, desire children, and yet abominate sexual intercourse. Thus fear of the pain occasioned by defloration and child-birth is not the cause of the frequent repressions of the feminine sexual instinct; indeed, repressed libido of this or other kinds (and more particularly the fear of defloration and conception) are not normal, but pathological phenomena.

Thus the causes of the widespread weakness of the feminine sexual instinct are *not* biological. The feminine sexual instinct, in itself of equal intensity to the masculine, is only repressed through influences originating in the cultural and social spheres. The woman is by nature always receptive to the male, i.e., she is always prepared to receive him, and if she has repressions in this direction, they are not biological, but cultural and social. The inadequate and inferior sexual life of women must be ascribed to the inadequate and inferior conditions of her development and existence.

These "inferior conditions of development" relate above all to woman's upbringing, which is, of course, based on age-old social prejudices. And a grotesque feature of this upbringing and education is the fact that the old-fashioned pedagogues with their anti-love principles usually blame the results of their own guilt on the theory of the alleged weaker sexual instinct of the "weaker sex." Fortunately, there are today many examples of women who, through enlightened upbringing and education, are in a position to prove the correctness of our view.

And that view is as follows: The sexual instinct of women is by nature *quantitatively* the same as that of men, but differs therefrom *qualitatively*. Women may be less sensual than men, but this is due to cultural, i.e., educational causes, no less than the frequent quantitative weakness and repression of the feminine libido. Undoubtedly, however, sexual life plays a far more important role in the life of a woman than in that of a man, and that is the ultimate reason for the qualitative difference between the feminine and masculine sexual instinct. This difference lies in the fact that the sexual instinct of a woman, unlike that of a man, is not concentrated exclusively on copulation, as the maternal instinct is a component part. The sexual instinct of women, as Marie Bonaparte so aptly remarks in her book *The Sexuality of the Child*, is diluted, since it is divided between copulation and the processes of motherhood.

CHAPTER 30

Days of Highest Sexual Excitability in Women

On what days of the month does intense erotic desire arise? Are there any special symptoms at these periods? Does ovulation play any part in arousing a desire for sexual intercourse?

The answer to these questions has been found as a result of practical observation. It has been observed that many women, at a certain time during the menstrual cycle, display a nervous excitability that considerably affects their mood and conduct. There is a physical and emotional disequilibrium. Today we know that these fluctuations, which in their manifestation frequently do not betray any sexual connection, are in reality the consequence of important physiological processes in the female genital organs. The erotic aspect of these phenomena does not reach the consciousness of some women, particularly, of course, if they are frigid, while other women are aware that they are due to sexual urges. The latter experience a keen desire for sexual intercourse at these periods. However, not all women who are conscious of the stirring of their sexual appetite show this, and the husband may completely fail to notice it.

The causes of this periodical nervous phenomenon lie mainly in the activity of the ovaries. In some women this condition recurs regularly and distinctly, while in others only a trained observer can notice slight changes. Indeed, the disturbance may be screened from observation by outside factors, such as excitement, worry and illness.

Opinions differ as to the exact days in the menstrual cycle when these changes in the emotional life of the woman occur. Some authors assume that they are the days immediately following menstruation. However, we think that this can only apply to few women,

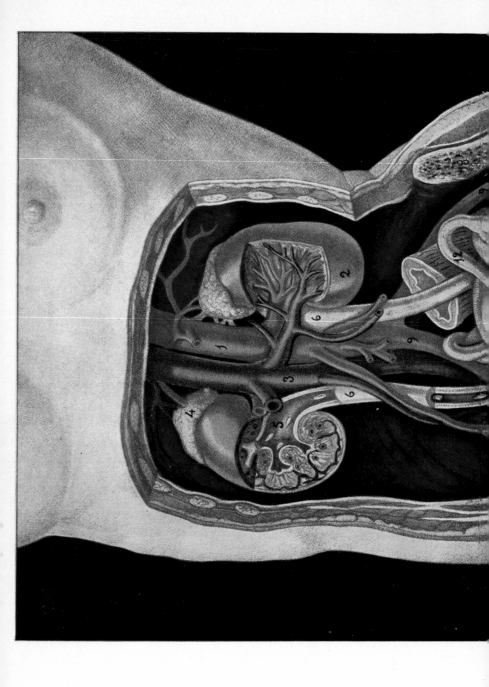

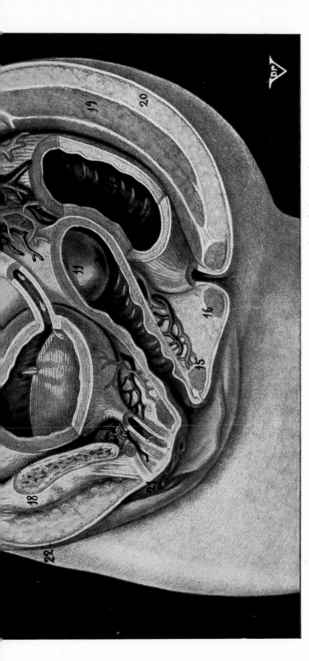

Fig. C-19—Complete color-picture story of woman's external and internal sex organs.

From abdominal aorta (1) the blood flows towards kidneys (2–2) through renal artery (in red) and leaves through renal vein (blue), from which it is collected by the *vena cava inferior* (3). Part of kidney is sectioned, in order to show more visibly the arteries and veins. Over kidneys may be seen the suprarenal glands (4) with their arteries and veins. The right kidney is also partly sectioned, in order to reveal pelvis (5) of kidney, which collects the urine, which then passes to the ureter (6–6) which opens into bladder (7). This is shown open, to illustrate the entry of the urine. Urine is eliminated by urethra (8), of which the orifice of the urinary meatus or passage is visible externally. The abdominal artery is subdivided into primitive iliac arteries (9). (10) The uterus. (11) Cervix of uterus with its orifice. (12) Fallopian tube with its funnel. (13) Ovary. (14) Vagina. (15) Vaginal contracting muscle. (16) Sphincter muscle of the anus. (17) Rectum. (18) Pelvic bone. (19) Muscle. (20) Fat. (21) Clitoris. (22) Mons veneris.

as there is no physiological reason for it, since the changes occurring in the genital organs are not at their peak immediately after menstruation. Further, specialists are aware that some women have a keen desire for sexual intercourse during the menstruation itself, though this is not frequent. In our view the phenomena referred to above generally occur shortly before menstruation, and during the maturing of the ovum, somewhere in the middle between two periods.

Fig. 104—Picture story of woman's excitation curve. The menstrual cycle of woman for two consecutive months.

The maturing of the ovum and menstruation have been discussed in detail in other chapters. The maturing of the ovum involves such a powerful process in the organism of the woman that it provides a sufficient reason for the simultaneous occurrence of emotional disturbances, since it is quite logical that nature should make ovulation and the desire for sexual intercourse coincide. Thus when the ovum has matured, the woman desires intercourse more keenly, so that the conditions are particularly favorable to procreation. A few days before menstruation the mucous membrane of the uterus becomes congested with blood, causing it to swell. This explains the second period of sexual excitability.

As already indicated, the psychological change before menstruation does not always manifest itself in the form of an intensified desire for sexual intercourse, but frequently appears in the form of nervous disturbances, irritability, depression, moodiness, contrariness, all of which may alternate with periods of elation and gaiety. This psychological disequilibrium is due, consciously or unconsciously, to the unsatisfied sexual desire, which may manifest itself in various forms. In the case of neurotic or hysterical women this may lead to serious conflicts between husband and wife, thus endangering the harmony of marriage. Husbands should know these periods of increased irritability, as there is frequently a conscious or unconscious desire for tenderness behind it.

In some women the inhibitions which have become fixed in the subconscious in earlier years, come to the surface at these times, and they are unable to open up. In this condition they unconsciously expect the man to uncover their emotional urges. If the husband understands these psychological processes of his wife, he can help to dissolve the psychological inhibitions. In this way the nervous disturbances of the woman manifest themselves to a less extent, and if during these critical days sexual intercourse gives real satisfaction to the woman, it produces a beneficial effect on her physical and emotional equilibrium. This is further proof of the importance of a proper regulation of the erotic aspect of marriage.

Single women can deal with these periodical nervous disturbances with the aid of hydrotherapy. Cool baths or showers of about fifteen minutes once or twice per day are most effective. Their action consists in stimulating blood circulation in the abdomen and thereby producing a soothing effect.

CHAPTER 31

THE COLD WOMAN

HAVING considered the nature of the normal feminine sexual instinct and the normal sexual desire of woman, let us now consider the irregularity of her sexual function commonly known as frigidity.

The term itself is to some extent inexact as applied to individual cases, for the actual complaint comprises two distinct pathological conditions—frigidity and impotence. Where sexual desire, i.e., the sexual appetite, is absent, we speak of frigidity; where the capacity for sexual sensation is lacking, i.e., where orgasm cannot be attained, we speak of impotence. In other words, frigidity may be defined as deficient libido, and impotence as inadequacy or total absence of orgasm.

In cases of frigidity, though very rarely, orgasm may occur. For instance, it happens not infrequently that orgasm is attained through masturbation, the normal sexual hunger for a man being absent. Conversely, in cases of impotence the sexual appetite is very frequently present in its normal intensity, that is to say, the endocrine activity (internal secretion) of the ovaries is perfect, but the attainment of orgasm during intercourse is prevented by certain physical or psychical repressions. The woman concerned desires intercourse, but fails to derive satisfaction from it, i.e., she is unable to attain orgasm.

In individual cases we distinguish absolute and relative, or total and partial frigidity and impotence. *Absolute frigidity* (in the case of non-homosexual women) is only present when a woman fails to experience sexual desire at any time throughout her life, although she has come in contact with all types of men. *Relative frigidity* is the case of a woman whose sexual desire remains dormant in relation to a certain man or group of men, though present and active in relation to other men. In the same manner, *absolute impotence* signifies the absence of orgasm during intercourse with any man, and *relative impotence* the absence of orgasm during intercourse with a certain man or one of a group of men. We speak of *total frigidity* when there is not even a trace of the feminine libido (which is probably impossible in non-homosexual women) ; but in most cases of this type we are confronted with *partial frigidity*, that is to say, a more or less considerable, but still only partial, lack of sexual desire, of which noticeable traces still exist. In the same way we speak of *total impotence* in cases where no satisfaction whatever is derived from sexual intercourse; and of *partial impotence* where a slight sensation of pleasure that does not approximate to orgasm is derived.

It will be noted that the concepts of absolute and total frigidity or impotence overlap, since for instance, an absolute impotence may at the same time also be total impotence (complete absence of all erotic sensation in relation to all men) , but it may also be partial impotence (slight erotic sensation in relation to all men). Conversely, not every total impotence is necessarily absolute. It *may* be (if all erotic sensation is absent in relation to all men) , but, on the other hand, it may be only relative (total absence of all erotic sensation, but only in relation to certain men, while normal in relation to other men) . The same applies to frigidity.

As these terms will be frequently employed in the following pages, we tabulate them below, together with their precise definitions for reference:

FRIGIDITY

Total..........	Partial......................
Absolute	*Relative*
All sexual desire absent in relation to all men.	All sexual desire absent in relation to a certain man or group of men; normal sexual desire present in relation to other men.
Slight erotic sensation in relation to all men.	Slight sexual desire in relation to a certain man or group of men; sexual desire of normal intensity in relation to other men.

IMPOTENCE

Total..........	Partial......................
Absolute	*Relative*
Erotic sensation totally absent in relation to all men.	Erotic sensation totally absent during intercourse with a certain man or one of a certain group; orgasm attained in intercourse with others.
Slight erotic sensation in intercourse with any man, never approximating orgasm.	Slight erotic sensation in intercourse with a certain man or one of a group, never approximating orgasm; orgasm attained in intercourse with other men.

Naturally the boundary between frigidity and impotence cannot be clearly defined in all cases, transitions being frequent. For, on the one hand, sexual hunger is partly also a cause of orgasm and, conversely, an initially present libido may become gradually repressed in consequence of unpleasant experiences in the form of unsatisfying intercourse. Thus it happens in many cases where sexual intercourse produces no pleasure, i.e., no orgasm, particularly when accompanied by pain, that frigidity finally develops. On the other hand, psychological impotence is only a mild form of frigidity. In all cases where orgasm is missed for psychological reasons the cause is in some way connected with aversion for the partner.

It is a most peculiar fact that even in the cases of frigidity, that is to say, when a woman has no sexual desire, she will nevertheless make attempts to participate in the sexual act. However, in such cases the motive lies not in the sexual instinct, but in rational considerations, impelled by sentiments of gratitude or friendship, even pity or vanity. In very many cases it is vanity, combined with curiosity and the urge to prevail, that drives a frigid girl into a love adventure for which she is not fitted, merely because she does not wish to appear inferior to her friends. In cases of partial frigidity, the woman concerned may be impelled to agree to physical union by the fear that she may lose the man with whom she may be emotionally in love.

Frigidity is frequently confined to the actual urge for copulation, while the maternal instinct—a component of the sexual instinct—

remains unimpaired. In such cases the hunger for children may lead to sexual union, or the maternal instinct may operate in relation to the man himself and impel the woman to play the part of protector to a weak man. A mixture of pity and the maternal instinct may frequently lead a frigid woman to sexual intercourse.

The *consequence of frigidity*, i.e., of inadequate or no satisfaction during sexual intercourse, are many and varied. They lie mainly in the nervous and psychological sphere and in the course of their development invade the sufferer's social life. However, we will only deal here with the purely medical consequences, which include *white and yellow flux* (due to protracted congestion), *backache* (due to lack of uteral relaxation), and *menstrual complaints* (also due to protracted congestion). In some cases a cardiac neurosis also develops, which may then become intensified to grave fear neurosis. Finally, there is a gradual transition from non-satisfaction to frigidity and aversion to all sexual approaches of the partner.

CHAPTER 32

ABSENCE OF SEXUAL APPETITE

As we have seen, normal sexual intercourse involves a very complicated process, beginning (1) with the local excitation of the sexual organs, (2) from which the excitation of the terminal nerves is conveyed, (3) through the spinal cord to the brain, (4) which reacts in a certain manner to this excitation provided that it is suitably "charged" through perfectly functioning endocrine glands.

It is clear, therefore, that the cause of feminine impotence, i.e., the absence of orgasm, must lie in some irregularity at the four points mentioned above, i.e., (1) in the sexual apparatus, (2) the spinal cord, (3) the brain, and (4) the endocrine glands. Basing ourselves upon this division, we speak of a genital, spinal, cerebral or glandular impotence.

Genital impotence in a woman is present when, owing to congenital or acquired peculiarities of the genital apparatus, the introduction of the male member, and therefore sexual satisfaction, is impossible.

Spinal impotence means that, owing to an organic irregularity of some sort, the erection center of the spinal cord is incapable of performing its proper functions.

The term cerebral impotence comprises all those cases of impotence that are due to irregularities, either physical or psychological, whose source lies in the brain.

And finally, there is glandular impotence, which is impotence caused by some defect in the germinal glands.

Frigidity, i.e., the absence of sexual desire in a woman, may be caused by irregularities in the brain on the one hand, and in the glands on the other. The genital apparatus and the erection center in the spinal cord cannot, logically speaking, play a part in this connection, for, as we know, sexual desire originates partly through the function of the germinal glands and partly through the images, fantasies and impressions (such as visual and auditory) registered by the brain.

Thus frigidity in a woman may be either (1) cerebral, or (2) glandular.

These forms of frigidity, and particularly of the far more frequent impotence, very often occur in combination. It is, for instance, typical that the psychological, i.e., cerebral, causes of sexual insensibility are connected with some physical factor. This occurs with particular frequency in the case of an unfortunate defloration. If owing to the unusual strength of the hymen the defloration has been very painful, recollection of the pain may lead in an otherwise neurotically inclined individual to frigidity. That would be a combined case of genital and cerebral frigidity. However, cerebral frigidity is by far the most frequent.

A combination of genital and cerebral impotence may also occur. It has been observed that psycho-sexual infantilism (infantile backwardness of psycho-sexual development) caused by defective endocrine activity may be accompanied by physical immaturity of the sexual organs. Thus there may be cases where adult girls who, owing to their impeded psychological development, could in any case not attain orgasm despite their age, also possess such small external and internal sexual organs that the introduction of the male organ would be impossible.

Another frequent introduction is spinal-cerebral impotence. This type of impotence is sometimes a concomitant of advanced syphilis which has attacked the brain and the spinal cord at the same time.

As already stated, the two forms of frigidity, cerebral and glandular, may also occur in combination. Indeed, it may be said that this is always the case, for strictly speaking no neurotic deficiency of feminine sexuality that goes so far as to cause even sexual desire to disappear, is imaginable without at least a not entirely normal glandular activity. Naturally, that is no reason why attempts to cure this type of frigidity by psychological means should be neglected, and indeed in the majority of cases such treatment would probably succeed.

For the sake of completeness we must, in conclusion, mention that there are women who have "grown cold," women who, as a result of the deadly monotony of their marriage, have gradually lost their former undoubted potency and sometimes even their sexual desire. In such cases the medical man can do nothing. Indeed, the abatement of potency and sexual desire would appear to be a just punishment for the abuse of marriage by partners to a humdrum alliance. Nature only endows with the gift of desire those who endeavor to conquer happiness anew every day of their lives. The flame of nature is for the mentally and emotionally young person a source of perpetual delight, but changes to ashes, and the grayness of ashes for the humdrum, satisfied person. These emotionally dead people should be left to their dead, and our efforts should be devoted to the countless other unfortunate people whom it is still possible to help.

CHAPTER 33

FREQUENCY OF FEMININE FRIGIDITY AND ITS CAUSES

ANY attempt to determine the incidence of feminine frigidity would be bound to meet with serious obstacles, and it would be practically impossible to compile reliable statistics on the subject. There are many reasons for this. Firstly, sexual insensibility occurs very frequently in *apparently healthy women*, in whose case a medical man has no opportunity to inquire. A great many of these women only consult a doctor if they are afraid that owing to their sexual insensibility they might remain barren. Secondly, even if a woman is aware of her defect, she is mostly too shy to confide it to a doctor—and sometimes even to her own husband. Indeed, some women feel offended if their doctor asks them as to their sexual sensibility. That is why doctors are reluctant to broach the subject.

It might be suggested that information should be sought from the husband; but the results would be unreliable. The husband of an impotent woman in a great many cases has no idea of his wife's infirmity. Owing to the low sexual civilization in Europe and America, comparatively few men have any idea whether their partners have attained orgasm. In the great majority of cases they do not even take any notice, so absorbed are they in their own sensations. At the same time, it would be impossible for a man to decide with absolute certainty whether the female partner has or has not attained orgasm.

In addition to these two reasons (lack of contact between impotent women and doctors and ignorance of husbands) there is a third that renders any attempt to establish the incidence of feminine impotence illusory. A considerable proportion of sexually insensible women *do not know themselves* that their sexual reactions in any

242

way deviate from the normal. Many women live to a ripe old age and die without having known the peak of sexual satisfaction and without even having had an idea that it existed in other women. However, it is ultimately women themselves from whom this information has to be obtained, to reliably establish the incidence of feminine impotence. Scientists are now engaged in gathering these data.

Of course, if a woman says that she misses something during sexual intercourse, or does not feel anything, her statement may be accepted without reserve. On the other hand, if a woman claims to have normal sensations, we have no reliable means of determining whether it is not a case of self-deception. No one can form a definite idea of sensation he has never experienced, and sensations or emotions cannot be exhaustively described in words.

For all these reasons we must estimate the number of impotent women at a higher figure than could be established from the sum total of practical medical experience. At all events, an approximate estimate of the prevalence of feminine sexual impotence may be arrived at on the basis of medical experience and the considerations detailed above. Certain it is that feminine impotence (as well as frigidity) is a phenomenon that has been widespread in all ages and in all countries.

Today sexual frigidity in women of certain social classes is so widespread that it is regarded as "normal" in those classes. In this connection some passages of *The Diary of a Little Girl*, by an eleven-year-old middle class girl of Austria, are illuminating. The girl describes what she had heard from her school friends concerning sexual life.

"So that is how little children are born," she writes, "and that was what Robert meant that time. No, I am not going to do that, ever, I am simply not going to marry. Because you have to do it if you are married; it hurts awfully, but you must do it." And a few days later there is the following entry: "It hurts so badly that you can hardly bear it. But you must do it, because the man can force you."

"It hurts," and "you must"—those are the ideas with which the unenlightened female children of this social class grew up—the surest way to prepare for their own psychological downfall in consequence of their defloration at a latter age, and for the impotence from which the ladies of this class, from whose bedrooms the stories of the writer's school friends probably originated, suffered.

Characteristically enough, the servant-maid at the home of the young authoress was considerably more optimistic, as the following entry in the diary shows:

"We asked Mali to tell us whether *it* was really so painful. She laughed and said: 'It can't be so bad as all that, otherwise they wouldn't all do it'." Which only confirms the old experience that plain, uncomplicated and psychologically healthier people generally have an easier and more successful sexual life. Unfortunately, however, the hard working women are not free from feminine impotence. Though here the influence of an artificial upbringing does not play such an important part in producing these sexual catastrophes, nevertheless overcrowding and unfavorable social conditions contribuate their quota to preventing the hard working women of low income from being happier in their sexual life than those who live in leisure.

We will now quote a few estimates of the incidence of feminine impotence by well-known sexologists. According to Otto Adler, the proportion of totally or partially impotent women ranges from ten to forty percent. Other authors place the figure at between forty and fifty percent, either generally or as regards certain definite regions. Professor Wilhelm Stekel, the world-famous Austrian sexologist, thinks that far more than fifty percent of all women are impotent. A famous woman doctor estimates the proportion of feminine impotence at sixty percent!

Otto Adler is right in pointing out that even "experienced" bachelors believe that the prevalence of feminine sexual impotence is less serious than it actually is, and that this may be due to the fact that they may not come into sexual contact with "well-bred" girls who, owing to mistaken methods of education, are apt to be repressed and subsequently to become sexually insensible.

Many important authors estimate the number of impotent women at anything from one-third to one-half of the entire female population of civilized countries. In the overwhelming majority of these cases the deficiency is due to psychological, i.e., cerebral causes, and it is recognized that cerebral impotence surpasses, both in numbers and gravity, all other forms of feminine impotence.

The number of frigid women is also considerable. But the majority of cases of deficient sexual sensibility is represented by partial impotence of psychological origin, while, in turn, the majority of these are cases of relative impotence.

The contention supported by a few authors that it is an error to assume a large proportion of impotence in women because women are less frequently in the mood for sexual intercourse and therefore necessarily remain unsatisfied on a great many occasions, may be of some importance as regards cases of relative impotence. Unfortunately, however, this argument cannot alter the fact that there is a very high number of absolutely impotent women, a fact borne out, in addition to earlier experience, by data supplied recently by medical consultants.

Before proceeding to a thorough examination of the causes of this prevalence of feminine impotence, it must be observed that despite the frequency of this phenomenon there is virtually no "congenital" sexual insensibility; it is practically always acquired, in most cases in the psychological sense. This discovery constitutes an indictment of our "civilization," and it is in this direction that we must seek for the causes of the wide prevalence of feminine impotence.

In this connection we cannot refrain from pointing to the fact that the so-called "ascetic outlook" on life, which is still the main foundation of our system of education and continues to dominate the views of our adult contemporaries, rests on a misinterpretation of certain religious commandments. And indeed, there is a causal connection between this tendency and frigidity.

The teaching concerning "mortification of the flesh" in its various interpretations, exercises a strongly repressive influence on sexual life, so much so, indeed, that the sexual organs are gradually numbed into greater or less insensibility and sometimes even become atrophied, i.e., degenerated through lack of use. This, undoubtedly, is considered as the highest ideal, and it is its widespread acceptance that has led to the typical psychological inhibition against every kind of carnal activity that even today dominates great masses of people.

Thus, for instance, certain Pharisaical circles in many cases exploited the discoveries of the cause of syphilis and gonorrhoea, not to spread enlightenment and a knowledge of hygiene, but rather to foster in wide sections of the population a panic fear of venereal disease, which was represented as a sort of evil spirit lying in wait behind all sexual pleasure. Needless to say, the medical men who lent themselves to this propaganda were probably unconscious of the fact that they were serving the cause of the ascetic ideal rather than that of social hygiene. However, the representatives of this philosophy of life have long bitterly opposed the dissemination of a knowledge of contraceptive methods, and are still continuing to do so, though with considerably less success than formerly. But where married people are in complete ignorance of any method of avoiding an undesired pregnancy, sexual intercourse is either completely eliminated, or, alternately, fear of pregnancy constricts not only the throat of the woman concerned, but also the nerves of her genital apparatus, and there can be no question of sexual satisfaction for her.

Thus it happens that in modern times, in addition to the expressly ascetic inhibitions of the feminine libido and potency, fear of infection or pregnancy has become a cause of feminine impotence, and even of partial frigidity.

The widespread prevalence of relative impotence in women is also due to a social cause, namely, the fact that it has been ingrained in us for many centuries to treat marriage as a business transaction. It often happens that a girl lacking all sexual experience makes a "brilliant match," but with a man for whom she has little or no affection, or who may perhaps have appeared desirable to her but proves in practice to be sexually unsuited to the girl concerned. It is no wonder, then, that such a girl should derive no sexual satisfaction from intercourse with her husband, even though she is not otherwise "cold." This is a typical example of matrimonial frigidity.

The situation is even more tragic if the man proves to be impotent on the nuptial couch, or suffering from some other defect, such as a premature ejaculation (*ejaculatio praecox*). Such a man is, of course, in any case incapable of satisfying his wife, so that a woman with a powerful sexual instinct will either "break out" of the marriage, or fall a victim to a severe neurosis in consequence of her enforced abstention, while a woman with a weaker sexual instinct (though still healthy), will gradually become frigid, or at least impotent in sexual intercourse. In such cases the impotence caused by the fears and anxieties arising from the husband's repeated unsuccessful efforts, at first appears in the form of a relative impotence, which, if this psychological condition becomes aggravated, may soon change into absolute impotence, and sometimes even into frigidity.

This development of feminine impotence is, owing to its frequency, so important that we must consider more closely its cause, the psychological impotence of the man. This type of masculine impotence is also a product of our civilization in so far as men are naturally also educated according to the ascetic ideal. As, however, they have a better opportunity for sexual activity among the women of certain classes and among prostitutes, and as they are not condemned for such indulgences to anything like the same extent as girls, they develop the "split between body and mind" in the matter of love which was so typical of the men of an older generation. This means that their capacity for sexual love is divided, on the one hand, into purely physical love, which they mostly practice with women of inferior status whom they despise and, on the other, a purely emotional love, admiring and worshipping the women of their choice, but at the same time making them unhappy owing to their sexual incapacity. Such men require a "Madonna" and a "prostitute," and if they happen to marry a "Madonna" they condemn her to sexual starvation.

Sigmund Freud, the father of psychoanalysis, writes in this connection in his classic work *On the Psychology of Love Life*, that he "cannot dismiss the conviction that the attitude of the man to love in our modern civilization bears the impress of psychological impotence. The emotional and sensual elements are very rarely merged to the proper extent among the educated classes; the man in his sexual activity nearly always feels embarrassed by his respect for the woman, and only manifests his potency completely when confronted with a debased sexual object which, again, is partly due to the fact that there is a perverted component in his sexual aims which he dare not attempt to satisfy on the respected woman. He only derives complete sexual satisfaction when he can abandon himself to that object, regardless of anything else, and he dare not do this, for instance, with his virtuous wife."

In a preceding passage Freud writes in connection with masculine impotence expressly: "I assert, on the contrary, that psychical impotence is far more widespread than is generally believed, and that a certain degree of this is characteristic of the love life of civilized man."

In addition to medical men, only a certain class of women is capable of supplying confirmatory evidence of this state of affairs, namely, women who, though respected in "society" as virtuous wives, have in their private lives discarded the prejudices of their world, and are capable of discussing the subject without embarrassment. One such lady made the following statements in a letter: "It is my experience that otherwise sound men are, or become impotent in their intercourse with me; *they respect me too much* and for that reason things do not seem to go so well (unfortunately, a frequent experience with me) . . . . There are men who cannot react properly to a 'respectable woman' and are impotent with her precisely because they consider her 'too respectable.' They dare not touch her, because intercourse with such a woman seems 'immoral' to them."

However, a thoughtlessly contracted marriage may also, indirectly, lead to feminine impotence or even frigidity in other ways than through physical aversion or through the psychologically determined physical failure of the man. We refer to the typical "tragedies" that so frequently occur on the wedding night. But the *immediate psychological causes* of feminine impotence occurring during the wedding night do not lie in the pain involved in defloration, but rather in two, usually allied, psychological peculiarities of a large number of modern girls, particularly those of the so-called "better classes."

Owing to their unpractical upbringing, such girls develop a certain enamoured pride in their virginity, that is to say, an artificially fostered self-love (narcissism) connected with the hymen. Through defloration this self-love, at the same time as the hymen, is injured, and it is this that constitutes the unconscious principal component of defloration impotence. Instead of a simple, uncomplicated exclusive love, the man who has "robbed" a girl of this type of her "innocence," even if he is her husband, evokes in her a love mingled with unconscious hatred, with the result that sexual satisfaction is missed and the girl becomes impotent. The social attitude to virginity that was up to a few years ago almost universal, and which overrates the hymen to such an extent that it regards this insignificant and sometimes non-existent membrane as the seat of a girl's honor, to which the social rating of a "lady" is attached—this attitude absolutely breeds defloration impotence, so that its widespread prevalence is not surprising.

That is the first of the two additional causes mentioned above. The second similarly relates to a psychological factor with a social basis: The divergence between *anticipation* and *realization* during the first intercourse, which must be ascribed to the typical inhibitions raised against all sexual activity in certain middle class or "better class" circles. By the raising of inhibitions in this connection we mean the fact that, owing to the influence of the ascetic outlook and the education based upon it, all extra-marital sexual activity is strictly condemned in a woman, thereby acquiring the lure of "forbidden fruit." This lure in a great many cases goes so far that none but forbidden—that is to say extra-marital—intercourse affords erotic pleasure, while conjugal intercourse, being permitted, evokes no erotic sensations. This is a frequent form of matrimonial impotence. Owing to this psychological attitude this type of girl experiences a double disappointment in marriage.

If a girl has already had intercourse with another man before marriage, with normal orgasm, then the unsatisfying conjugal intercourse not infrequently provides the impulse to adultery, which in the experience of the woman concerned at least afforded the normal amount of sexual pleasure. Here again, as so often in other directions, we are confronted with the grotesque fact that the ascetic attitude to life with its "moral" sysem of education achieves the precise contrary of its aim—in this instance it promotes adultery on the part of the woman.

Of the cultural causes of the enormous prevalence of feminine impotence the most universal is the so-called intellectualization of our age. We mean by this the artificial estrangement of the people from all that is natural by means of a wrong ideal of education, which is further reinforced by the whole trend of our technical age. Intellectualism is being introduced everywhere, even where it is entirely out of place, and therefore also into sexual life. And it is a well established experience that when you start to work out "systems" of loving, or to love in accordance with "theories," the immediate experience is bound to be missed, and it is this immediateness, this directness and naturalness that provides the best safeguard for the organically happy conclusion of the sexual act for the woman.

At the same time, it would be unjust to ascribe the frequency of feminine sexual irregularities *solely* to cultural influences. The latter, in fact, operate in addition to certain anthropological difficulties.

In the course of development from animal to man, the form of copulation changed from the *front-to-back* method which is still practiced by animals, to the *front-to-front* attitude; and we think it is safe to assume that the anthropological root of human love should be sought in this circumstance. Animals procreate; man, and man alone, is capable of love. Animals copulate from behind. They sniff at each other, but do not look into each other's faces. The absorption of one pair of eyes in another, the kiss—these are rewards of the erect bearing, which is at the same time probably also the principal source of our sense of beauty.

As, however, in front-to-back copulation the point of excitation in the female was the clitoris, which in front-to-front intercourse is hardly touched by the man, erotic sensitiveness in the course of the ages has been gradually transferred from this erogenous zone of the clitoris to the interior of the vagina—and this change still occurs in every human female at the beginning of puberty. The lateness of the process in the development of the individual female today is itself proof that (measured in anthropological ages) this "new" front-to-front method of copulation and its consequences are of "recent" origin.

It might almost be said that this newest process of development is in the biological sense as yet insufficiently missed in the development of individual women. In that case the clitoris alone remains sensitive to erotic excitation by friction, while the vagina fails in this respect. In other words, the frequency of feminine impotence may be a consequence of, among other things, the fact that we are still in a transitional phase of anthropological development, in which the transposition of the terminal sensory nerves from the clitoris to the vagina is not yet sufficiently "fixed."

In view of all this, it is not surprising that sexual disequilibrium of various kinds should be particularly frequent in women. But as we are still on the subject of the wide prevalence of feminine sexual frigidity, there is something we must add at this stage, namely, the fact that this evil is particularly great in Europe. This is due to purely social causes, and particularly to overcrowding, which is one of the worst features of a post-war period. Where an entire family must live in a single room, it is inevitable that even small children should observe the intimate intercourse of their parents, and it may also happen that the father will violate one of the older girls. All these unfavorable influences on the child mind are bound to produce an adverse effect on the sexual development of children and young people, and it is therefore hardly surprising that people brought up in such environment are literally overloaded, so to speak, with all kinds of sexual irregularities: hysteria, anxiety and other neuroses are the order of the day, and the feminine impotence that nearly always accompanies such neuroses almost becomes the rule, and normal sexuality the exception.

The peak point of this deplorable state of affairs is reached fifteen or twenty years after a war, in which so many girls who have just reached adult age have lost their fathers. Those who have peered into the depths of the child mind will know that, particularly in early childhood, the influence of both parents is necessary for normal development. The children of widows or widowers therefore frequently develop all kinds of neurotic symptoms. In particular, girls require, for their undisturbed sexual development, the presence of their father, on whom they "learn to love," and on whom they can, for the first time, exercise their psycho-sexual personality.

If the father is absent during the first critical years, that is to say, between the ages of four and six years, then the inter-sexual inclination that is present in all children, both in the physical and psychological sense, cannot be sufficiently differentiated; the masculine impulses of the little girl will not be sufficiently repressed. In addition, there is the fact that the daughters of the war dead are in many cases later obliged, professionally or domestically, and to some extent also, though quite unconsciously, in the sexual sense, to "take the place of father," and this circumstance fixes their masculine inclinations all the more strongly. Such girls in their subconscious minds could not develop a real femininity, and owing to this subconscious aversion to their natural feminine role in sexual intercourse, they "refuse to take part in it" and therefore remain insensible.

No wonder, then, among the generation of girls born during war sexual neuroses are particularly frequent. Thus a Viennese sexual consultant with a practice in a lower income district reported at the Vienna Congress of the World League for Sexual Reform in the year 1930 that more than fifty percent of the young men and nearly ninety percent of the girls in his sphere of activity appeared to be affected by some sexual complaint. Although, naturally, these figures cannot be accepted as applying to the youth of all classes and of other ages, they are based on practical experience and could no doubt easily be confirmed among the lower income groups in other large cities.

What is most appalling to the initiated about these figures is the fact that the daughters of these girls, the majority of whom have no doubt married, might probably develop into frigid women as a result of wrong standards imposed upon them by their mothers, standards which the latter evolve through subconscious influences. In addition, there is the normal tendency of a girl to imitate the attitude and bearing of her mother, which only reinforces other baneful influences. In this way the evil is transmitted from one generation to the other, a perpetual chain of sexual and, therefore, also of domestic and social unhappiness.

Nevertheless, we are able to conclude this chapter with a word of hope. Looking far ahead, we find that the prospects for the future are somewhat better. The cultural restriction of feminine sexuality is gradually losing its influence, and, consequently, feminine frigidity and impotence are gradually diminishing (despite temporary increases in countries affected by war and overcrowding) because the psycho-social influences are improving. For this reason we will conclude by quoting the words of a witty Frenchman who predicts a diminution of frigidity for the future. The following passage occurs in a book by the French psychoanalyst Laforgue:

"It is a fact that women have only conquered the right to experience orgasm, and also their freedom, in recent years, so that they must go through an immense emotional development within a very short time which will probably wipe out the frigid middle class type of woman of the turn of the century, as well as the bigoted school ma'am and the pale-faced other-wordly 'ascetic.' Literature, which only a few years ago was subject to a strict censorship, as well as public opinion, of which it is an expression, is free and gaining more freedom still. The sexual problem, owing to the increasing influence of psycho-analysis, is being treated more objectively, and new discoveries are everywhere leading to enormous changes in the life of States as well as in the life of individuals."

CHAPTER 34

HYGIENIC AND SOCIAL SIGNIFICANCE OF FEMININE FRIGIDITY

THE complete sexual insensibility arising from frigidity produces no consequences as far as the woman herself is concerned, except that she may have to suffer the reactions that manifest themselves in her domestic life if the husband is affected, physically or psychologically, by the weakness of his wife's sexual instinct. If, however, the husband does not regard the wife's sexual reserve as a fault and (not being aware of the deficiency) simply exercises his "rights," then everything may be in order in the domestic sphere, apart, of course, from the possibility that the wife finds intercourse painful either for physical, but more probably for psychological reasons.

The position is very different if, though the wife's sexual appetite is normal, she cannot attain orgasm; in other words, if erection (congestion) of the internal sexual organs occurs, but no contraction of the uteral muscles. The accumulation of blood occurring during intercourse does not abate sufficiently, the libidinous congestion in the abdominal organs becomes a permanent phenomenon, and the consequences may be inflammation of and fluxes (discharges) from these organs. Thus the prevalence of feminine impotence is one of the causes of the frequency of these female complaints, though of course these complaints may also arise for a variety of other reasons. In addition, there are irregularities in the monthly period, such as also frequently occur in the case of particularly sensual virgins who do not indulge in sexual intercourse.

If intercourse is entirely avoided as unsatisfying or even burdensome, then all those troubles that are ascribed to sexual abstemiousness arise, i.e., symptoms which in cases represent the indirect consequences of feminine impotence. Skin troubles, loss of the rounded feminine forms, and all kinds of neurasthenic and neurotic complaints are some of these indirect consequences. The sexual urge is deflected, the woman's erotic fantasy revels in all sorts of perverted imaginings, and an increasing nervous irritability gradually develops; the subject becomes easily exhausted, develops an exalted, capricious character, with changeable moods that may not always be due to any visible cause. In severe cases, that is to say, where the woman's libido is particularly strong, there may be psychopathic features, i.e., she may have sexual hallucinations.

But this does not mean that such psychological consequences would not arise if the impotent woman does engage in sexual intercourse. On the contrary, the psychological consequences are even more serious in that case, because the woman's psychological equilibrium is severely shaken by the disappointment of her anticipations, by the constant unrelaxed tension, which is usually accompanied by disturbances in cardiac activity. Nearly all the "nervous" complaints, from exhaustion, depression and a quarrelsome disposition, to muscular weakness, gastric complaints and fits of terror and cramp, may arise in such cases. All these symptoms are partly of a hysterical character and partly of a neurasthenic character, so that they must be regarded partly as organic nervous complaints, and partly as psychical troubles, the two mutually aggravating each other. A large number of serious nervous (psychical) symptoms have been observed in impotent women, of which it is impossible to say with certainty that they are rooted in impotence itself. On the contrary, many definitely diagnosed cases of psychogenic impotence (or impotence arising from psychical causes) seemed to indicate that the impotence itself, together with its apparent consequences, is only one of several symptoms of a more profound psychical trouble.

Stekel, the world famous sexologist, includes among these symptoms: all kinds of phobias and fears (fear of particular locality, of confined spaces, of height, of blushing, of climbing; giddiness, stage fright, stammering, etc., etc.), gastric troubles, nervous vomiting, congestion, swooning, insomnia, trembling, periodic loss of weight, muscular cramp. If these symptoms occur in conjunction with sexual insensibility, then they are undoubtedly due to sexual causes, perhaps in some cases more or less direct consequences of an insensible but libidinous sexual life.

If, therefore, the cure or, better still, the prevention of feminine sexual insensibility would evidently be of immense importance from the point of view of health, the hygienic and cultural struggle against this evil would almost seem to be of greater importance still from the social point of view. The gravest social consequence of feminine frigidity is the disintegration of married life. The negative attitude of the wife to the husband's natural sexual needs (in the numerous cases in which the husband becomes aware of it) and also the inadequate orgasm of the wife during sexual intercourse, are fruitful causes of marital disloyalty on the part of the husband. Dr. Magnus Hirschfeld, author of *Sexual History of the World War*, wrote in this connection:

"According to my experience, most cases of adultery arise from this cause, which is particularly tragic where, as I have frequently observed, the husband retains his affection for his wife. The 'misunderstood' woman is also frequently the victim of this inadequate sensibility."

If the husband is a man of refinement, he will naturally suffer from the perpetual conflict between the compelling urge of his sexual instinct and his conscience, so that psychological troubles in the husband, or at any rate, serious nervous crises, are not rare. Since perfect health presupposes harmony between body and mind, which must share the individual's experiences in unison, a normal sexual life is obviously an indispensable condition of psychological and social harmony between husband and wife.

But marriage is also the basis of the family, and where married life is unhappy, the children are bound to suffer as regards their psychological development. If, on the bases of the latest discoveries of psychological research, we are able to establish the dictum "happy marriage—happy children," the reverse of this formula is unfortunately also true. The "nervousness" of the parents always produces a disastrous effect on the children, thus implanting the disposition of psychological troubles in the next generation.

The sexual coldness of the mother and the unrelaxed tension arising therefrom, is particularly harmful to the development of her daughters. For the secret of good education does not lie in the various externally imposed and applied "measures" and "methods," but in the *identification of the children with the parents based on love,* that is to say, in the natural bent of the children to imagine themselves in the position of their parents. In most cases this applies to the parent of the same sex, and the child, partly consciously, and partly unconsciously, tends to imitate father or mother in bearing, mood, conduct and mode of life. Thus modern psychology has strikingly confirmed the old dictum that "Education is example and love —nothing else." And since the example of the parent is in fact the decisive educational factor, the parents, whether they are or are not aware of it, are the examples the children will follow for good or ill.

A fixation, or inhibition of the psychological development of children, is all the more likely to occur where the mother is sexually insensible, because experience shows that the mother transfers her unsatisfied love from the husband to the children. In other words, a mother who in her married life is incapable of receiving or giving sexual love, lavishes the surplus of love, as such, on her children. Such children are bound to be spoiled, and thereby made unsuitable for practical life.

In this manner the identification of the daughter with the mother is fixed for the latter's later life, and it frequently happens that the daughter in adult life develops the same deficiency (impotence or even frigidity) as her mother. In general, the occurrence of irregularities in sexual sensibility in mother and daughter may be assumed to be due to one of the following three causes:

1. A conscious education to "abominate" men. Though probably not well known, it is nevertheless a fact that a great many husbands are represented to their own female children by a neurotic wife, for no other reason than the perfectly normal and natural sexual demands they make, as "monsters." Naturally, such statements are bound to implant in a great many cases an aversion to normal sexual contact.

The complaints of the mother about the burdens of motherhood, the tyranny of men, the brutality of the father, etc., cause the small girl to develop a hatred of the men who inflict all these troubles on women, and ultimately a fear of the object of feminine sexuality. She will endeavor to be as strong and as well educated as a man, in order to be able to resist men. This solution, of course, can never be a happy one, as even the most masculine woman cannot be a man. Such women constantly suffer from injured vanity, as narcissism is really what constitutes the basis of their lives.

We ourselves know of a case in which a woman had been forced into marriage by her mother against her will. The marriage was unhappy. The woman experienced no erotic sensations during intercourse with her husband, who was really a stranger to her, and even repellent, and as a result, "men" and marriage to her became synonymous with everything that was evil. She brought up her daughter on this principle, teaching her to hate her father and men in general. When the daughter left home to study chemistry, the mother warned her (unnecessarily by now) never to marry and to avoid love and men at all costs. The girl appeared to have absorbed her mother's teachings very thoroughly, and although she always sought the friendship and affection of other girls, she could be very annoying, even unbearable, when she discovered in her friends the least interest for men. She used to preach to them about the repulsivness and danger of love for men. Her aversion to masculine sexuality had penetrated into her subconscious mind so deeply that, to the consternation of her teachers, she was incapable of handling, in the university laboratory, a syringe, evidently because this harmless instrument was to her a symbol of masculine generative power, with which she had decided "to have nothing to do." We do not know what became of this unfortunate girl, but the beginning of this fresh tragedy is sufficient to show what a serious crime her grandmother committed when she forced the mother of this girl to marry against her will.

2. But the descent of a sexual irregularity arising from psychological causes may, and in most cases actually does occur in another way, *through the operation of the child's undigested psychological impressions.* Every child has a normal and natural curiousity in

respect of everything connected with sexual life. This tendency of the infant is utilized by the modern teacher to *encourage* the child to observe correctly and without embarrassment, and to ask questions, and these questions are answered truthfully and in a manner that the child will comprehend, thus building up an organic system of enlightenment. Unfortunately, however, this method of education is not applied by the great majority of parents, and indeed cannot be applied, because this modern method of education presupposes the ability on the part of the parents to discuss the question of sex with complete naturalness. This naturalness, particularly in the case of frigid or impotent and, therefore, mostly neurotic mothers, does not exist, and their children must rely on their own imaginations in the matter of sex. That is the source of the well-known ingenuous ideas concerning the origin of children and the meaning of the anatomical sexual differences between boys and girls, which are known to medical science as "infantile sex theories."

If such a child at an early age happens to observe the sexual activities of its parents, it will, in its utter ignorance of the process, regard it as a brutal act of violence. The child's interest in this mysterious subject, which, foolishly enough, is in most cases covered with a veil of secrecy by the adults, will never abate. It will feed on snatches of conversation between the parents and others, and further observations, and if, in addition, the child has to witness quarrels between the parents arising, in the last resort, from sexual discord, permanent psychological injury to the child is bound to result, hence it, too, will be "nervous" in adult life.

Now, the neuroses arising through this sort of domestic discord are in the case of women nearly always linked with some irregularity of sexual sensibility and sexual life, and the atmosphere of such a home therefore usually contributes to the transmission of defective sexual sensibility from mother to daughter. Thus although the daughter does not "inherit" the disability in the biological sense, she acquires it through the psychological "projection" from her mother.

3. However, in the great majority of cases the psychological transmission of feminine sexual insensibility from one generation to

another occurs *by means of a particularly strongly fixed identification of the daughter with the mother.* If the mother is physically and psychologically affected through lack of sexual satisfaction, she will not, naturally, radiate the same good temper and vitality as a sexually satisfied woman, and she will therefore be regarded by her daughter as a "martyr." Hence her female child will be more attached to her. In this way the father automatically becomes an object of hatred, instead of an object of childish love. The girl regards herself as her mother's ally against her father, and may even unconsciously identify herself with the unhappy mother, and the crown of thorns of the mother's destiny imperceptibly glides down on the child's head. Thus the identification of the daughter with the mother, which is otherwise the magic formula of rational education, becomes a curse to the daughter through the neurotic character of the mother. Together with the unconsciously hated father, the girl will in her later life also hate "men"—and this already confronts us with a complete case of impotence or even frigidity.

This is only a rough outline of a mechanism that is extremely complicated in its operation, but it will suffice for our purpose. The more detailed particulars are only of interest to the professional psychologist. Our object here is only to show *the extraordinarily extensive social effects* of feminine sexual insensibility. This endless chain of inadequate sexual satisfaction, discordant domestic life, disastrous upbringing, and transmission of the sexual evil to the children, and by the latter to their children, constitutes a serious danger to the health and internal peace of the people, particularly in view of the enormous incidence of feminine sexual insensibility.

For the many sexually unsatisfied women who are tormented by (mostly unconscious) desires, are not only imperfect wives, not only bad mothers unsuited for their task of bringing up children; their inner restlessness and lack of equilibrium also deprives them to a considerable extent of the joy of life and a healthy desire for work, and many husbands, leading a discordant married life as a result, are thereby impeded and injured in their professional progress.

The evil should be attacked from two directions, i.e., *preventively,* which can be done by educational means, by enlightening parents

and promoting educational reform; and therapeutically (i.e., cura-
tively), which is the task of the medical profession, and involves
early diagnosis and treatment of the sexual irregularity. However,
both the educational expert, who must be trained in sexual science,
and the doctor must be supported by public opinion, for it depends
on public opinion whether the individual will consult the medical
specialist and the educational specialist in time and follow their
advice.

But the medical man can only help and bring about an improvement in individual cases. The *root* of the evil lies in the cultural
prejudices of our age and its educational principles. That is the
proper objective of the attack.

CHAPTER 35

POSSIBILITY OF A CURE FOR SEXUAL IMPOTENCE

IMPOTENCE arising from physical causes, that is to say, mainly genital impotence, will usually have to be treated physically. If the introduction of the male member causes pain or other technical difficulties owing to some anatomical peculiarity in the woman herself or in the man, then the doctor must see to it that a painless passage should be made possible, or, if necessary, he must advise the couple as to a more convenient performance of the sexual act, which may only be rendered difficult by a slight displacement of the organs in relation to the normal or by the fact that one of the partners is too corpulent. If the orgasm of the woman is prevented by pains in the pelvis, the causes of the pains must naturally be eliminated.

Somewhat more difficult is the treatment of masturbation impotence, that is to say, the form of feminine impotence which is a consequence of former frequent masturbation on the clitoris. In such cases a re-education of the sexual sensory nerves is necessary.

However, in a great many cases the cause of the evil is in the man. For if the man, owing to inadequate potency, or possibly owing to clumsiness, cannot perform the sexual act normally then it is naturally impossible for the woman to attain orgasm, either. In such cases it is the man who must be treated for his impotence, or for his precipitate completion of the act owing to premature ejaculation. In the less serious case of mere clumsiness on the part of the man, he must be taught to acquire a better physical, and what is even more important, a better psychological technique. Deficient technique, and particularly badly performed or entirely neglected preliminaries, are very frequently the decisive cause of feminine failure to attain orgasm.

As sexual insensibility is due either to purely mechanical or psychological causes, medicinal treatment should only be resorted to in order to reinforce the psychological treatment. This warning needs to be emphasized, as wide sections of the people still believe, as a result of the publicity of the chemical industry, that there are miraculous remedies for masculine and feminine impotence. Nevertheless, the so-called *hormone preparations* that have in recent years appeared on the market, such as ovarial tablets, may produce an improvement in cases where impotence is due to glandular causes. On the other hand, preparations whose action consists solely in setting up an excitation, should be avoided. At most, a combination of ovarial tablets and one or other of the excitant preparations *prescribed by a doctor*, may be used. The result would be to encourage glandular activity, intensify the desire for intercourse, and strengthen the nerves by means of a specific nerve food. At the same time, the ultimate object is to deal with the causes of the complaint, and not merely with the symptoms. And that is why, in the medicinal reinforcement of the psychological treatment which feminine impotence usually demands, the important question is not *what* is prescribed, but *how* the medicine is prescribed. For in the medicinal treatment of impotence it is the psychological effect of the prescription that determines the results—the faith that moves mountains.

However, the overwhelming majority of cases of feminine sexual insensibility is due more or less to psychological causes. In all cases of sexual irregularity the physician must proceed very carefully and gradually in interrogating the patient concerning her sexual life and the history of the complaint; but this applies particularly in cases where the causes are psychological, as a prolonged and methodically conducted connection between physician and patient is necessary before the former is able to investigate properly the inhibitions and psychological difficulties. In most cases it is necessary for the patient to tell her entire life story, and nearly always her dreams must be communicated to the physician.

Such "cures" are, of course, disastrous. The sexologist must be a man of refinement and understanding, and his task is to encourage and cheer, not to intimidate. In particular, it is advisable to impress upon the patient at the beginning of the treatment that there is *no* congenital and therefore incurable sexual insensibility, and that where it is caused by psychological entanglements, it can be eliminated by unravelling these.

The sexual specialist will have frequent opportunities to prevent by his advice the development of an obstinate impotence. In this connection considerable importance attaches to the advice, where applicable, that the patient should allow herself to be *deflorated artificially* by the doctor. This advice is applicable particularly to women who marry older in life for the first time, who are still under the influence of their upbringing, which may have been based on the ascetic ideal, involving an overrating of virginity. Artificial defloration, which is a very minor operation and heals in about three days, removes this "stumbling block." It is true that the already existing psychological conflict, which may be described as the "virginity complex," is not removed by such an operation, and may subsequently still lead to other psychological entanglements and complaints; but as regards this one *decisive* occasion "derailment" is prevented, and unless there are other physical or psychological difficulties, there is every probability that soon after the patient starts to engage in sexual intercourse, normal sensibility will be re-established.

At the same time, a physician is only consulted in the vast majority of cases when impotence is already present, so that there can be no question of prevention, but only of a possible cure. The methods of psychological treatment may vary a great deal according to the nature of the individual cases. In this connection it may be said that there is little scope for treatment by suggestion. In cases of sexual insensibility little can be done by suggestion, except perhaps when the complaint is particularly mild and due to a certain sexual anxiety. Hypnotism is more effective, and may sometimes, though certainly not always, be employed in cases of defloration impotence or vaginismus, i.e., excessive vaginal contraction. However, the primary object of hypnotic treatment is also only the re-establishment of sexual self-confidence. If this is not achieved, that is to say, if owing to sexual inhibitions there is a strong resistance, then this particular method of treatment must naturally be dropped. It is particularly undesirable to inculcate orgasm by hypnotic means, as there is a danger of fixation on the doctor, and consequent estrangement from the husband.

In serious cases of psychological impotence, as well as of psychological frigidity, psychoanalysis is often the correct treatment. The object of this treatment is, in the case of frigidity, to release the repressed libido, and in both cases—frigidity and impotence—to uncover the sexual complexes in the subconscious mind and thereby eliminate them. (A complex is a pathological or unhealthy combination of various psychological elements to one psychological unit; the psychoanalysis is the analysis or dissection of the complex. The term psychoanalysis has frequently been misinterpreted to mean that the psychological unit constituting the personality of the individual is disrupted, which is impossible; whereas the purpose of psychoanalysis is precisely to re-establish the normal attitude of the personality by disrupting unhealthy psychological combinations.)

The question, What are the events whose psychological traces psychoanalysis uncovers?, is answered by Sigmund Freud, the father of psychoanalysis, as follows: "There is a variety of such events. Principally impressions that are apt to exercise a permanent influence on the budding sexual life of the child, like observation of sexual processes between adults, or the child's own sexual experiences with an adult or another child—which is not at all rare—and also the hearing of conversations which the child understands at the time or only subsequently, and from which it believes to have obtained enlightenment concerning mysterious or terrifying things. Also, statements and actions of the child itself proving a tender or sensitive attitude to other persons. It is particularly important in psychoanalysis to induce a recollection of the child's own sexual activities, and also the interference of adults which brought them to an end."

This treatment, of course, can only succeed if a special kind of intimate relationship is established between the patient and the analyst, a so-called "transference." It has been observed that the patient transfers to the physician during treatment his former childish attitude to the adult person in authority over him, for instance, his father, and this applies for good or ill.

It is clear that the analyst must possess not only an adequate training and experience, but also a particular solidity and reliability, in order not to abuse, unconsciously or consciously, the transference of the patient.

On the whole, it may be said that feminine sexual impotence of psychological origin represents a most favorable field for the application of psychoanalytical methods. Professor Wilhelm Stekel, the world famous psychoanalyst and sexologist, wrote in this connection: "The condition of sexually insensible women is sometimes subject to sudden changes and surprises, even when they do not change their sexual partner. Which means that in feminine impotence the prospects of a cure are never hopeless."

It is therefore highly advisable, as we have already pointed out, for the physician to impress upon the patient right at the beginning of the treatment that feminine impotence is curable, and this may even considerably facilitate the treatment itself.

At the same time, all the physician can do is eliminate unconscious inhibitions and psychological obstacles. The rest depends on the husband, to whose skill and experience it is left whether the woman who is now capable of sexual enjoyment will, in fact, find in his arms the happiness which has so far only been a vague dream to her.

Before we conclude this chapter on the cure of feminine frigidity and impotence, we must say a few words about the *prevention* of these sexual troubles, as prevention is proverbially better than cure and should be the most important aim of medicine.

As the basis of our preventive suggestions we reiterate once more that the great majority of sexually insensible women *are the victims of wrong upbringing and education, and of the clumsiness or lack of consideration and gentleness of the men,* who are themselves the victims of similar methods of education. *Deliberate brutality on the part of a man during sexual intercourse is rare.* Frequently the "guilt" of the man in this connection is due to prolonged recourse to prostitution, the "safety valve" of an antiquated and unhealthy sexual morality. The preventive requirements are therefore as follows:

1. Abolition of sexual ignorance both in men and women by means of educationally correct enlightenment of children.

2. Medical enlightenment of young people concerning healthy sexual satisfaction and the faults to be avoided during sexual intercourse, such enlightenment to be afforded not later than shortly before marriage.

3. War on the present biologically and socially untenable sexual morality by propagating a new, eugenically oriented *sexual morality of Love, honesty and a sense of responsibility.*

CHAPTER 36

PHYSICAL CAUSES OF FEMININE SEXUAL PROBLEMS

As we have seen in the preceding chapters feminine sexual insensibility may be due to physical and psychological causes. In this chapter we will deal with the former group of causes, mainly in connection with feminine impotence, as frigidity of purely physical origin is almost non-existent.

The physical causes of feminine impotence may lie in the woman herself, but in many cases this complaint is brought about by the male partner. We will therefore consider the two groups of causes separately, beginning with the former.

Congenital and acquired peculiarities in the female body come first among the physical causes of feminine impotence. In the majority of cases of this type we are confronted with genital impotence or glandular impotence. The latter form of impotence is caused by deficient functioning of the endocrine glands, in consequence of which the growth and development of the sexual organs have not kept pace with the rest of the body.

Genital impotence may be caused by a number of congenital anatomical anomalies, such as a closed vagina due to congenital features or inflammations, or contraction or narrowing of the vaginal canal. Sometimes there is a double vaginal passage, in which case medical science can sometimes help by surgery. The same applies to hermaphrodites or "men-women" who, although psychologically feminine, have external sexual organs that are too large (clitoris developed almost to a penis and large lips grown together) to render sexual intercourse in the feminine sense possible. Finally, these congenital anatomical anomalies also include severe rupture (hernia) which, if it penetrates into the large lips may sometimes close the vaginal passage. However, such rupture is operable.

All these are really circumstances that render sexual intercourse difficult or impossible, but which at the same time cause impotence. For a woman who is incapable of sexual intercourse is nearly always also impotent, since, as we have seen, despite the fact that erotic sensations may be experienced in various parts of the body, the posterior part of the vagina is normally the principal seat of erotic sensation. This part of the membrane cannot be excited in women who are incapable of sexual intercourse, because the male member cannot penetrate. Women suffering from this disability may nevertheless attain orgasm if there happens to be a displacement of their erogenous zones in such a manner that orgasm can be attained by the excitation of another area of the body, but such cases are probably extremely rare.

But obstacles barring the penetration of the vagina may also be acquired. These are usually tumors originating in the vagina or even in the uterus.

If despite the presence of such painful obstacles to penetration sexual intercourse is attempted or forced upon the woman, an abatement or extinction of the sexual appetite or libido may result. In such a case we would be confronted with a change from genital impotence to frigidity, fear of the pain involved finally suppressing the desire for sexual intercourse.

The same consequences, i.e., genital impotence and frigidity, may, of course, also arise if the woman is suffering severe pain during intercourse for other reasons, such as a wound or inflammation. In such cases the introduction of the male member is possible, but the violent pain prevents the attainment of orgasm by the woman. At first an internal erection of the feminine sexual organs will still occur; but if the attempts to perform the sexual act despite the pain are obstinately persisted in, then the female genital apparatus will cease to be congested sufficiently even to produce the preliminary stage of sexual excitement.

In addition to cases of inflammation in the external genital organs, violent pain may be—and indeed is far more frequently—caused by internal growths and displacements or by inflammatory changes in the fallopian tubes and ligaments of the womb, which frequently occur after abortion, particularly in the case of inadequate convalescence, and also after criminal (illegal) abortions performed without proper antiseptic precautions and post-operative care. This is a common cause of sterility. The displacements, however, are usually amenable to treatment by the physician, and the post-abortion troubles may also be eliminated by means of suitable treatment and, above all, rest.

Thus if sexual intercourse, particularly the pressure of the male member against the uterus, causes pain, an immediate visit to the doctor is indicated, particularly as in that case, especially after unpreventable spontaneous abortion, the oviducts are frequently

Picture story of abnormal states in female sex organs, compared with uterus in normal condition.

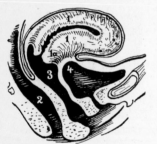

FIG. 105—(1) Uterus; (1a) Cervix; (2) Rectum; (3) Vagina; (4) Bladder. Uterus in normal position.

FIG. 106—(2) Retroflection of uterus.

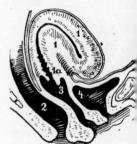

FIG. 107—Uterus tipped forward.

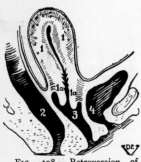

FIG. 108 — Retroversion of uterus.

FIG. 109—Slight prolapse of uterus.

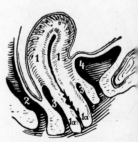

FIG. 110—Severe prolapse of uterus; projecting from vagina.

also inflamed. Neglect may lead to the tragic consequence of the closing of the oviducts and therefore barrenness. In view of this grave danger of so many feminine complaints, it is always advisable to consult a doctor immediately on the appearance of the least flux or pain in the pelvis and the back, or pain during sexual intercourse.

In the same category as the above-mentioned causes of feminine impotence belongs the so-called vaginismus, i.e., a convulsive contraction of the vaginal muscles, which closes the entrance of the vagina almost completely, so that the introduction of the male member becomes impossible. In the majority of cases this excessive contrac-

Uterus in abnormal positions.

FIG. 111—(1) Uterus; (2) Rectum; (3) Vagina; (4) Bladder; (5) Small ulcer on cervix.

FIG. 112 — Cancer of the uterus.

FIG. 113—Very advanced cancer of the uterus.

FIG. 114—(1) Uterus; (2) Rectum; (3) Vagina; (4) Bladder; (5) Tumor in uterus (small).

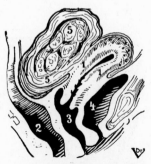

FIG. 115—Large tumor (5) in the posterior part of the uterus pressing against intestine.

FIG. 116—Same tumor (5), considerably enlarged, pressing against bladder.

tion is due to psychological causes; we will revert to this subject later. At this stage we only wish to deal with the physical causes of the complaint.

Irregularities in connection with the hymen need not necessarily lead to vaginism immediately, yet they may cause genital impotence. It happens during the first intercourse quite frequently that the hymen, being particularly strong, is not broken, but only distends, causing pain at every subsequent intercourse. In such cases artificial defloration by a doctor is necessary. Operative defloration should preferably be carried out by means of three or four radical incisions, i.e., from the center outwards. A local anaesthetic like cocaine usually suffices. The wound heals in three or four days.

However, it may also happen that although the hymen is pierced during the first intercourse, painful tears remain, and as these are disturbed at each subsequent intercourse they do not heal up. In that case the physician must see to it that a painless passage is provided. If, however, there are scars after the healing of the tears, these scars are covered with highly sensitive terminal nerves, and vaginism may be the result.

So far we have only mentioned cases in which anatomical anomalies, swellings, painful inflammations or badly healed remnants of the hymen cause the vagina to be impenetrable or too narrow, so that intercourse is either impossible or painful. But the reverse of these cases may also lead to feminine genital impotence. For instance, after child-birth the tears in the vagina may be sewn up wrongly, so that it becomes too wide. In that case the mucous membrane of the vagina does not adhere closely enough to the male member during intercourse, so that the excitation required to produce orgasm cannot take place. Impotence arising in this manner can usually be cured by means of a minor operation.

The anatomical causes of feminine genital impotence further include certain peculiarities in the physical make-up of otherwise healthy women which renders the introduction of the male member difficult. If the partners are unable to solve the problem, then sexual intercourse does not take place at all. In such cases the surgeon must help. He will do this, for instance, by endeavoring to correct an

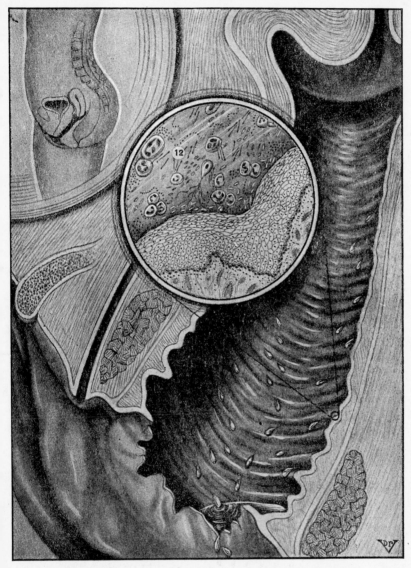

FIG. 117—Picture story of how a discharge is produced in the vagina.

White flow. The circle shows a portion of the mucous membrane of the vagina, considerably enlarged. Vagina has been invaded by a large number of dangerous pathogenic microbes (12), which have overcome the normal microbes indicated in the drawing of a normal vagina (10). This causes inflammation, and therefore a discharge (flux) is produced.

anomaly in connection with the position of the vulva, i.e., the external genital organs, which may be situated either too high, or too low,
or he will advise the husband and wife as to the manner in which
sexual intercourse may be carried out without surgical intervention.
The specialist must in such cases indicate the precise positions. Such
special positions may also be necessary if one or both of the partners
are particularly corpulent, though this is generally an obstacle to the
man rather than to the woman.

Finally, we must mention the anatomical causes operating in
cases where both partners are physically and psychologically, as well
as constitutionally, normal, yet either incapable of sexual intercourse
at all, or only in a manner involving severe pain to the woman,
owing to a dimensional discrepancy between the genital organs of
the partners. This, however, is a rare phenomenon. During such
painful sexual intercourse the attainment of orgasm is naturally
impossible. If intercourse is repeatedly attempted without medical
aid being invoked, then an inhibitional frigidity may develop in a
woman, which, however, would in the majority of cases be a relative
frigidity. In some cases the excessively narrow vagina widens after
child-birth and the formerly painful intercourse can now be performed with complete orgasm. Unfortunately, however, in the majority of these cases pregnancy and child-birth do not occur at all.
Then, the doctor must try a careful process for the widening of the
vagina, which is comparatively easy up to a point.

At the same time, a discrepancy of the sexual organs, which is a
purely genital cause of impotence in the woman, is extremely rare.
In the vast majority of cases where the vagina is too narrow to allow
of the penetration of the male member, it will be found that the
entire sexual apparatus of the woman concerned is under-developed.
Women with such infantile under-development of their genital
organs are usually to a certain extent also infantile and immature
in the psychological sense, and have a naive attitude to love that is
not equal to the psychological requirements of sexual life.

We have so far dealt with cases of impotence caused by congenital
or acquired *anatomical* defects. We now come to those cases where,
although the anatomical make-up of the subject is perfect, the attain-

ment of orgasm is prevented by the *defective functioning* of individual organs.

We will commence with the form of impotence in which, although the muscles of the oviducts and the uterus contract during intercourse, so that the physical conditions of orgasm are present, orgasm cannot be attained because owing to the destruction of certain nerves in the spinal cord the sexual excitations do not reach the brain. In such cases the impotence is due to a conductive defect. However, impotence is caused far more frequently by the destruction of the nerves at a certain point in the lower part of the spinal column, near the small of the back, known as the sacrum, where the erection center is situated. The erection center is that part of the spinal cord through which excitation the internal erection of the female organ is effected, i.e., the strong congestion that renders possible the intense excitability of the genital zone, thereby creating the foundation on which all the other physiological causes of orgasm depend. If this erection center is destroyed, then excitation and satisfaction in a woman become impossible.

Destruction of the erection center may be caused by injury to the spinal cord, inflammation of the spinal cord, and particularly by the so-called tabes of the back. This is a severe infectious disease of the spine, which frequently appears as the after-effect of syphilis. In consequence of the organic changes produced by the causative agent of syphilis in the spinal cord, women affected with tabes of the back sometimes have fitful orgasms accompanied by intense secretions from the vagina and the vulva. Child-birth in such circumstances is usually entirely painless. Tabes of the back, like any other post-syphilitic disease, is in case of early diagnosis usually curable.

Complete absence of sexual desire owing to glandular defects usually arises from two entirely different causes. We know today that all the endocrine glands, i.e., glands that convey their secretions direct to the blood, in contrast with the exocrine glands, whose secretions are discharged, influence each other both favorably and unfavorably. As it is always the combined mixture of all the secretions that determine the physical and psychological attitude of the individual, one and the same external symptom may be due to several causes connected with the internal secretions of the glands.

The exact number of the endocrine glands in the human body has not yet been determined. We know of at least nine, but there are probably more. Some of these endocrine glands *promote* development, while others exercise a contrary influence. Thus lack of sexual desire, or rather inadequate sexual desire in a person may be due either to a preponderance of inhibiting endocrine secretions or a deficiency of the secretions that promote development.

Thus the first though rare possibility of glandular frigidity lies in a retarded or slow retrogression of the thymus gland; for the thymus gland (which is situated in the chest) is an endocrine gland that impedes sexual development. In normal individuals this gland degenerates when sexual maturity is reached, and, naturally, its adverse effect on the development of sexual desires also ceases. If, therefore, the degeneration of this gland is retarded, then sexual desire will also appear later, or at any rate, it will be weaker.

The other possibility of a glandular frigidity lies in the absence or under-development of the ovaries. This is usually accompanied by inadequate development of the feminine sexual organs.

This second glandular frigidity usually goes hand in hand with glandular impotence, because owing to the absence or under-development of the ovarial glands the brain cannot be adequately eroticized.

We now come to the influence of narcotics on feminine sexual insensibility, i.e., those causes which operate adversely to sexual sensibility through the brain. We refer to morphine, cocaine, nicotine, and, above all, alcohol. In the case of advanced alcoholism complete impotence may be produced, both in men and women, by failure of the brain to respond to sexual excitation, and minor degrees of impotence as a result of the abuse of alcohol are not at all rare. The same applies to excessive use of tobacco, while in the case of morphine and cocaine the effect is far more intense.

The influence of alcohol on sexual life as a whole will be dealt with in a separate chapter.

CHAPTER 37

FEMININE MASTURBATION—CLITORIC AND VAGINAL SEXUALITY

WE have already mentioned that the seat of highest excitability in a woman should be the posterior part of the vagina. Unfortunately, however, in the case of a very large number of women this most intense sexual sensitiveness is absent, or almost absent, and is replaced by an exclusive sexual excitability of the clitoris.

In order to make this and the following more detailed observation clear to the reader, we must first deal with the intensely interesting but somewhat complicated role of the clitoris in the sexual development of the woman.

First, we must remember the fact, unfortunately frequently ignored, that man in the course of his development from the lower creatures has been bi-sexual. To explain this, we must digress a little and outline the history of that development.

Science has established that man's first ancestor was a unicellular creature. We also know that this process of development is still going on. For instance, it is well known that the appendix, which still plays an important part in ruminants, performs no ascertainable function in man. This organ is gradually degenerating, so that, perhaps after thousands of years, it will finally disappear.

In contrast to the appendix, the brain is still in a state of development. During the thousands of years of human progress it has continually grown in size, because the progress of civilization has made increasing demands on the brain.

The same process—retrogression on the one hand, and further development on the other—is taking place in the sexual organs. The cells, the primitive creatures from which man has in the course of billions of years developed, had no sexual organs, and multiplied

277

by a process of division. When a cell had absorbed a certain quantity of nourishment, when it was "overfed," it simply split into two or more parts, thus producing a new generation of cells, which in turn continued the process.

At a higher phase of development these cellular creatures developed sexual organs, but there was no differentiation—each cell having both masculine and feminine sexual organs. Thus, they were bi-sexual, and they now multiplied by fertilizing themselves.

At the third phase of development came sexual differentiation, that is to say, some of the organisms developed masculine, and others feminine sexual organs, and multiplication now occurred by means of sexual intercourse.

Naturally, these processes did not take place by leaps and bounds, but very slowly, over billions of years and particularly the differentiation from the bi-sexual creatures to the hetero-sexual (of different sexes) has been very slow and is, indeed, to a certain extent still proceeding. Traces of certain organs of each sex are still present in the other sex. For instance, men still have nipples on their breasts, though these would be superfluous to them even if they were more fully developed, as the suckling of new-born infants is a feminine function. In the same way women have a clitoris, which is a degenerated form of the male member.

Now, every individual human being must pass through the same process of development through which the primitive cells have passed from sexlessness to bi-sexuality and from the latter to differentiated sexuality.

We know that the fertilized ovum in a woman during the first stage of its existence is sexless. (It is true that the future sex of the new being is implanted at the moment of fecundation, but that does not concern us here.) It is only between the sixth and eighth weeks of the development of the embryo that the sexual protuberance evolves, but this contains both the masculine and feminine elements (vestiges of the ovaries and the penis), so that it is bi-sexual. During the subsequent development of the embryo certain furrows grow together, while other vestiges evolve more strongly, the germinal glands developing either into ovaries or testicles. In this way during

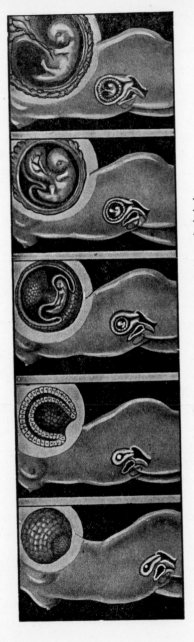

Picture story of development of child inside mother's body.

Transparent development of child inside, in the different stages, and five inset pictures of development of foetus to child.

Fig. 118—In circle: form of ovum anchored in uterus.

Fig. 119—Structure of ovum in next phase.

Fig. 120—Foetus starts to take shape.

Fig. 121 — Foetus receives nourishment through vessels of placenta.

Fig. 122—Foetus after three months.

the eighth month the originally bi-sexual creature develops its separate sexuality.

However, the process is not complete until the sexual glands, i.e., the testes or ovaries, commence their endocrine function. This occurs between the ages of twelve and fourteen, which period is called the age of puberty.

It will be seen that children retain a certain degree of bi-sexuality, which is in continuous retrogression until the age of puberty. In the case of the female child this bi-sexuality is greater than in the male. The explanation is as follows:

As we have already stated, the clitoris is an organ in process of retrogression, and represents a rudimentary penis. As such it is, so to speak, superfluous in the normally developed female body, a remnant of an earlier bi-sexual phase of development.

During the phase when man was half animal, copulation was carried out from behind, as animals still do today, and the clitoris then still played an important part, in that it was the chief seat of sexual excitation. In the adult human female the clitoris is in process of retrogression, since during front-to-front copulation the clitoris is hardly touched by the male member.

But that is not the case in female children. During childhood, and in fact during the age preceding sexual intercourse, the clitoris occupies an important position in the imagination. Infantile masturbation is carried out on the clitoris, and this organ retains its sexual significance until the age of puberty.

During the period of puberty in a girl the point of greatest sexual sensibility should be transferred from the clitoris to the interior of the vagina and the last vestige of masculinity (and the clitoris is a rudimentary penis) should also disappear in the psychological sense. In a word the period of puberty should serve to prepare the human female, both organically and psychologically, to attain marital happiness, i.e., orgasm in sexual intercourse.

Unfortunately it happens far too frequently that this stage is not reached, and the vagina remains insensitive to sexual excitation, as it has been during childhood, so that only the clitoris is susceptible to excitation. That means that the individual concerned is impotent.

This happens, where the cause is not psychological, particularly when exclusive sexual sensibility has been fixed on the clitoris too strongly through excessive masturbation during childhood. It is therefore clear that masturbation frequently plays an important part in the causation of feminine impotence, the exact nature of which we shall examine in detail. (Thus impotence through masturbation, which is frequently assumed to arise in men, but does not in fact exist, does in a great many cases occur in women.)

The determination of the frequency and temporal extent of feminine masturbation is immensely difficult in individual cases (though the question whether a woman has ever indulged in masturbation must in nearly all cases be answered in the affirmative). False modesty and, above all, more or less powerful subconscious resistances, usually make it difficult for female patients to state the true facts. Thus it requires a very careful technique of interrogation and a capacity for deduction based on considerable psychological knowledge and experience on the part of the doctor to obtain really reliable results.

All this naturally only applies to the kind of infantile masturbation which is exercised by rubbing the clitoris. In consequence of frequent excitation over a long period, the terminal nerves of this organ do not retrogress, so that the nervous cells in the mucous membrane of the vagina are inhibited in development. The clitoris therefore remains the center of sexual sensation in the women concerned, and when they engage in normal sexual intercourse, they prove to be impotent, owing to the insensibility of the mucous membrane of the vagina, since, as we have seen, the clitoris only plays a secondary role in sexual intercourse.

However, in all cases where masturbation is in any way involved in the causation of impotence, it is only the *direct* cause. *Indirectly*, those psychological and social factors which have led to the fixation of masturbation to the clitoris, play an important contributory role. These psychological and social causes which lead to masturbation of the clitoris as the sole method of sexual satisfaction, include sexual solitude (lack of a partner), fear of infection, of pregnancy, and of defloration. The last-named is particularly strong, because owing to the psychological and social overrating of the hymen, from which fear of defloration arises, such girls choose masturbation of the clitoris as the only method of satisfaction, as vaginal masturbation would destroy the hymen. The result is tragedy—for the clitoric sexuality becomes fixed, the vagina remains insensible, and if marriage is nevertheless attempted, the woman is impotent from the outset. And the ideas of such women concerning the awful nature of feminine sexual satisfaction appear to stand confirmed, since they themselves derive no pleasure from it. If they had engaged in vaginal masturbation, sacrificing the physical symbol of virginity, they would have suffered little or no harm, exactly like men who masturbate in the ordinary masculine way. And later a satisfactory sexual life would have been possible at any time as soon as a partner had been available.

It will be seen from this that prevention of feminine masturbation impotence is not a matter of combatting the practice of masturbation, but is only possible if the psychological and social causes which fix masturbation to the clitoris are eliminated. Above all, the overrating of the hymen as part of feminine education must be abolished. In a word, this is another difficulty of sexual life which, like most others, could be overcome by the propagation of a natural moral outlook, which regards human actions according to their intrinsic nature, and not according to external viewpoints.

Let us now examine the question of infantile masturbation.

It should be noted, to begin with, that clitoric masturbation of infants, i.e., children of up to five or six years, is neither unnatural nor in the least dangerous. It only becomes dangerous if as a result of wrong methods of education, it is carried on to excess, or beyond the age of five or six years.

These methods include the two notorious extremes of *excessive severity* and *excessive leniency*. In the case of excessive severity, and particularly threats and rigorous measures intended to force the child to give up masturbation, the intensified consciousness of guilt and the child's fear of the hostile attitude of the adults, drives it all the more to resort to masturbation as a consolation. In this manner masturbation may literally become a compelling urge, so that the parent or guardian who employs these strict methods achieves the precise contrary of what is intended.

But experience shows that excessive leniency, the spoiling of a child, also leads to increased masturbation. In particular, too many caresses, games and larks with children in the parents' bed may lead to bad results. Such things arouse in the child (and our general remarks concerning masturbation apply equally to both sexes) all sorts of sexual desires that can only be realized in adult life. The child takes such jokes, however harmless they may appear to be, in earnest, so that it is continually exposed to a sense of injury, and again seeks consolation in masturbation.

The brutal suppression of infantile masturbation by adults produces one further result. Masturbation is given up—apparently; but the child will be bound to continue it in secret. But these secret manipulations will always be accompanied by fear of discovery, so that the sexual instinct will become associated in the mind of the child with fear. And as fear of various kinds plays an important role in the sexual life of a woman (fear of the unknown, of the pain of defloration, pregnancy, child-birth, etc.), it is easy to see how fear may take root in the subconscious mind of a female child, to become inseparable from everything connected with sex. This fear is one of the deepest causes of feminine frigidity and impotence, for it is bound to eclipse any sensation of pleasure in sexual life.

As regards the curability of feminine impotence caused by clitoric masturbation, that naturally depends on whether the masturbation was practiced in childhood or only at the age of sexual maturity. The latter, of course, is far more easily cured, as it is only a substitutive masturbation, to which the girl concerned has been driven for lack of a male partner. What happens is that the sexual sensibility of the masturbating woman becomes fixed on the clitoris (where masturbation takes place, since the vagina is closed by the hymen), and when normal intercourse is eventually attempted the vagina is entirely insensitive to excitation; but in such cases a cure is possible, usually through variations of position during sexual intercourse, designed to discover the most sensitive erogenous zone, if possible away from the clitoris. In addition, it may be necessary for the man at first to employ a particular method of intercourse, varying the speed, force and rhythm of the friction in a manner similar to the earlier movements of the girl during masturbation. This new method of intercourse must be practiced for some time, and when orgasm is regularly attained it may be gradually varied, until orgasm is attained by the woman by the normal method of intercourse.

Naturally, such "treatment" of masturbation impotence is only possible if the woman has a very skillful and experienced partner, who in addition has the gift of understanding.

However, a cure is particularly difficult in cases where, as a result of prolonged clitoric masturbation, the woman concerned has become so accustomed to the use of her hand in this connection; but a cure may nevertheless be achieved by systematically deflecting this habit. The treatment would have to begin by manual friction, which may the first few times be carried to the point of orgasm, in order to establish a psychological link between the woman and her partner. Later the man must also use his member, as far as possible unobserved by the woman, while continuing the excitation of the clitoris with his hand. Once the woman attains orgasm through this "combined" intercourse, purely genital intercourse, with only vaginal excitation, may be begun.

The mechanism of treatment is far more complicated, however, in cases of impotence arising from infantile masturbation.

How infantile clitoric masturbation leads to impotence in the adult woman has already been described, and we have seen that this type of impotence is mostly psychological, so that it can only be cured by psychological means. An experienced psychoanalyst will therefore have to be consulted, though the physical method indicated above may also be carefully attempted in mild cases.

In concluding this chapter we would further point out that clitoric sexuality in a woman, that is to say, the *tendency* to place the clitoris in the center of sexual life, is usually also a matter of constitution, and therefore to that extent congenital. Thus it is probable that children who masturbate on the clitoris and later fix their sexuality to this organ, are impelled by constitutional causes.

However, in such cases the entire physical appearance betrays this constitutional tendency. Women of masculine appearance, with broad shoulders, narrow hips, long legs, angular outlines, flat chests, a deep voice, growth of facial hair, etc., are likely to have a clitoric sexuality (the clitoris being a rudimentary penis). Conversely, women with soft, round outlines, and full breasts, that is to say, women of feminine appearance, are more likely to have attained the stage of development where vaginal sexuality predominates.

Women with a "boyish" figure mostly belong to the type of clitoric sexuality. And so long as the "child-woman" remains the fashion, men will hardly find a proper "helpmeet" in this physically, and also psychologically somewhat immature type. For although clitoric sexuality may in certain individual cases be associated with intellectual and artistic gifts, *it is the capacity for vaginal orgasm that makes the woman,* and only a physically and psychologically fully developed woman can be an equal partner in a physically and intellectually harmonious union. Recognition of this fact has nothing to do with the political and legal equality of women, but this quality only acquires true significance through the *full expression of the difference between the sexes.*

CHAPTER 38

Hysteria of Sexually Unsatisfied Women

THE word "hysteros," from which "hysteria" is derived, means "womb." The Greek physicians associated the complaint with the womb, and in this they were right in so far as it suggests a sexual basis, but wrong in actually linking hysteria with the physical organ.

However, this error had far-reaching effects on the subsequent investigation of hysteria, as the complaint was automatically regarded as a typically feminine one, masculine hysteria being completely ignored. Indeed, it is largely ignored in medical literature even today. Where the designation "hysteria" is used in connection with women, men are said to be afflicted with sexual neuroses or sexual hypochondria.

Hysteria, in fact, is not confined to either sex, and scientists of considerable experience in this field hold that there are probably more hysterical men than women. However, in this chapter we shall consider the case of women only.

It is a most difficult task to give the layman a correct idea of hysteria, for this is a pathological phenomenon that presents the entire psychological and even physical life of the woman so affected like a distorting mirror. Imagine a distorting mirror in which one portion of the body appears to be abnormally large and thick and another abnormally small and thin. Convert this into psychological terms, and you have a fair conception of the nature of hysteria.

In order to make it easier for the reader to follow our analysis of feminine hysteria, we quote the following seven cases from the records of Dr. Magnus Hirschfeld:

Case 1.—A girl of twenty-five had severe hemorrhages from time to time, introduced by violent coughing, without any tubercular affection being present in the lungs. Highly intelligent, and an efficient private secretary, the girl's thoughts, emotions and volition were intensely engaged in the sexual sphere. She preferred effeminate men. The hemorrhages sometimes resulted in the discharge of half a pint of blood, so that her condition frequently appeared to be desperate. But several examinations, checked by a number of doctors, failed to reveal any organic trouble. After about nine months the girl established intimate relations with an author who showed a tendency towards effeminacy, each being violently attracted to the other in the erotic sense. From then on the hemorrhages completely ceased, and never recurred during the next seven months, during which time the girl was aware of a tremendous physical and psychological improvement. Then the lovers had a serious quarrel. The hemorrhages from the lungs re-started immediately with renewed violence. After an interval of about three months, when the girl entered into another harmonious affair, the hemorrhages again ceased.

Case 2.—Mrs. T. went for a short holiday to a mountain village. At her hotel she made the acquaintance of a family. One night, at about ten o'clock, when her new friends had gone to a musical performance, Mrs. T. decided to go up to bed. In order to do so she had to pass through a corridor, along which the apartment of the family was situated. She suddenly thought of the clothes rack she had seen during a previous visit in one of their rooms, entered, and took from the rack a blue silk raincoat, a blouse belonging to a fifteen-year-old girl, and a skirt that went with it. She took these garments to her room, and took a great delight in them, without, however, intending to make use of them. She laid the clothes aside and later, when a search was made for them, she cut them up into small pieces, which she hid. However, some buttons that were lying about betrayed her, and she confessed everything to the policeman who was then called.

Mrs. T. says that she took the clothes not because she needed them or because she had a mania for bedecking herself with fine things, but owing to an irresistible impulse, which comes upon her particularly during her *period*. She did not intend to use the garments, and only took them because the process gave her sensual pleasure.

Her upbringing had been strict, and her childhood embittered by quarrels between her parents. At school she learned quickly, but also forgot quickly what she had learned. At the age of eight she had been attacked by a man, who attempted to violate her.

Among the physical symptoms in this woman, the following are noteworthy: Headaches, exhaustion, restlessness, insomnia or nightmares. The sexual organs are under-developed. Psychological characteristics: Deep depression, the patient easily bursts into tears and cries for a long time. She feels unhappy even when there are no external causes. Suicidal thoughts. Has attempted suicide twice. Forgetfulness and weak memory.

Case 3.—In a small village the women, and particularly spinsters, had for several years been annoyed by anonymous letters making the grossest reflections on them. The authorities had a strong suspicion, and intended to arrest the daughter of a local landowner. However, they first consulted a detective in a nearby city. As the detective interrogated the woman who had made the complaint, and who received most of the anonymous letters, it occurred to him that she herself might be the culprit. He followed his "hunch" and found his suspicion confirmed. The woman was a severe case of hysteria.

Case 4.—A young couple had been married for two years without engaging in sexual intercourse. The wife, who had studied medicine for a few terms, had discovered that the husband had a strong homosexual component, but at first she had hoped that the genuine camaraderie that linked them together was a sufficient basis for a permanent, harmonious "married" life. After a few months, however, she began to cry day and night, lost a great deal of weight, her arms and legs trembled, and her whole body twitched. She stayed in bed and said she could not walk. Suggestion and medicines proved useless. The only thing that calmed her was when the husband she loved placed his hand on her forehead. But even this contact caused the man a feeling of discomfort. Later, the woman suffered from violent fear; she frequently screamed, and this afforded her a certain relief. She refused to eat and was badly constipated, so that she had to be fed and relieved artificially. After six months her condition became so bad that the worst was feared. Then she read in a medical journal that the sexual tendency of a homosexual man could be changed by the grafting of masculine germinal glands; *there was an immediate improvement in her condition.* Thus even the thought that there was a possibility of conquering the man she loved, gave her relief. Above all, the immobility to which she had condemned herself for several months ceased. She left her bed, and made all the preparations for a joint journey for the purpose of having the grafting operation carried out. The operation was successfully performed, but although the man was still unable to carry out the sexual act, he developed a deeper psychological attachment for her, and what was most important to the woman, he was now able to bear her caresses. The woman's condition now improved to such an extent that the marriage could be considered as a comparatively happy one, and all the hysterical symptoms in the woman regressed. In fact, she regained her former robust appearance and happy disposition.

Case 5.—A girl of twenty-five became engaged to a very worthy man whom, however, she did not like. A few days after the engagement she became deeply depressed. She could not sleep, was very restless and anxious and had times during which she screamed and flailed with her arms and legs. She was afraid of her fiance's caresses, and thought with horror of the possibility of cohabitation. The girl states that she had suffered a severe sexual shock when she was eight; since then, she says, she is nauseated by anything connected with sex.

Case 6.—A bachelor of about fifty-five was frequently visited by the daughter of a friend from the country, a woman of about thirty. One Sunday, when the girl came to his flat, the man opened the door himself, and suddenly kissed her on the lips. As she did not resist, he laid her on the bed and indulged in all sorts of manipulations, which she permitted. After this the girl declared that the man must marry her, as he had robbed her of her innocence. The man tried to calm her, and explaining that she had not lost her innocence at all, he refused to marry her. The girl then had a severe attack of hysteria. She ran to her own and the man's relations described everywhere in vehement language what had happened, wrote the man alternately ardent love letters and letters of abuse, and finally became so excitable that she had to be sent to an institution.

Case 7.—A woman of thirty-six, who had been a widow for eight years, and was highly respected in the small town where she lived, married a non-commissioned officer upon his return from captivity. *The day after the wedding night* she showed symptoms of acute derangement. She declaimed aloud, addressed her second husband by the name of the first, and was generally so excited that she had to be sent to an asylum. The man petitioned for divorce. But as soon as she learned about this, the woman suddenly became sane and was released from the asylum. The hysterical attacks never recurred and the marriage was quite happy.

It will be noted that the common feature of all these cases is the fact that they are centered in sex. Where the individual case could be precisely analyzed, there was always some physical trouble due to hysteria. Continuous headaches, restless sleep, screaming during sleep, are common. Even hemorrhages, paralysis of the limbs, and digestive troubles may be caused by hysteria. Thus all these physical troubles are due not to physical but to psychological causes.

We will mention a few more symptoms of hysteria, though not all, since that would take some hundreds of pages.

Nearly all hysterical persons are changeable in their moods, suddenly changing from gaiety to deep depression, the latter being generally more prolonged. During their periods of depression hysterical women often play with the idea of suicide, and although this is never serious, there have been cases in which a hysterical woman has killed herself by taking an overdose of some poison in error.

Among the physical symptoms we have already mentioned headaches. These may appear in the form of migraine, i.e., affecting half of the head, or there may be pain at the back of the head, and even the scalp may become hypersensitive. The senses are sometimes also affected. Thus over-sensitiveness to noise is very prevalent, while the sense of smell may also give trouble, and the eyes may be affected by constant blinking. The tendency to lachrimosity is very common and malapropism, in the sense that a hysterical woman "blurts out" something she does not really want to say, is also frequent. Stammering is more frequent in men, arising from a sense of guilt on account of masturbation in childhood. Other characteristic symptoms are nervous coughing, intensified secretion of saliva, severe perspiration, frequent blushing and paling, defective heart action, loss of appetite, frequent eructation, impeded digestion, constipation, stomach noises, as well as heartburn, nausea, vomiting, diarrhoea and colic. Then there is sudden paralysis of the arms or legs. which sometimes only affect one side, and at others both.

The hysterical character of all these symptoms only become clear to the physician retrospectively—when he sees how quickly they disappear when the trouble in the woman's sexual life is eliminated.

In order to understand the cause of these hysterical aberrations, we must know that every individual has certain special requirements as a condition of sexual satisfaction. A normal woman will be satisfied by sexual intercourse with a normal man. But if such satisfaction is impossible in the case of a strongly sexed woman, either on account of the inadequate potency of her partner, or on account of the lack of a partner, the result may be hysteria. However, this type of hysteria is extremely rare, since strongly sexed women generally break the bonds of marriage and morality and find satisfaction in some other manner.

Most frequent, and most serious are those cases of hysteria in which the subject's sexual desire is directed to a form of satisfaction that is uncommon and therefore difficult to obtain.

In this connection early childhood experiences play an important role. We have seen in previous chapters how decisively the clitoris affects the sexual development of the female child. But before the child's attention is directed to the clitoris as a sexual zone, it derives erotic pleasure from other parts of the body. Thus, for instance, suckling is in a certain sense sexually tinged. Later, the child sucks its thumb or its teeth. The infant takes everything into its mouth, as at that stage it is the mouth through which it derives most pleasure.

At another stage the child derives pleasurable sensations from the anus. We know that in a former phase of development, the sexual cavity and the rectum had a common duct. (Birds, for instance, have no separate ducts for sexual activity and for emptying the bowels.) Naturally, this common excretory and sexual canal is supplied with sensitive nerves, and in the infant the anus is still capable of producing pleasurable sensations. And it usually does produce them through the frequent washing, powdering, etc. of the anus carried out in the case of infants. The attention of the child is thus attracted to this pleasure-giving part of its body, and is afterwards further fixed during the period when it is trained to the use of the chamber.

But it is usually shock-like sexual experiences in childhood—scientifically known as traumas—that determine or affect the form of satisfaction of an individual woman. Such traumas generally consist in attempts at violation, a perverted adult playing with the child's genitals, or children indulging in such games among themselves. According to whether the child reacts to such play with fear or pleasure, the hysteria in the adult woman may assume different forms, because, as a result of such traumas, the manner of sexual satisfaction desired by the woman vary.

Finally, we must refer to the quasi-erotic attachment that links every child sometimes to the father and at others to the mother. This attachment may easily, through a complicated psychological process, change into hate. Since Freud, these emotions have been known as the *Oedipus complex*. In a normal child the Oedipus complex dissolves and has nothing to do with the child's subsequent sexual life; but where it does not dissolve in a female child, complications arise in adult life as regards the manner of sexual satisfaction.

Thus we see that hysteria may arise, on the one hand, where a normally sexed woman is deprived of normal sexual satisfaction and, on the other hand, where a woman rejects the normal method of satisfaction and desires other methods which are not available in normal circumstances. *Hysteria is therefore a physical and psychological reaction of women, often arising from the non-satisfaction of special sexual desires, regardless of the fact whether they are natural or unnatural.* But once the sexual desires of a hysterical woman are satisfied, psychological equilibrium is instantly restored and the physical symptoms disappear as though by magic.

That the hysterical reaction sometimes manifests itself (as in the cases we have quoted) in hemorrhage from the lungs, at others in headaches, colic, or attacks of perspiration, is due to the various childhood experiences that determine the sexual desires of the woman concerned in each case. It is the duty of the doctor trained in psychoanalysis to trace the sources of these infantile experiences and render a cure possible by uncovering them.

In order to prevent misunderstanding, we must add something to our remarks concerning the special sexual desires of hysterical women. These desires are sometimes incomprehensible and even ridiculous. Thus, in one of the cases quoted above, the woman in question could only find sexual happiness with effeminate men. Other hysterical women want men with white hair, or a long beard or even a cripple, while still others—and there are many of them—are completely frigid in the normal sex act.

Women with such special sexual desires are often fortunate enough to find a partner who answers their requirements, or is prepared to meet them with regard to the form of the sexual act. In such cases there is, of course, no hysteria. But otherwise this affliction is almost inevitable.

CHAPTER 39

THE SINS OF THE MALE

STRANGE as it may sound, it is nevertheless a fact that the investigation of feminine impotence must always begin with an examination of the man. Very frequently the imperfections of the man, and particularly his complete or partial impotence, or on the other hand his inexperience and clumsiness in sexual intercourse, are the only cause of feminine impotence, which may not have existed at all at the *beginning* and has only developed gradually as a result of the shortcomings of the man. In such cases the impotence of the woman is nearly always only relative, that is to say, only as far as that particular man is concerned.

Cases in which masculine failure is due to physical causes are extremely rare. An example is a considerable discrepancy between the genital organs of the man and the woman, i.e., the very exceptional case where the man's member is really too large, and it is not a case of normal male member and an extremely small vulva. It may also happen "once in a while" that owing to an anomaly in the cavernous bodies in the male member, erection occurs at an abnormal angle, so that it cannot be introduced into the vagina. This is a rare form of masculine genital impotence. Much less rare are the cases where the only obstacle to sexual intercourse is the size of the man's stomach, but this situation can usually be remedied by means of a change of relative positions between the man and his female partner.

Let us now consider the most most important causes of feminine impotence due to the male partner.

(*a*) The first of these is *complete impotence of the man*, whether it is due to physical or psychological causes, or whether it exists in relation to all women or only in relation to the particular woman concerned. We do not propose here to go into details as to the causes of masculine impotence as such, as this problem will be dealt with separately elsewhere in this work. It will be sufficient at this stage to observe that in the majority of cases masculine impotence is due to psychological causes, and that present methods of education are important contributory factors. That applies particularly to the kind of masculine impotence which is a typical concommitant of the so-called masturbation hypochondria, that is to say, a psychological complaint which sometimes arises from the severe treatment of the problem of masturbation during the patient's youth. The treatment of masculine impotence naturally differs from case to case, and may, according to its nature, be treated either by physical or by psychological means. At all events, unless a change of partners is contemplated, a cure for the impotent woman whose impotence is due to the man is impossible unless the man is first cured.

(*b*) A similar role to the male partner's complete impotence may be attributed to absolute *ejaculatio praecox* on the part of the man, that is to say, premature ejaculation occurring before or immediately after the member is introduced into the vagina. This phenomenon is a kind of impotence, and the man suffering from it may be said to be half impotent. Premature ejaculation is a sign of sexual neurasthenia, which includes all those phenomena of sexual exhaustion (lowered potency, fatigue, irritability, etc.) that were formerly ascribed exclusively to sexual overstrain, but whose causes have now been found to lie in psychological factors. Sexual overstrain, which may in fact produce temporary neurasthenia, only occurs very rarely. In some cases ejaculation praecox is only due to the psychological fixation of the first over-anxious attempt at coitus.

(*c*) *Relative premature ejaculation* differs very materially from the absolute ejaculatio praecox discussed above. As the designation suggests, this is an ejaculation that is only relatively too early, that is to say, relatively to feminine excitation. We have seen in the early part of the present work that a certain simultaneity of excitement during inercourse must be achieved if the woman is to derive the same enjoyment as the man. In some cases, however, the man with the best will in the world, is at first unable to attain even approximately this coordination of the mutual orgasms, and the discrepancy between the two orgasms occurs again and again. In such cases the difficulty is mostly due to *differing physiological temperaments*, but (unless the difference is overwhelmingly great) this can be eliminated by consulting an experienced doctor.

(*d*) However, impotence in a woman may also develop in consequence of lack of practical skill in the male partner, which in its effect is equal to masculine impotence. The cause of this clumsiness may lie in one of two factors—inexperience or anxiety. Erotic inexperience even in men who had had ample experience of sexual intercourse as such, is not rare. In particular, men who have made frequent use of prostitution sometimes fail completely in intercourse with a woman who really loves them and expects love in return. A "Don Juan," who has never learned how to treat a loving woman (and whose experience is, in fact, confined to prostitutes who are always ready for their clients), frequently realizes when confronted with a "technically" inexperienced woman who nevertheless expects tenderness and consideration for her feelings, that he is a fool.

But the clumsiness of the man may also arise from anxiety, fear of the "mystery" of woman, which is implanted in every man from early childhood, and which, if too strongly developed, will prevent him from gaining any "experience" at all. For the man must have a capacity for experience. Passing through an act or an event does not constitute experience; the event must also be digested. The main fault in this connection is *haste and a false recklessness* arising from an inner uncertainty. In such cases the art of the "preliminaries" is lost, with the consequences described in the early part of this work in connection with the so-called pleasure curve. The woman wants to be placed in the right mood, she must be physically and psychologically prepared if the embrace is to make her happy. She is repelled by haste and impatience on the part of the man, in the same way as by his depression "afterwards." A man who, immediately after the sexual act, turns away from his female partner is in the end bound to lose her affection, and will also be robbing her of her capacity for the more subtle kinds of sexual enjoyment.

(*e*) Finally, even if the man is neither impotent nor clumsy, his

wife may nevertheless become impotent owing to his fault. That
will be the case if, as a contraceptive measure (either from ignorance
or laziness) he practices *coitus interruptus.* This (entirely unreliable
and therefore impractical) method of birth control consists in withdrawing the member immediately before ejaculation takes place,
that is to say, at a moment when the woman's excitement has hardly
reached the climax. Just when the woman's excitement is approaching the orgastic climax, the man withdraws his member and leaves
the woman to her fate. The consequence is an unsatisfactory abatement of the woman's sexual excitement after the interruption, and
an undue continuance of the blood congestion in her internal organs.
This frequent unfinished and therefore frustrated excitation produces not only a high degree of nervous irritability in the woman,
but also leads to a gradual abatement of her sexual responsiveness,
i.e., to impotence.

What is the process whereby, in all the cases mentioned above,
feminine impotence usually develops? It should be noted, first of
all, that it does not *always* develop. In cases where the woman's
sexual appetite is too strong, the permanent impotence of the man
may sometimes lead her to dissolve the marriage partnership and
find another conjugal partner.

However, the alternative to this explosive solution of the conflict
is usually a neurotic complaint in the woman. Particularly in the
case of coitus interruptus, but sometimes also in the case of the man's
impotence, the repeated disappointments and unrelaxed tensions
produce an *anxiety neurosis* in the woman (and in most cases of
coitus interruptus also in the man), so that whenever sexual intercourse is attempted orgasm is suppressed by fear. Finally, a stage is
reached where orgasm cannot be attained at all, even if the mechanical conditions are entirely favorable.

As regards coitus interruptus, this is being abandoned to an increasing extent as a result of the introduction of rational methods
of contraception. In the case of impotence of *ejaculatio praecox* in
the man, the woman cannot be cured of impotence thus caused unless
the man is cured first. Finally, uncoordinated orgasm and clumsiness on the part of the man may be cured (except in pathological

cases) by means of good advice. In more difficult cases of this type, it may be necessary for the man to submit to psychoanalytical treatment, in order to be freed from faults in intercourse based on a deep-rooted sexual anxiety. It should be noted, however, that in cases of relative premature ejaculation—that is to say, where the man's orgasm occurs before that of the woman—the advice that the man should try to postpone his orgasm may produce the contrary result.

There are two further possibilities in cases where the cause of feminine impotence does not lie in the woman alone, but partly also in the man.

(*f*) There may be a specific aversion on the part of the woman to the particular man who is her sexual partner, that is to say, she may have a strong aversion for certain sights, sounds, smells, etc., associated with the man.

(*g*) The other possibility is represented by brutal or clumsy defloration, which unfortunately occurs very often. However, this subject will be discussed in a separate chapter.

CHAPTER 40

Tragic Wedding Nights

As we have seen, the great majority of women engage in sexual activity before defloration, mainly in the form of masturbation. But there are also other activities of a sexual nature, such as kissing, caresses and the like, which are natural in young girls, so that normally the sexual impulse is awakened long before the first sexual intercourse. A young girl anticipates with all the greater interest and curiosity her first real sexual experience which is, of course, associated with defloration. It represents the fulfillment of all her desires and dreams. Naturally, therefore, the man must proceed during the act of defloration with the greatest care and consideration.

Many primitive peoples have recognized the importance of successful defloration. Among certain Australian native tribes it used to be the custom to have the hymen of the bride, before the consummation of the marriage, perforated by an old woman. Among the Massais, an African tribe, the act of defloration is a solemn ceremony preparatory to marriage. Among certain tribes in the Malay Islands defloration is carried out by the bride's father or another male member of the family. In the Philippines there used to be men whose profession it was to perforate the hymen of girls in whom it had not been perforated in childhood by an old woman. Among certain Eskimo tribes defloration is carried out by the priest.

These and other examples show that in many cases defloration was not the task of the husband. As the perforation of the hymen was often carried out as part of a ceremony, it is easy to understand why the idea of sacrificing virginity to a god arose. In addition to this interpretation of the artificial act of defloration, it may be assumed that the harmful effect of an unsuccessful defloration on the nuptial couch was known to the primitive races, and that is why they had it carried out by a third person.

In this connection the "right of the first night," (*Jus primae noctis*) which prevailed until the late Middle Ages all over Europe, is interesting. The bride on the wedding night was sent to the squire, who carried out the defloration. It may be assumed that this custom arose from the tradition that defloration must be carried out by a person of authority, or a member of the family.

Unfortunately, today the importance of successful defloration is not appreciated by the majority of men, yet, as we have already pointed out, the first sexual intercourse and the manner in which it is carried out, are of decisive importance as regards the entire future sexual life of a girl. The slightest psychological or physical disturbance may produce lasting consequences and, in particular, may lead to sexual insensibility in cases where the psychological tendency is present.

For, in any case, the first sexual act is not pleasurable to the girl, since it usually involves pain and a slight hemorrhage, and if the foundation of sexual insensibility has been laid during childhood, this pain may recur at each subsequent intercourse, long after the physical causes have disappeared. At any rate, recollection of the pain of defloration may suppress orgasm, or even the sexual impulse itself, thereby leading to impotence or even frigidity. Such an inhibitional impotence through recollection will arise all the more easily where the brutality or clumsiness of the man has made defloration particularly painful for the woman. Thus, brutality, clumsiness, and even a humiliating negligence on the part of the man during defloration have been known to cause prolonged and even permanent sexual insensibility in a woman. In such cases the sexuality of the woman, in view of its initial tendency to sexual insensibility, is confirmed in that tendency, so that the result of wrong education is reinforced by the wrong attitude of the man and his failure to bring out the remaining inclination to full feminity.

Such defloration tragedies are sometimes fully aggravated by the wrong ideas which one or other (or both) of the partners have about sexual intercourse. In a good many cases the man thinks that he must break down the resistance which every decent girl must put up during the first intercourse. Such stupid ideas may lead a man to use violence against a psychologically insufficiently prepared woman, thereby destroying the basis of psychological harmony between the partners, which is certainly the most important condition of true sexual happiness.

On the part of the woman wrong ideas concerning the sexual act are usually evolved if she has an "old maid" attitude. Such girls, although they make a cult of their own virginity, nevertheless long for sexual intercourse, and in the course of the empty years they evolve in their imaginations so many unrealizable "fairy tales" of unspeakable bliss, that they are bound to be disappointed even if the man is most considerate. *Fact and fancy* necessarily differ, and once a girl is filled with such unrealizable fancies, there is no escape for her, for natural defloration will be bound to lead to the inevitable tragedy. And if a man of experience were to suggest in such a case artificial defloration, he would be refused with horror as a man without a sense of "romance"—the sort of "romance" which, at its first clash with reality, would be shattered.

We have already discussed the causes of vaginal cramp (vaginismus) in another part of this book. We have seen that owing to the painful tears in the hymen, or other painful abrasions, there is a convulsive contraction of the vaginal muscles, so that the male member cannot be introduced into the vagina and sexual intercourse cannot be carried out.

But it may also happen that the convulsive contraction of the vagina occurs *after* the male member has been introduced. In that case the male member can only be withdrawn when this contraction has ceased. As, however, the contraction may last a considerable time, unless immediate medical assistance is available, the male member is, so to speak, imprisoned in the vagina. This is called "an imprisoned penis," or in Latin, *penis captivus.*

However, it frequently happens that vaginismus appears whenever sexual intercourse is attempted, even though the tears and other painful phenomena have long disappeared; in such cases the cramp is independent of the physical pain by which it was originally caused. This vaginismus, which is mainly due to psychological causes, is the expression of recollections of the pain experienced by the woman. Sometimes this "recollective vaginismus" may be the result of memories of rape, or even only of a sudden brutal defloration for which the woman was not adequately prepared.

Now, whereas the so-called physical vaginismus is always partly due to psychological causes, and whereas in the case of "recollective" vaginism the physical factor is involved at least to some extent, there are cases of purely psychological vaginism. Here there is no "recollection" of anything, the complaint is not indirectly due to physical causes, since there have never been any inflamed tears or painful scars in the hymen, nor inflammations of any part of the vulva, nor has the defloration been carried out brutally or in an abnormally painful manner. This type of vaginism is due to the purely psychological cause of anxiety hysteria, a hysterical fear of pain, fear of the subsequent child-birth, fear of coitus itself and, above all, fear of the male in general.

Finally, there are cases of defloration impotence, examples of which are quoted by Freud, and in which the woman after the first intercourse, and even after each subsequent intercourse, expresses her antagonism for her male partner by abusing him and even striking him. This happened in one particular case observed by Freud, although the woman was deeply in love with the man, was in the habit of inviting coitus, and derived evident satisfaction from it.

The present writer has also observed a similar case. It relates to a strikingly beautiful and strongly sexed woman who welcomed the "preliminaries" and also derived considerable satisfaction from the sexual act, but was immediately afterwards overcome with nausea for her own sexuality and for the man. In this way she was deprived of the enjoyment of the period of contentment following upon the act, and was never able to relax. She has developed a tendency to avoid any situation that may lead to sexual relations, because she knows that she will be unable to control herself "afterwards."

Thus with regard to defloration we concur with Freud when he says: "Defloration produces not only the cultural consequence that it ties the woman to the man permanently; it also releases a primitive reaction of antagonism towards the man which may assume pathological forms. These frequently manifest themselves through inhibitions in the sexual side of marriage, and this is why second marriages so often succeed far better than first marriages."

CHAPTER 41

LESBIAN WOMEN

THERE are two forms of feminine homosexuality, i.e., the conscious and the unconscious. Feminine homosexuality is conscious when the woman concerned deliberately refrains from the natural satisfaction of her sexual impulse with a man, and feels attracted by women.

The position is very different in the case of the type of feminine homosexuality whose cause does not lie in the defective function of the sexual glands, but in a psychological factor. We have already discussed the role of the clitoris in infantile sexual life, and know that the sexuality of many women remains fixed to that organ even during the age of sexual maturity. Considering that the clitoris is a rudimentary penis, it is not difficult to understand how such a woman comes to evolve a masculine, i.e., homosexual attitude. It only requires an accidental external fixation, say on a friend or a female teacher, to carry the homosexual attitude of a girl right through to adult age. Freud calls attention to the fact that the absence of an energetic father in childhood may also promote a tendency towards homosexuality in a female child. This does not mean that the child is fatherless, but that her father plays a subservient role in the home to a mother with masculine qualities, though, of course, a similar result may arise where the father is dead or absent and has no share in the upbringing of the girl.

It is easy to see what an immense part war plays in bringing about feminine frigidity and impotence by promoting the development of homosexual tendencies in the generation of girls then in its infancy.

However, a particularly strong impulse towards the choice of a homosexual objective on the part of girls is represented by the anxieties connected with the biological experience of motherhood, of which even the child has a presentiment in the form of the contradictory fear which has been so aptly described by a Swedish woman doctor: "Partly the fear of having to go through this mysterious and awful experience, and partly the fear of never being allowed to go through it." In order to avoid these fears, nearly every girl, between the ages of five and twelve, assumes certain masculine characteristics, which usually disappear with the arrival of puberty. But if through wrong methods of education, such as constant complaints about the cares of family life, the burdens of motherhood and the brutality of men, the little girl comes to abhor motherhood, it may happen that when she grows up she will have a subconscious aversion to motherhood, and will consequently be incapable of taking her due share in any intercourse with men.

Another educational factor that may inhibit the evolution of complete femininity is the custom prevailing in many families to give preference to the boys over the girls. Even at the birth of a female child there are expressions of disappointment, especially where it is a first child and an "heir" has been expected. This attitude arouses envy and jealousy in the girl towards her brothers. She wants to be a boy. She turns away from games proper to girls and engages in the more robust boyish games, i.e., she manifests her desire to become a boy in the physical sense. Though this is naturally impossible, psychological boyishness and, later, psychological masculinity, can be developed quite easily. Girls of this type, whose sexuality is, as such, in any case fixed in a clitoric, i.e., masculine, direction, can easily develop a psychological masculinity.

This tendency on the part of a woman to acquire masculine psychological and emotional characteristics is called the masculinity complex. This complex, therefore, is a hidden homosexual trait in a woman, and if the female child does not succeed in shedding this complex during puberty, then this initially unconscious complex may later develop into conscious homosexuality.

Women who think and act like men are not as a rule the happiest among their sex, and it is given to very few women to be able to think like men, and nevertheless feel like women. Thus the treatment of the masculinity complex should be the most important part of the education of girls, and it naturally requires considerable tact and knowledge on the part of the parents. And the lack of such knowledge today is to a considerable extent to blame for the deplorable prevalence of clitoric sexuality and impotence in modern times.

CHAPTER 42

The "Misunderstood" Woman's Dream Man

"Love is blind." This is an age-old proverb, a version of which exists in every language in the world. Thus its truth is universally recognized. It means that people in love attribute to their partners qualities which they do not possess, or fail to notice their faults.

The overrating of the loved person, his or her importance and views, which Freud calls "sexual overrating," is a question that has been frequently discussed in scientific literature, as well as in fiction. We do not propose to deal here with this form of sexual overestimation, since this is entirely normal and natural, and it is safe to say that a woman who does not think highly of her love partner, must think very little of herself.

However, it frequently happens that the intellectual or physical superiority of the man becomes a *condition* of his being chosen as a partner. This is the opposite of the overestimation discussed above, where a woman first falls in love with a man, and out of her love overrates him; for in this case the woman first sets herself a high standard, a "type," then endeavors to find the embodiment of her dreams. Thus in the first case the loved man is endowed with certain qualities, while in the second case loved qualities are attributed to the man.

Now, if a woman attributes this sort of superiority to a man, she will probably discover, sooner or later, that he does not possess it. But as the woman's sexual emotions are fixed to the imaginary superiority, and not to the personality of the man, the awakening will bring not only disillusionment, but also sexual impotence or frigidity.

In order to make this clear, we must add that a woman who attributes to a man an imaginary *superiority* does so because she herself wants to have a feeling of *inferiority,* and cannot attain sexual happiness without it. And with the disappearance of the man's superiority, her own sense of inferiority also vanishes and, at the same time, her sexual desire for the man concerned.

It also frequently happens that the man actually possesses the social or intellectual quality which the woman has made a condition of her affection, but if fate deprives him of it later, he loses the love of his wife at the same time. The same may happen if the man loses his physical strength where this is a condition of the woman's love.

But whether the man's superiority is imaginary, or whether it is actual and is subsequently lost, the tragedy for the woman consists in the fact that there is a split between her idea of him and his real personality. Science designates the image or idea of a man evolved by the woman in opposition to reality, the *imago* of the man. It is interesting to note that the *imago*-man usually resembles the woman's own father. The resemblance may be positive or negative, that is to say, the *imago*-man either possesses the same qualities as a loved father or the contrary qualities of a hated father.

It sometimes happens with these women, under the operation of the maternal instinct, that if their desire for a "superior" man is not fulfilled for a long time, they finally accept a man who does not correspond to their *imago*-man, but towards whom they have a feeling of *pity*, but no sense of inferiority.

But the consequence of marriage based, in these circumstances, on pity, is frigidity. If, afterwards, the "ideal" man turns up, then the "marriage of pity" sometimes goes on the rocks with remarkable rapidity. The new relationship appears to be all the more blissful because it brings (perhaps for the first time) sexual sensibility. But the new happiness also rests on a shaky foundation, for the wonderful qualities attributed to the new partner are in most cases imaginary; in certain favorable circumstances he may *appear* to possess them, but he is bound very soon to reveal himself, in the course of his daily contact with the woman, as a man with all the usual faults and weaknesses. If, as a result, the new relationship is not severed altogether, then at least, the woman loses her sexual sensibility, and impotence appears in exactly the same way as in all other cases.

The process may be repeated again and again, either with another man in each case, or with the same man, if a kindly fate happens to restore his halo in the eyes of the woman.

Without going into details with regard to the precise influence which the father's personality may have on a woman's choice of a sexual partner, we need only point out that the essence of the peculiar requirement of the type of woman under discussion is the exercise of authority by the man (the father being essentially a person of authority). The *imago*-man must always maintain his authority if his wife is to accept him as her sexual partner. If he is unable to do so, or if he goes so far as to reject, as a matter of conviction, the old-fashioned tyrannical attitude of husbands, and tries to regard his wife as his social and sexual equal, then his wife will inevitably become impotent in relation to himself.

This type of woman *needs* a tyrannical husband. They are used, from childhood, to an imperious superior in the person of their father, and in their subconscious minds they regard the husband's attitude as a continuation of the father's authority. It will be seen from this how an education based on oppression and servility breeds servility in the adult woman, so much so that she is incapable of enjoying sexual happiness otherwise than as a slave. Free men and women can only be produced if education is based on the principle of freedom. That applies in the political as well as in the domestic sense. A famous educationist once said: "Woe to him who brings up a child in fear, for he thereby degrades generations."

Some women solve their problem by imagining, during intercourse, that their partner is another man, one who answers the requirements of the *imago-man*. For ethical, social or other reasons, the woman does not wish to be unfaithful to her husband, but in order to attain orgasm she must be unfaithful to him in her imagination. This process occurs far more frequently than is generally believed, and as far as appearances are concerned there would be nothing wrong in this, since it does not involve actual infidelity.

But in some cases the woman is tormented by remorse for this mental adultery, abandons it, and (since the husband does not possess the qualities of the *imago*-man) reverts to impotence.

The type of woman discussed above is a well-known variant of the "misunderstood" woman whom we know from countless novels and plays. The latter type of woman also seeks superiority and authority in the man, and as life usually only produces ordinary, human men, she is disappointed, "misunderstood." The "tragic" longing that characterizes these women is part of their personality, and the perpetual (and necessarily vain) search for their super-man drives them into the arms of one man after another.

But the opposite of this type is also no rarity. There are women whose husbands are particularly cultured and considerate men, and who nevertheless fail to derive sexual pleasure from their embraces. These women are afflicted with a masochistic tendency and tenderness is not what they require for happiness. But if such a woman happens to come across a brutal, inconsiderate man with sadistic tendencies she receives him with slavish submissiveness and feels herself "understood" by this "dispenser of happiness."

The separation of physical and emotional love referred to above in connection with the "mental adultery" of a certain type of woman, also occurs in men. However, whereas in the case of the woman the substitution consists in raising the man to a higher level, in the case of the man the separation of physical and emotional love involves a contrary process. The man's physical love, that is to say, his potency, depends on the degradation of the woman. Thus the grotesque situation may arise that a man is only fully potent if he despises the woman with whom he is having relations, whereas if he loves and respects her he has no physical desire for her, and proves impotent when it comes to actual intercourse with her.

Freud writes about men who are incapable of concentrating their entire sexuality on one subject: "The love life of such men is split into two parts, which are respectively designated in Art as 'heavenly and earthly' (or animal) love. Where they love, they do not desire, and where they desire, they are unable to love."

Although this particular form of relative impotence occurs far more frequently in men than in women (since owing to the dual code of morality it is easier for men to indulge in extra-marital sexual activity with women whom they despise), there are some women in whom the separation of physical and emotional love is accompanied by contempt for the sexual partner. That applies in those cases in which "the world" is staggered by the news that this or that well-brought-up daughter of highly respected parents has eloped with a primitive male of her acquaintance. It often happens that a rich man's daughter runs away with her father's chauffeur or valet, and many a girl of the "best circles" has sunk to a level hardly above prostitution.

The cause of such peculiar occurrences lies in an education based on the ascetic ideal of "chastity," which conveniently ignores the sexuality of unmarried girls. What happens in the case of a well-brought-up, well-educated and cultured girl who associates with a man of low class, is this: The girl is too strongly sexed to abstain from sexual intercourse altogether. But as, from early childhood, all sexual activity has been represented to her as sinful, she can only derive pleasure from sexual intercourse where it is associated with conditions that are regarded in her social stratum as particularly degrading. Such a condition is, above all, a relationship with a man who, although he may according to ordinary standards be all that can be reasonably expected, is a "low class" man in the estimation of the so-called upper classes. And in order to emphasize the forbidden nature of her action, such a girl will further aggravate the contrast between the "culture" and "morality" of the parental home and her association with the "low class" man by eloping with him. The "disgrace" is explained by the family by some such argument that the girl is afflicted with some mental or moral defect, and it will not occur to them to attribute the "catastrophe" to the girl's education or to the atmosphere in which she was brought up.

CHAPTER 43

Age of Sex Maturity in Boys and Girls

THE sexual glands normally start to perform their proper functions during the second half of the second decade of life. The ovaries of the girl then already produce ova suitable for fertilization, while the testes of the boy already secrete semen capable of fertilizing an ovum.

However, although at this age the sexual glands are already mature, and boys and girls are already capable of performing the sexual act, in our civilization parents and teachers take good care that young people should not indulge in sexual intercourse. Sexual intercourse at this age would be purely physical, almost animal, as physical capacity is not accompanied by psychological maturity.

But even those who hold that in the case of very young people the psychological element should be ignored for health reasons, cannot deny that under the present conditions, the sexual life of youth before marriage must be restricted for economic reasons. Marriage between minors is nowadays impracticable, while sexual life outside marriage is contrary to the present conception of morality and responsibility. We will not go into the question whether this conception is right or wrong. The fact is that it is the prevailing conception, and very few people would dare to defy it, and our object here is to consider the discrepancy between the arrival of sexual capacity and the beginning of sexual life in its relation to feminine frigidity. For the state of affairs referred to above represents a conflict between that which is natural and that which is imposed by social convention (of necessity because of the responsibility involved—those who beget must be prepared to provide the necessary love and care for the begotten), and as such conflicts are bound to produce harm in some direction, the comparatively long sexual abstinence of girls must necessarily produce deplorable consequences.

In order to realize this ascetic ideal of modern society, parents and guardians display extraordinary zeal. The worst sins in this connection are committed in the nursery. What the children know, they are forbidden to show; what they would like to know, they are forbidden to ask. Every honest manifestation of their sexuality is condemned as sinful. In this manner children acquire very early in their lives a distorted and unsound attitude towards sex. They learn to regard everything pleasurable as sinful, and it is therefore not surprising that they lose the capacity to regard any manifestation of the sexual instinct without prejudice.

In particular, if the belief that everything pleasurable is forbidden and sinful takes firm root in the child-mind, it is only logical that the adult into which the child has grown should, subconsciously and automatically, reject sexual pleasure even in marriage and prevent the development of a sensation of pleasure. That attitude spells impotence and frigidity for life.

But an "ascetic" education may also lead to a very different psychological process. It is a well-known fact that, particularly for children, "forbidden fruit" has a special lure. This has frequently been observed in connection with sweets—a child who receives more than adequate quantities of sweets legitimately, will risk punishment by stealing extra sweets of perhaps inferior quality. In the case of strongly sexed children the same happens in the sex domain. Despite the strictest injunctions they continue their sexual manipulations and find them all the more pleasurable *because they are forbidden.*

The lure of that which is forbidden then becomes fixed and continues into adult life. A girl so treated in childhood may not be able to attain orgasm except through forbidden intercourse, that is to say, with an extra-marital partner. A husband, however loving and devoted he may be, can never give sexual happiness to a woman of this type. It must be a lover, *a forbidden partner.*

Thus we see that the strict application of the ascetic principle produces the opposite result to that for which it is intended. The severe repression of the female child's sexuality results in the adult woman breaking her marriage vows, as transgression is an indispensable condition of her sexual happiness.

The question of *fear* in connection with sexual activity has already been discussed elsewhere in the present work. Fear of the unknown, of the pain of defloration and child-birth may deaden a woman's sexual sensibility, since fear is always destructive of pleasure.

The most frequent cause of anxiety impotence in woman is probably the practice of *coitus interruptus*, or interruption of the sexual act, which is discussed in detail in another chapter. This practice may induce impotence even in a woman of normal sexual sensibility. Anxiety neuroses of this type are so frequent that Freud is able to say in this connection: "Careful interruption of the sexual act, if carried on as a regular practice, is so frequently the cause of anxiety neuroses in men, but particularly in women, that in such cases this should be looked for first of all in establishing the cause of the complaint. It will then be found in countless cases that the anxiety neurosis disappears as soon as the sexual abuse is stopped."

Fear of defloration and infection are less frequent causes of feminine impotence. Rather are these fears the cause of frigidity. But the fear of conception is a possible cause of impotence, owing to the widely held erroneous view that fecundation is impossible unless the woman attains orgasm. However, this error does not play a particularly important role in the causation of impotence in such cases, as fear of conception is usually accompanied by an unconscious aversion to the man and his sexual approaches, which would in any case deprive the sexual act of all its pleasure for the woman. But fear of child-birth may also lead to impotence *without* the erroneous belief referred to above and *without* any aversion for the man, if neither the man nor the woman employ a contraceptive of any kind (either chemical or mechanical) and fear of conception deadens the responsiveness of the woman's sexual organs. This factor of uncertainty is nearly always present where *coitus interruptus* is practiced. This view is confirmed by the fact that a woman who is otherwise not frigid, becomes so when she engages in intercourse without a contraceptive for the *first time*, this being a case in which inadequate excitation and lack of orgasm do not arise.

Finally, there are two other forms of anxiety impotence. One form occurs in the years before the climacteric and is probably due to a considerable extent to the erroneous belief that feminine sexual sensibility dies with the climacteric (whereas the fact is, as shown elsewhere in this work, that feminine orgasm may be aroused long after the cessation of reproductive capacity). Women thus affected go round in a vicious circle, they become sexually insensible for fear that they are going to become insensible.

The other form of anxiety impotence is due to overcrowding. It is the fear of being overheard, which occurs anywhere where the lovers cannot isolate themselves sufficiently. Where partition walls are too thin, or where a young couple is obliged to live with the parents of one partner, such situations frequently arise. If the attention of the woman is distracted by the thought that the neighbors may be listening, she cannot concentrate on her own sensations, and in such circumstances it is not surprising that she misses all sexual pleasure. This fear of being overheard or of being "caught," also operates in extra-conjugal intercourse.

For the rest, in all cases of psychological impotence, but particularly in the case of anxiety impotence, this condition is only aggravated by worrying, sometimes to the point of vaginism. If a woman racks her brain over the causes of her impotence, which in any case mostly lie in the subconscious mind, this leads to an *autosuggestive aggravation* of the evil itself. All natural "experience" occurs to a certain extent unconsciously, and the harmony of the experience is disturbed by such concentrated conscious thought. However desirable it is that the modern woman should be governed by logical thought in all her professional, political and social activities, and also as regards the main principles of her sexual life, in the most intimate moments of sexual activity she must eliminate logical thought as far as possible if she is to attain real happiness.

CHAPTER 44

FRIGID ONLY WITH MARRIAGE PARTNER

CONJUGAL impotence is a special form of impotence, in which the woman possesses normal sexual sensibility in relation to all men, *except her own husband.*

We have already referred in earlier chapters to this special form of feminine impotence. It arises in the case of women who derive no pleasure from sexual intercourse unless it is prohibited, and also, very frequently, in the case of the "misunderstood" woman who, as we have said, is dominated by a "tragic longing" for a sexual partner who is superior to her own husband and who, in reality, does not exist, particularly in marriage.

But whereas these two types—the woman who only enjoys sexual intercourse if it is forbidden, and the "misunderstood" woman—evolve as a result of wrong methods of education, conjugal impotence on the part of the woman may also arise owing to *forced* marriage. It is obvious that a marriage of convenience, a marriage whose principal object is to provide for the woman, cannot be happy from the sexual point of view. Marriages contracted at the wish of the parents, or in which financial or social considerations play the most important role, that is to say, marriages where mutual affection is not the decisive factor, must sooner or later end in sexual indifference, i.e., frigidity or impotence.

If, in addition to the forced choice of a partner, the husband inspires aversion during intercourse by being inconsiderate, then sexual insensibility in the woman is all the more certain to arise. And if the husband insists on intercourse unduly, the woman's sexual insensibility may develop into frigidity. A single tactless or rough act suffices to produce this tragic consequence.

After the dissolution of such a marriage, or in extra-marital intercourse with a man whom she loves, the woman naturally ceases to be "cold." The legitimate husband who has been forced upon her, and in relation to whom she has been frigid, need not be surprised to find that she is not only absolutely normal in relation to another man, but more strongly sexed than usual.

The same situation, that is to say, frigidity and impotence owing to a forced choice of partners, may also arise outside marriage, where a woman, owing to economic dependence, is forced to enter into a sexual relationship in which love plays no part. Such cases frequently occur in the theatrical and film world, where an unknown actress may have to pay with her body for her professional chance, or in business, where the female secretary sometimes has to yield to the will of her employer. In such cases frigidity and impotence may arise just as quickly as within the bonds of a forced marriage.

It is an immutable law that love cannot be bought, and on this point even the most cunning financier must fail. A forced marriage, as well as an extra-marital "affair" entered into for economic or other "sensible" reasons, differs but little from plain prostitution.

CHAPTER 45

The Child-Woman

WE cannot conclude this section without referring to the interesting type of woman known in literature as the *child-woman*.

This is a borderline case between potency and impotence, though it is somewhat doubtful whether the term impotence is applicable at all here. Physically, the child-woman appears to be normal and she usually attains orgasm without difficulty. Yet she lacks something essential to real sexual satisfaction—the feeling of unity arising from complete surrender, which in a really mature woman becomes intensified during coitus to an overwhelming sensation of *mutual penetration*, a sensation that only those who have actually experienced it can imagine.

Real sexual satisfaction, that is to say, an explosive bursting of the tension of mature sexuality, is only possible where, in addition to the physical excitement of orgasm, this emotional "orgy" of *mutual merging* into one another is also present. It is this mutual merging into one another that the child-woman cannot experience. Her physical orgasm appears in an incomplete form, because there is no inner relationship between herself and the man. The only difference between such intercourse and masturbation is the fact that instead of the hand or a mechanical instrument of masturbation *another person is used as the instrument*. This sort of coitus might almost be defined as masturbation by coitus. Indeed, masturbation by an adult might be regarded as a more mature form of sexual activity in that it usually involves at least an *imaginary* emotional connection with another person.

Those who have studied child psychology know that infants in their emotional life are completely egotistic, even egocentric, i.e.,

318

self-centered. The infant's world is bounded by the limits of its own body, and it judges every impression, i.e., the entire outside world, from the one viewpoint whether it is physically pleasant or unpleasant for itself. The infant's intelligence is not sufficiently developed to enable it to pay any attention, or to wish to pay attention, to events that do not affect its own body.

If we consider the attitude of the child-woman in sexual life, we shall find that, as in the case of infants, their attention is concentrated on their own bodies, so that their psychological attitude is an *infantile attitude*. The number of these infantile women is very large, so large, indeed, that they are "the vogue." The child-woman is self-centered like an infant in arms; she seeks satisfaction in herself, employing for the purpose some object from the outside world, preferably a man, just as an infant sucks its thumb or a comforter.

But it is just this infantile quality that is fatal to the man who loves a child-woman. For his type of infantilism usually involves cruelty, and the child-woman, precisely because she is not emotionally concerned with her male partner, "consumes" a large number of men. What is a man to a child-woman? She will not be unfaithful to him in her imagination, just as an infant does not think of the red comforter while it is sucking away at the yellow one. The one is as good as the other. But actually they are unfaithful to their partner in a manner that cannot really be described as unfaithfulness, since they have no idea whatever about faithfulness.

Why it is that this self-centered aspect of the instincts, which plays a far more important role in the infant than in the adult, survives so long in this type of woman, it is difficult to say at present. Certain it is that *extraordinary beauty*, which attracts everybody, and causes everybody to treat a child thus endowed differently from others, is apt to increase the child's self-love beyond measure, and to fix it permanently. And it is also certain that the attitude of men to the extremely beautiful child-woman is such that she sees no reason to doubt herself and to abandon her attitude of self-love. To men who expect more of a woman than that she should be a willing toy, and always prepared to engage in sexual intercourse, the child-woman presents a grave danger. They, too, allow themselves at first to be dazzled by her beauty, and may fail to notice her lack of emotional participation in sexual intercourse. They assume that they are receiving the genuine love of a mature woman, expect comradeship and participation in the cares and sorrows—and these are things that the child-woman can never give. He who loves a child-woman sails in shallow waters. The child-woman can neither be happy nor make a man happy.

And that is why this form of feminine impotence had to be included in the present section of this work. It may not be of equal importance from the viewpoint of sexual hygiene as real impotence, but its social consequences are no less grave, for it leads to broken marriages and carries the seed of unhappiness.

BOOK V

Delaying Sexual Death

CHAPTER 46

WHAT IS "TO GROW OLD"?

WHAT does "growing old" consist of? All vital processes rest on the perpetual decay and re-birth of the constituents of the body, and particularly of its smallest units, known as the *cells*. To live means to produce substances for the nourishment of the body cells, which in turn reject from the nourishment they receive the portions which they are unable to utilize.

It will be seen that the cell must perform a considerable task in separating the useful from the useless in the nutritive substances conveyed to them. As everything that is engaged or involved in continuous effort must sooner or later wear out, the process of "wearing out" is also bound to begin at some time in the cells.

Investigators have established that the wearing out process consists in a change in the chemical composition of the cells. As age creeps on, the water content of the cells steadily decreases. In plain language this means that the cells become hard. Thus the body of an adult is composed of 60 percent water, 16 percent albumen, 19 percent fat, and 5 percent ash, whereas the body of a newborn child is composed of 71.2 percent water, 11.4 percent albumen, 13.4 percent fat, 2.4 percent ash and 1.6 percent other substances.

But the hardening of the cells referred to above only represents one aspect of the ageing process. We know that there is a limit to the growth of every individual. On an average, the process of growth continues until the twenty-first or twenty-second year of life. Now, growth is equivalent to renewal, and just as there can be no unlimited growth in the individual as a whole, so there can be no unlimited renewal in the world of cells. Once the limit has been reached, a gradual descent begins. The cells shrink and perish, superior cells change into inferior ones. Finally, a stage is reached where the process of retrogression predominates. It does not start suddenly; it is a slow, almost stealthy process and what is more important, the process is *uneven*.

This is what we call the process of "growing old."

As we have said, the decaying of the cells is uneven. That means that the more superior a cell is the later it starts to decay. *Now, the most valuable cells in the human organism are the germinal cells, therefore the ageing process reaches them last.* We emphasize this fact particularly, in order to counter the erroneous belief that ageing begins with the limitation of the sexual functions. It is, in fact, the sexual functions that continue longest in the healthy human organism.

The process of ageing starts earliest with the inferior cells, the so-called connective tissues. These cells fill the niches and cavities of the body, upholster, so to speak, the skin, connect the various parts of the body with each other, and constitute the basis of the bones and joints. It is therefore clear that wherever the connective tissue shrinks, the skin must become flabby, thus forming wrinkles. But the strength of the bones is also diminished and they become fragile. Finally, the attractive rounded forms of the woman (for instance) are lost. Very frequently the place of the connective tissue is taken by deposits of fat. But this is too soft to keep the skin supple, so that the fat deposits, having no adequate support, become pendent, thus destroying the impression of beauty.

In the process of ageing, the connective tissue is followed by the *nervous tissue*. Next comes the muscular tissue, of which our muscles are composed. The so-called ephithelic cells, of which the mucous membranes are composed, live longest. Their structure is very similar to that of the germinal cells.

As regards the skin, it is the lower layers under the outer skin, which are composed of connective tissue, that age first, while the cells of the outer skin continue to be renewed throughout life.

Of all the organs the arteries perform the hardest work, for it is not only the heart but also the arteries that continuously contract, forcing the blood into all parts of the organism. The arteries of a

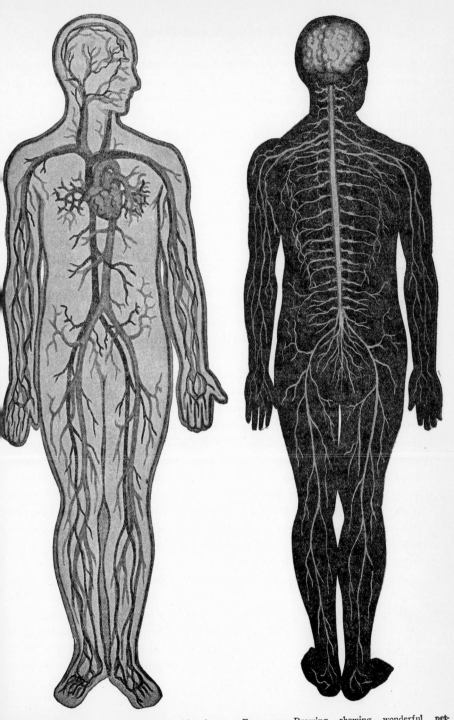

FIG. 123—Drawing of human body with cir-   FIG. 124—Drawing showing wonderful *net-*
culation system.   work of nerves in the body.

person of sixty will have performed more than two thousand million contractions. It is therefore not surprising that the elasticity of the blood-vessels should already start to diminish after the age of thirty. After the fortieth year of life it is even possible to determine by a microscopic examination the decay of the fiber of the walls of the blood-vessels that give them their elasticity. All the arteries harden, and the heart, which has to pump the blood into them, has a harder task. In order to be equal to this more strenuous task, it must grow in size, and this growth can be determined with the aid of measurements. For instance, the heart of a man of twenty-one, i.e., an age when growth is practically complete, weighs approximately from 7 to 8¾ ounces, while that of a man of forty weighs about 9¾ ounces, that of a man of sixty, about 10¾ ounces, and, finally, the heart of a man of seventy weighs about 11 ounces.

In consequence of the hardening of the arteries, a familiar phenomenon of old age, the so-called arterio-sclerosis, arises. The arteries accumulate poisonous substances which had formerly been ejected through their elasticity.

Arterio-sclerosis really consists in the excessive growth of the inner walls of the arteries and the accumulation of calcium and fatty subtances, which reduce the internal diameter of the arteries. In other words, the arteries become narrower and cannot pass the normal amount of blood. This narrowing of the interior of the arteries may sometimes affect one part of the body, and sometimes another part. In most cases sclerosis may be observed in the lower extremities. People who are suffering from arterio-sclerosis in the feet and legs walk with difficulty. Frequently they are unable to move at all, owing to local congestion, and they must then wait until this is relieved.

In other cases it is the arteries of the abdomen that become sclerotic, and this manifests itself in sudden attacks of colic.

Sclerosis very frequently occurs in the region of the heart. This is a very serious disease, since it is the function of the heart to supply the entire arterial system with blood, and if the blood-vessels of the heart itself become narrow, then the nourishment of the heart is decreased, and it cannot pump blood efficiently enough to the rest of the body. The brain may also be seriously injured through the hardening of the cerebral arteries, as the brain is then prevented from receiving an adequate flow of blood and nourishment.

In consequence of the ageing of the brain, the individual becomes less receptive to new impressions, and his creative imagination diminishes, although his judgment remains unaffected, and is even clearer than in youth. The memory is in all cases affected. Remarkably enough, this weakening of the power of recollection applies far more to immediately preceding events than to the impressions of early youth. Indeed, childhood scenes are remembered with particular vividness in old age.

Naturally, the hardening of the arteries does not affect everyone equally. There are a great many old people in whom no hardening of the arteries can be observed, while, on the other hand, people between the ages of thirty and forty have been found to be suffering from this disease.

The symptoms of old age also include a weakening of sight, hearing and the sense of smell, the trembling of the extremities, the changes in the skin, and the changed reactions of the lungs, kidneys and digestive organs.

As regards the sexual organs, the germinal cells, as we have stated at the outset, live longest.

The male genital organs continue to produce fertile spermatozoa far into old age. However, the other tissues of the sexual apparatus decay with those of the rest of the body, while the sexual apparatus itself shrinks, including the cavernous bodies of the male member. As, however, the cavernous bodies are made up of muscular cells which, as we have seen, are long-lived cells, it goes without saying that the cavernous bodies also have a long life. Thus the capacity for erection frequently remains till late old age, when other cells are already decayed.

It is clear from this that artificial rejuvenation of the human organism based on a revivification of the genital apparatus, is nothing but a vain dream.

Ageing is a biological process which takes place in the cells, including those which have nothing to do with glands. How, then,

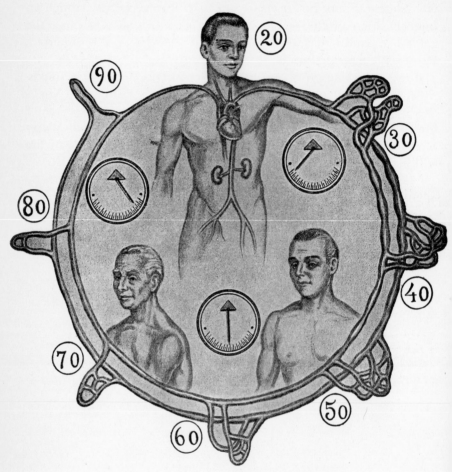

Fig. 125—Picture story of man at different ages.

Schematic representation of activity of the capillary blood-vessels at various ages—with intensity diminishing as age advances.

could such cells be rejuvenated by intensifying the sexual functions? No, Nature cannot be "tricked" so easily. Rejuvenation through an intensification of the sexual functions is only possible where the genital apparatus has aged *earlier* than the rest of the organism. However, such cases are extremely rare.

But if rejuvenation of an organism that has become old is impossible, it is in our power to delay the process of getting old. Nor is this particularly difficult. All that is required is a rational mode of life. We have seen that certain poisons (alcohol, nicotine, etc.) may accelerate the ageing process. What we call a rational mode of life will be discussed in detail in a later chapter.

CHAPTER 47

Is There A Masculine Menopause?

IT is well known that the climacteric in a woman, which occurs between the ages of forty and fifty, is accompanied by profound changes. The climacteric is popularly known as the "change of life," and the period has been described as the "dangerous age" of women.

Now, the question we wish to answer is whether the climacteric is peculiar to women only, or whether men also experience a critical phase in their sexual life which may be compared with the feminine menopause, and which is accompanied by grave physical and psychological disturbances.

Many authors have investigated this problem and have, on the basis of practical observations, evolved some interesting theories on this hitherto unexplored subject.

It was the German scientist, Kurt Mendel, who first postulated a "masculine climacteric," having observed it in a large number of men. At the approach of the critical age the majority of the men he had studied, and who up till then had been in perfect health, without any unusual nervous tendencies, began to complain of fits of periodical anxiety and attacks of nerves. Some of them experienced a state of debility aggravated by sudden changes of mood, but all of them showed—and this is the characteristic symptom of this condition—an excessive sensitiveness, to the point of bursting into tears on the slightest provocation.

"I suddenly find I am as sensitive as a woman," said one of the men observed by Mendel. "I burst into tears for any trifle."

Another complained that he could not bear to read the papers, because he burst into tears when he read about a murder or a bad accident. A third confessed that he refrained from mixing with other people because he was afraid of "making a fool" of himself by bursting into tears during an attack of nerves.

The similarity of these confessions—of which Mendel quotes many more—shows that these are not exceptional cases, but that the symptom in question is fairly frequent at a certain age. And the German scientist adds that all, or nearly all, these men were normally masculine men, not in the least effeminate, and that some of them were of robust constitution; in none of the cases was there a previous history of nervous trouble.

But in addition to an intensified sensitiveness, which alone irresistibly points to a comparison with the female menopause, the men observed by Mendel also complained of flushing, giddiness, palpitations, sudden perspiration, general fatigue, headaches, insomnia at night, or, on the other hand, somnolence by day. Mendel also observed a weakening of the subjects' memories, particularly as regards proper names, figures, dates, addresses and recent events, and also a diminution of interest in the outside world, coupled with a morbid egotism, neurasthenia and hypochondria. The patient became more and more misanthropic and less and less sociable, and would never expand except to his doctor.

As the symptoms characteristic of this state appeared, the sexual appetite decreased. In some of the cases it was totally extinct by the end of the critical period, while in others the cessation of the symptoms was followed by a recrudescence of sensuality. However, although in many cases this is not a serious matter, it may sometimes be due to pathological causes. In the case of men whose prostate is hypertrophied, or overgrown, an irritation of the genital apparatus frequently arises, and this may sharpen the sexual appetite, out of all proportion to the sufferer's capacity.

According to Professor Mendel, the climacteric process is progressive, and reaches its culmination after a certain period, which may be anything between ten months and four years, but in most cases lasts from eighteen months to three years.

Other scientists who have also studied the problem have reached fairly similar conclusions. Thus, for instance, Professor Hollander observed in his patients the following symptoms: lassitude, impa-

tience, irritability, lack of confidence both in others and in themselves, loss of energy, diminution of the power of imagination, and
generally of the intellectual faculties. In the physical sphere the
professor observed headaches and insomnia.

Some physicians, as for instance Dr. Hoche, confirm the changes
that occur in men during the critical age, but at the same time
they hold that it is difficult to draw a clear distinction between the
symptoms heralding the advent of old age generally and the climacteric symptoms proper. Thus, while women frequently acquire
masculine characteristics during the critical age, the converse has
never been observed in men. Moreover, certain manifestations of
sclerosis and other troubles due to external causes, such as the abuse
of alcohol and nicotine, may sometimes erroneously be taken for
climacteric phenomena. Then, generally speaking, the principal
psychological symptoms of the feminine menopause, like irritability
bordering on hysteria, do not occur in men. Finally, men never
experience the arterial tension which is so frequent in women during
the menopause.

However, the one fact that emerges from this controversy is, that
there is a period in the life of men that is comparable to the feminine menopause. According to Havelock Ellis it starts in certain
men as early as thirty-eight, according to Marcuse between forty and
fifty-five, and according to Kenneth-Walker between fifty-five and
sixty.

What is the immediate cause of this profound change in the
sexual life of men? It is generally admitted that it is due to genital
decay arising from the slowing down of glandular activity. According to Mendel, functional deficiency of the testes is responsible, while
Marcuse ascribes the critical change to the slowing down of the
prostate. The French scientist, de Fleury, attributes the "masculine
climacteric" to a deficient activity of the thyroid gland. It will be
seen that virtually all the scientists trace the troubles of the critical
age to genital causes, since, as we know, not only the testes and the
prostate, but also the thyroid has an important connection with
sexual life.

In addition to the temporary symptoms that mark the critical period, the masculine "change of life" sometimes also brings about a profound change in the character and personality of a man. A man in possession of all his faculties, active, aggressive, optimistic, may from one month to another change into an abject pessimist with a veritable phobia for any sort of effort. The change is particularly striking in the jovial type of man, who may suddenly become morose and unbearably brusque with his environment.

In some men the direction of sexuality changes. Normal heterosexual men may at the period of the "climacteric" suddenly develop homosexual tendencies. The torments of the hero of *Death in Venice*, by Thomas Mann, who becomes enamoured of a young man, provide an excellent illustration of this type of sexual evolution.

Professor Hoche, in his book on the masculine climacteric, quotes a letter of a patient who was perfectly normal up to the critical age. We reproduce the following passage from this remarkable confession. "No doubt, I did not always succeed in satisfying my wife, whom I married at the age of twenty-six, but she was sufficiently tactful and considerate not to make me feel it. As I approached the fifties, I discovered a great change in myself. To put it plainly, women ceased to interest me and I found, to my horror, that my imagination was beginning to be preoccupied with young men, a thing that had never happened to me before. I took pleasure in gazing lingeringly at adolescent boys, picturing in my mind their naked bodies, and imagining the pleasure it would give me to touch them. However, I never gave way to the temptation, and I am sure I never shall. At the same time, quite objectively I find that a new element, not without charm, has entered my life. Young girls do not interest me in the least."

Thus the view of those who hold that the critical age in men is a turning point towards perversion is not entirely without foundation. Many men have confessed that the climacteric has produced in them a tendency to sadism and fetishism. We also frequently read in the papers of old gentlemen who molest school girls in the street or in railway carriages. Other old men find themselves unable to satisfy their sexual appetite except by acts of exhibitionism. Certain authors have observed a recrudescence of sexual crime at the critical age. There are statistics to show, for instance, that in most cases of incest the guilty man is in his forty-seventh year.

All these examples show how profoundly the "change of life" may affect a man. Indeed, according to Professor Vaerting, the physiologist, the "menopause" manifests itself with far greater intensity in men than in women. In support of his theory he argues that the cessation or serious diminution of semen production is an entirely new phenomenon in a man, whereas a woman generally has some experience, before the menopause, of a suspension of the activity of the germinal glands, which, as we know, always occurs during pregnancy.

This author attributes the greater mortality among men than among women during the critical age, i.e., between forty-five and fifty, to the more violent effect of the climacteric on men, particularly as after the age of sixty mortality is approximately equal in the two sexes. The sudden cessation of the activity of the sexual glands is also made responsible for the frequency of suicides during the critical age, which is proved by statistical data.

Without going as far as Professor Vaerting, whose conclusions we regard as too extreme, we may consider it proved that there is a kind of masculine climacteric, although it cannot be considered a counterpart of the feminine climacteric.

CHAPTER 48

HOW TO PREVENT PREMATURE OLD AGE

WE have seen in the previous chapter that the great problem in connection with the masculine climacteric is to know whether the symptoms that appear during the critical age are those of the climacteric or simply manifestations of the ageing of the organism. However, this question is mainly of theoretical interest, and is far less important from the practical point of view. The fact is that between the ages of forty and fifty and, in some cases, after fifty, the organism of a man starts to decay or, in other words, to grow old.

What is "to grow old"? The process may be defined as a slowing down of the bodily functions by the accumulation of waste substances, and generally by the wearing out of the human organism comparable to the wearing out of a machine. This has been more fully described in the previous chapters.

The first suggested remedy for old age will be found in the Old Testament, where, in the Book of Kings, we read how King David, when he was "old and full of years" sought to keep warm by taking unto himself a young virgin, Abisag the Sunamite, who slept "on his bosom."

This method was also in use among the Ancient Greeks and Romans, who were firmly convinced that contact with young virgins produced a rejuvenating effect on old men. Indeed, this belief has had its advocates in all ages, even modern times. For instance, Dr. Kaldor, in his book on geronto-therapy, i.e., the means of delaying old age, expresses the view that the supposed rejuvenating effect of contact with young girls is not without scientific foundation, as the sight of and contact with young girls is apt to stimulate the activity of the genital glands. Naturally, this effect is only possible if the capacity to react to sexual stimulation is still present.

The secret of perpetual youth was also sought by the great Chinese philosopher, Lao-Tsu, author of the mystic work, *Tao-Toe-King*. The wise men of Nebuchadnezzar, King of Babylon, had various formulae for avoiding senility. The Greeks and Romans were similarly exercised by this problem, as witness the beautiful legend of the fountain in which Juno used to bathe in order to appear always young to Jupiter. However, the legendary fountain was never found, and the Romans therefore sought other means of rejuvenation.

Hufeland, author of a book on the art of prolonging life by observing certain health rules, expressed his doubts as to the value of the various rejuvenating elixirs which the alchemists of the age were so zealously trying to discover, and which Paracelsus claimed to possess. Hufeland held that in order to extend the frontiers of youth the best thing to do was not to shorten youth by an insensate waste of one's energies.

For many centuries no progress was made with the solution of the problem. Then, at the end of the nineteenth century, Professor Brown-Séquard, who had made a profound study of the activity of endocrine glands, arrived at the conclusion that the internal secretions played a cardinal role in the preservation of youth. He thus conceived the idea of combating old age by means of injections of extracts from the testes of animals.

On June 1st, 1889, at the age of seventy-two, Brown-Séquard announced to the Société de Biologie in Paris that, having injected under his own skin "a liquid consisting of powdered dog's and guinea-pig's testicles and a little water," he had experienced an invigorating effect. This sensational news spread all over the world, and was received with tremendous enthusiasm. Unfortunately, it was soon discovered that the hopes raised by this interesting experiment were not sufficiently well founded.

Soon after the war, the Austrian scientist, Steinach, taking as his starting point Brown-Séquard's theory that old age was to a considerable extent due to the slowing down of the genital glands, particularly as regards the production of hormones, invented an operation known as vaso-ligature. This operation was based on an observation made by Steinach, namely, that if external secretion of the germinal glands, that is to say, the production of spermatozoa, was prevented, their internal secretion became intensified, thus conveying to the organism the rejuvenating element, i.e., the hormones. Thus vaso-ligature consists in tying up the *vas deferens*.

It was found that, in many cases, this operation was followed by a general improvement, and also by a veritable rebirth of the sexual appetite. However, this method was for various reasons opposed.

Almost at the same time, Voronoff, also taking Brown-Séquard's principle as his starting point, evolved grafting operations, whereby the testicles of a chimpanzee were transplanted into a man. His method created an unprecedented sensation, but although it proved successful, at least temporarily, it failed to restore the subject's virility.

Some scientists have recommended, as a method of rejuvenation for both men and women, the employment of X-rays, said to produce a stimulating effect on the sexual glands. Dr. Holzknecht, a collaborator of Steinach, claimed to have achieved excellent results in this manner.

Among the various suggested methods of rejuvenation, we must mention that of Dr. Jaworsky, though this is still at the experimental stage. This scientist has injected into a fifteen-year-old (and therefore "senile") he-goat some cubic centimeters of blood from a young animal. Dr. Francesco Cavazzi gave subcutaneous injections of testicular blood from young animals, and has obtained some surprising results.

These, in brief, are the modern methods of "rejuvenation." However, none of them has been accepted unanimously, or even by a majority in the medical world, and the truth seems to lie with those who prefer natural methods, which, though not so sensational, are sometimes astonishingly effective.

One of the principal weapons with which the man of forty may combat approaching old age, is diet. It is the almost unanimous view of the experts that after that age men generally eat too much. At all events, "good living" has far more victims than malnutrition. By taking in immoderate quantities of food, a strain is placed not only on the digestive organs, but also on the organism as a whole, which must therefore wear out more quickly. The imperfect assimilation of food leads to gradual auto-intoxication, which considerably accelerates the advent of old age.

It is this auto-intoxication that Metchnikoff, the great Russian, endeavored to combat. He based his theory on the action of the phagocytes, i.e., cells capable of enclosing and digesting certain organic and inorganic particles, decayed cells, foreign bodies, and particularly toxic bodies. Metchnikoff called attention to the injurious effect of the microbes that are settled in the large intestine, and which produce toxins. The phagocytes, whose action is promoted by lactic acid, are contained in large quantities in yoghurt, and Metchnikoff advised that yoghurt should play an important part in the diet. It is said that the longevity of Bulgarian peasants is due to the popularity in that country of sour milk produced with a special ferment called *maya*. The action of the phagocytes is also promoted by such foods as cucumbers, cabbage, rice and barley. At the same time, Metchnikoff goes to extremes with his theory that old age is due to the microbe cultures in the large intestine, and he even advises surgical intervention in some cases.

Many people, in their struggle against the toxins that operate so destructively in the blood, adhere to the age-old tradition of enemas and fasting. Some years ago the Paris *Revue Médical* published an article under the signature of Dr. Guelpa, in which the author recommended, as a means of preventing premature old age, a thorough periodical disinfection of the alimentary canal by means of a strict diet confined to weak tea, water and vegetable soup. After the second day no hunger is felt, and this condition lasts until the system has been thoroughly disinfected. This may take from three to eight days, according to the individual's condition. Such disinfection reduces arterial tension and eliminates all the troubles due to the action of the toxins.

Among the special diets recommended for the preservation of youth, we must mention the milk diet (one and a half to two pints per day), which was praised by Hyppocrates and Gallenius. Then there is the fruit diet. The Schrott treatment, also deserves mention. It is similarly designed to de-toxicate the organism, and consists in swathing the body in blankets to induce intense sweating, and in administering strong purgatives.

The question whether a meat diet was advisable for middle-aged men has been frequently discussed, and a great many experts attribute various ailments, such as rheumatism, to the excessive consumption of meat. Some practitioners forbid meat entirely at that age, but in our opinion this is an extreme measure, as meat is generally an easily digestible concentrated food. What is harmful is the excessive use of meat, like excess in any other thing.

We have said that over-feeding has more victims than under-feeding. But we do not mean to imply that forced reducing is a method of preserving youth. A man of forty, more than anyone else, should beware of the reducing preparations advertised so largely these days. They contain either strong laxatives or thyroid extract, or other more modern drugs which are not without danger when used without careful medical prescription and supervision. The former impose a heavy strain on the alimentary canal and may damage the mucous membranes, while thyroid extract puts a great strain on the heart and may sometimes produce exophthalmic goiter.

Here is another point concerning food. Whereas young people can afford to take a hasty meal or snack, middle-aged people must take their time over meals, masticating their food slowly and carefully, in order to prepare it for digestion. This point cannot be sufficiently emphasized. It is of cardinal importance, and it is quite true, as Dr. Finot in his *Philosophy of Longevity* says, that "we dig our graves with our own teeth."

A further point in this connection is the necessity of a mixed diet containing all the vitamins required to maintain the body in youthful vigor.

As in the case of meat, so there are extremist doctors who would deprive their patients of the use of stimulants that they have been accustomed to all their lives, such as tea, coffee and tobacco. It is true that all three contain poisonous substances. Even a small dose of the poisons contained in coffee and tea may cause palpitations, insomnia or, in larger doses, convulsions. For instance, a cup of black coffee contains from ten to twenty centigrams of caffein, i.e., a medicinal dose. But that is not a sufficient reason, unless there are definite counter-indications, for depriving a man of the pleasure represented by these aromatic beverages. It must be remembered that in endeavoring to prolong youth it is important not to impose too great sacrifices, otherwise the principal effect of youth, i.e., the joy of living, might be destroyed.

As regards nicotine, it is well known that this is a virulent poison. Two drops of nicotine placed on the tongue of a dog are sufficient to cause convulsions, and sometimes even death. It is also well known that the abuse of tobacco may promote arterio-sclerosis, and may affect the sight, hearing, power of recollection and the nervous system in general. Moreover, experiments carried out by the Belgian scientist, Dr. Hertoghe, appear to prove that nicotine exercises a considerable influence on the thyroid gland, particularly in the case of young women. But here again, moderate smoking cannot cause serious trouble in an otherwise healthy organism.

Rest, of course, is also an essential factor in the preservation of youth, by which we do not mean the few hours of sleep which the organism demands in any case, and which modern man unfortunately does not always accord it in full, but also complete physical and mental relaxation after every considerable effort. Distractions and amusements which some people regard as a luxury are in fact a necessity, particularly to those whose work involves considerable physical or mental exertion. Naturally, proper sleep is one of the most important conditions that must be observed by all who wish to maintain their youthful vigor. The organism utilizes the pause in its activity that is represented by sleep to eliminate the toxins and re-establish the disturbed equilibrium in its strength. As we know, metabolism during sleep proceeds very slowly, so that less energy is used up in that direction, and the organism is therefore able to gather fresh energy. At the same time, too much sleep is unhealthy and conducive to laziness.

Fresh air and sunshine are also necessary to the maintenance of youth. Fresh air, being rich in oxygen, regenerates the blood by increasing the number of red corpuscles. Its tonic effect may be gauged by the contrast presented by people who are obliged to work or live in confined spaces, such as slum-dwellers. It is a well known fact that slum-dwellers, even if they are otherwise "well off," age very early.

It is not without reason that the ancients—Egypt, Greece, Rome— venerated the sun as a god. Heliotherapy, or sun cures, are not a new thing. Hippocrates praised the beneficial effects of sunshine and so did Paracelsus, at a later age. Recent experiments have proved that the red corpuscles of animals kept in a dark place for a long time gradually decrease.

It happens very rarely that an individual is forbidden to take sunbaths for medical reasons, but naturally, sun-bathing must not be carried to excess. In particular, neurasthenic subjects and people suffering from heart disease or arterio-sclerosis must exercise moderation, and should preferably consult a doctor before indulging in sun-bathing.

Those who think that the suppleness of the muscles which is characteristic of youth can be maintained without deliberately cultivating it, are badly mistaken. Systematic exercises and sport are the obvious method. It is advisable to choose games that do not affect a certain set of muscles only, but re-invigorate the entire organism. Gymnastic exercises, walking, swimming and tennis are all useful in this direction. The benefits of tennis are strikingly illustrated by the case of the King of Sweden, who, at the age of ninety, still had the suppleness of a much younger man. Apart from other favorable effects, sport is a remedy for metabolic irregularities. In certain cases of heart disease, specialists prescribe a "mountaineering cure," which is carried out progressively and is designed to re-educate the muscles of the heart to perform their proper functions.

CHAPTER 49

Does Life Begin at Forty?

FORMERLY, the forties were universally considered as a sort of "ante-chamber of death," the age of renunciation, of little pleasure and much suffering, of illness and decay.

If we survey the conditions of life in past periods, we shall find that, in the great majority of cases, that view was justified. The reasons are many, ranging from ignorance of hygiene to super-human strain of daily life and the low standard of living.

At the beginning of World War I, the Recruiting Commissions in England reported that a large proportion of the workers, from the age of thirty-five upwards, showed signs of ageing. Most of the industrial workers in Lancashire were, at thirty-eight, "old men" as far as military service was concerned. Even today, men who perform strenuous physical work, such as miners, certain categories of industrial workers, longshoremen, etc., etc., grow prematurely old, because their organism is worn out at an early age. And there is a saying that "premature old age means premature death."

This idea is the starting point of Professor Walter B. Pitkin's famous book, *Life Begins at Forty*, in which he says that "only stupid people die early." Although, at a first glance, this dictum sounds rather paradoxical, since it is easy to quote cases of really great men who died early, there is nevertheless a great deal of truth in it, and we will endeavor to trace the argument that led the author to this pronouncement.

Max Rubner, the biologist, published a remarkable essay, in which he tried to establish a connection between the weight of animals and their span of life. He arrived at the conclusion that for each $2\frac{1}{5}$ lbs. of its weight the organism produces and consumes 191,600 calories of heat. Thus the organism may be considered as a mechanism capable of producing a given amount of energy, and once that is exhausted, death follows. Thus it is sufficient to know the weight of an animal, and the rate at which it consumes energy, in order to determine approximately its normal duration of life.

Other scientists have tried to establish a similar connection between the weight of the brain and the duration of life. H. Friedenthal, for instance, evolved the idea of cephalization, i.e., the correlation between the volume of the brain and that of the body, without the bones, and he concluded that the larger the brain as compared with the body it governs, the greater is the expectation of life. The equation is as follows:

$$\text{Cephalization} \quad \frac{\text{Weight of body}}{\text{Weigh of brain}} \quad 0.666.$$

The coefficient of cephalization varies in the various species. In mice it is 0.045, in deer, 0.35, in man, 2.7. As the two animals referred to live, respectively, for two or three years and fifteen years, a simple calculation will show that man ought to live an average of 100 years.

The volume of the brain, which relatively determines the degree of intelligence, also determines to a considerable extent the amount of energy expended for a given effort, and it is here that the two theories, Rubner's and Friedenthal's, meet. A rat, for instance, uses six times more energy in its efforts to escape from a complicated trap than a monkey, which is infinitely more intelligent. A man, whose brain is far more highly developed, only requires a hundredth part of the energy used by the rat for the same task. And if we pursue this argument further, we must come to the conclusion that man, being the most intelligent animal, and being capable of husbanding his energies, should live longest.

If we consider Professor Pitkin's dictum from this point of view, we shall find that it is not just a witty saying, though, of course, it cannot be accepted as absolute truth. At the same time, statistics prove that unskilled laborers, on an average, have a lower expectation of life than skilled workers, and these, again, do not live so long as the experts under whom they work; and statistics have also established that the average expectation of life of the intellectual *elite* is considerably higher than that of the average. Thus we are justified in drawing the conclusion that "wise men live long."

There are those who argue that it is not worth while to live long, as, once youth has passed, life is only a burden. But that view is wholly erroneous, for whereas youth has incontestable attractions, the age of maturity, which begins at forty, is nevertheless, the happiest period of life.

"Youth is the loveliest flower on earth," writes Mme. Swetchine, "but maturity is the tastiest of fruits. There is more sweetness in ripe fruit than in the unripe."

How could youth enjoy life to the full? Up to a certain age, human beings lead an almost animal existence while engaged in the laborious task of adapting themselves to their environment. Up to the age of seventeen or eighteen they are imperfectly developed, and are incapable of creating anything lasting, except for those child prodigies who prove the rule, and most of whom cease to be prodigies once they are out of their teens. The period between the ages of seventeen and twenty-four is one of more or less helpless groping. Then follows a time struggle, during which the young man or woman must "carve a career," and they have little time to live their own lives. That is why Professor Pitkin is right in saying that until the age of forty a man may be compared to a student of music who is only capable of executing set exercises, and who as yet derives little pleasure from his art. It is not until the age of forty that the student of the art of living can become an artist and stand on his own feet.

That is particularly true in the case of professions requiring extensive knowledge and experience, such as medicine, architecture, the law, etc.

There is a widespread belief that after forty a process of decline is inevitable. We have already shown how mistaken that view is in the light of scientific experience. It is true that a runner, boxer or footballer of forty cannot measure himself with an equal chance of success against an opponent of from twenty to twenty-five, although it has frequently happened in all branches of sport that the younger men were defeated by the older. The tennis player, Bill Tilden, when he was far on the wrong side of thirty, frequently defeated opponents younger than himself. The Finnish runner, Kohlenmaien, gave a marvelous performance in a Marathon race at the age of thirty-eight. The French fencer, Gaudin, at forty, was still unbeatable. All this shows that even in sport, which really belongs to youth, "age" is not always inferior. As regards industry, skilled workers, contrary to the general belief, only attain their best in trades requiring intelligence and initiative at around forty. H. Sorenson examined a group of people between the ages of twenty-five and eighty-seven, and he found that 25 percent of the older persons worked faster and more skillfully than the average. The twelve oldest men, whose average age was seventy-nine years, were only inferior to the average by from 20 to 30 percent.

All this is easily understandable when we know that the human brain increases in volume up to the age of forty and does not reach its full development until then.

The history of art and science provides many examples of men who have done nothing noteworthy in their youth, and whose gifts only began to manifest themselves after their first youth had passed. Joseph Conrad, for instance, published his first full-length work at the age of thirty-nine. Titian was an obscure provincial painter before that age. Milton was, according to himself, an old man when he wrote *Paradise Lost.* We could cite countless further examples to show that even at a time when physical strength declines, the intellectual powers continue to develop. There was Plato, Goethe, Michelangelo, Victor Hugo, Newton, Leibnitz, and so many others whose cases leave no doubt as to the truth of this statement.

In the previous chapter we stated that towards the age of forty sexual capacity decreases to a certain extent. But that is far from being the rule, and in any case, even if the sexual activity of mature men could not be compared with that of younger men in the quantitative sense, that cannot be said in the qualitative sense.

The great French naturalist and philosopher, Buffon, married a young servant girl and had children by her. It is well known that

Victor Hugo, who was a rather reserved lover in his youth, became all the more ardent after forty, and remained so to the end of his long life. Ancient history provides many examples of "great lovers" who were long past youth. A distinguished Hellenist has calculated that Helen of Troy, for whose sake two rulers flung their peoples into a bloody war, must have been forty at the time, while her lovers were nearly sixty. Historically more certain is the fact that Julius Caesar was not less than fifty-six years old when he conceived a violent passion for Cleopatra. Then there was the French King, Henri IV, who, when nearly sixty, disguised as a groom, called on Charlotte de Monmorency, who was only sixteen.

Naturally, we must assume that these "aged" lovers of history maintained their vigor because they did not waste their energies in their youth. At forty, a man should take stock of himself and decide to be less prodigal with his energies in future. He must slow down the pace of his life. He must *simplify* his life, give up some of the aims he has set himself and concentrate on a few. In our mechanical age, when a great deal of the world's work is accomplished by machinery, such simplification is not difficult. It is only then that the man of forty will be able to look at life with the conviction that, in fact, "life begins at forty."

CHAPTER 50

CAN SEXUAL POTENCE BE RETAINED?

WHAT is the position with regard to the sexual impotence of men? In previous chapters we have endeavored to show that ageing is a biological process that may be delayed for a long time by a rational mode of life, but cannot be escaped completely. The same applies to the sexual potency of men.

In this connection we can only repeat that sexual potency can also be retained until late old age, but in the end it must diminish. Fortunately, the masculine genital glands are composed of cells capable of regeneration for a very long time, and the cells of the erection apparatus are also long-lived. Experience shows that in an otherwise healthy man the capacity for erection and impregnation continues far into old age.

In view of this, the question poses itself: How is it that diminution of potency is so frequent in men during their forties? The explanation is simple. This diminution of potency is not a typical phenomenon of the "ageing" of the masculine germinal glands.

Firstly, it should be noted that 90 percent of all cases of impotence are due not to physical but to psychological causes. But even where impotence arises from physical causes, the role of the sexual glands is not so important as is generally assumed, since, as we have said, these organs are the most resistant in the human organism. In cases of physical impotence, syphilis or its after-effects, and other diseases, are usually more to blame than the germinal glands. We refer to the disease of the spinal cord known as tabes. Potency is also seriously affected by diabetes. But perhaps the most important physical cause of impotence is inflammation of the prostate. We are dealing with the prostate in a separate chapter, and we will only mention here

347

that those diseases of the prostate that lead to impotence may arise from the practice of coitus interruptus and gonorrheal infection. However, all the physical forms of impotence will be discussed in the following chapter. What we wish to emphasize here is the fact that 90 *percent of all potency troubles are not of a physical but of a phychological character.*

But if that is so, why is it that the majority of the men who consult a doctor on account of potency troubles are in the forties? Are we to assume that at that age the psychological tendency to impotence is more pronounced? And, consequently, are we to regard this type of impotence after all as a phenomenon of old age, though relating not to the body but to the mind? The answer is that, as we have said, complete mental maturity is only reached between the ages of forty and fifty, so that there can be no question of psychological ageing.

Twenty-five years experience as a specialist has taught the author of the present chapter that men in the forties who consult a doctor about potency troubles, always admit, after careful interrogation, that their potency was not particularly strong even in former years. It should always be borne in mind that potency is partly a muscular function, and that, of course, there are men who are more muscular, and men who are less so. This does not mean that athletic men generally have a greater potency than physically less well developed men. Indeed, the contrary is frequently, and even mostly, true. Our reference to muscles is only intended to convey that some men are born with a stronger potency than others, for potency is determined, even to a far greater extent than by muscles, by the sexual appetite, by the individual's libido.

Now, if a specialist interrogates his patient expertly, it will be found that the latter's sexual appetite was not particularly keen even in his youth, or if it was, then he was unable to enjoy intercourse without certain disturbances. And if the patient is further interrogated, he will admit that he had never attached too much importance to sexual intercourse. In this manner a somewhat tragi-comic aspect of masculine impotence is revealed. The expert interrogation shows that there are many men who lead an intensive sexual life, not from an inner urge, but as a matter of convention. They have affairs out of vanity, or to compensate an inferiority complex—if they cannot conquer in life, they want to be conquerors at least where the favors of women are concerned. However comic it may sound, it is nevertheless true that the most pitiable figures in the world of sex are the so-called "Don Juans," who are driven to more and more conquests of women, otherwise they cannot compensate their inferiority complex; they go from one woman to another, and derive satisfaction from none. Nor can these people ever find satisfaction, as love to them is not an end, but a means to an end. They do not love because they have a strong sexual appetite, but for other reasons.

And all sexual relationships that are based not on libido but on some other factor, as in the case of the "Don Juan," must end in impotence with advancing age, since the other factor recedes more and more, and so does the potency that is so strongly linked with it. That is also the case with husbands who, during their forties, complain of a diminution of conjugal potency. When such men are interrogated, they inevitably realize that their sexual appetite in relation to their wives has been almost extinct for years, and that they only coninue to engage in sexual intercourse with them because the woman wanted it, or out of "masculine pride."

"Masculine pride" plays a curious role in the sexual life of such men. It happens far more frequently than it might be assumed that the sexual act is carried out in order to save this "pride," and without any genuine libido. And if a man finds himself incapable of satisfying this "pride" several times in succession, he gradually develops a sense of inferiority and, finally, the *fear* of incapacity actually leads to incapacity.

Fear and a sense of guilt are very important factors in the causation of psychological impotence. We refer to the states of fear that exist in men who masturbated in their youth, and owing to ignorance on the subject believe that their sexual potency will diminish in consequence. This fear produces impotence as its psychological reaction.

We know today that masturbation in childhood has nothing to do with impotence in later life. Unfortunately, however, parents and teachers make many grave mistakes in this connection. Children are threatened with hellfire, irreparable damage to their health, and the like, and it is therefore not surprising that they are in adult life burdened with a sense of guilt that only too frequently leads to impotence. But other, apparently insignificant, events of childhood may also lead to impotence in later life. There is such a variety of events of this type, varying in their effects according to the individual, that we cannot even attempt to deal with them here. They can only be brought to the surface and rendered harmless by expert psychoanalysis of the afflicted individual.

Unfortunately, few physicians possess an expert knowledge of impotence. This is not surprising since the problem of impotence is usually treated as an unimportant branch of urology. Apart from that, however, impotence is treated in the same hypocritical manner as venereal disease was treated some decades ago, and the patient himself is just as shy to reveal his trouble to a doctor as people afflicted with venereal disease were at that time. The latter relied on all sorts of quack remedies, and many impotent men do so today, buying the advertised "hormone preparations" at the drug store, or even having them prescribed by inexpert doctors.

We consider it our duty to state here that no aphrodisiac that has to be taken orally can produce the desired effect. All these preparations, whatever they are, are absorbed and cannot, therefore, be efficient. But injections of hormone preparations, whether natural or synthetic, are also, in the great majority of cases, useless, as hormone preparations can only be effective if there is a deficiency in the glandular functions themselves. As we know, the glands continue to function far into old age, and in most cases have nothing to do with impotence.

When, some years ago, it became the fashion in the medical world to treat impotence with hormone preparations and methods of rejuvenation, the author was at first an enthusiastic adherent of these treatments. Later, however, he realized, in the course of a fairly extensive experience, that apart from their suggestive effect, they produced no genuine result in any single instance.

On the whole, we must repeat that diminution of potency is in the overwhelming majority of cases due to psychological factors and must be treated by psychological means.

We have said above that men who in their forties consult a doctor on account of their diminished potency, have mostly been thus afflicted in their earlier life. If this is true, the question arises: Why did they not consult a doctor earlier? The answer is that the false shame of the patients plays a considerable role in this connection, in addition to the "masculine pride" referred to above. Now, in the forties this "pride" diminishes, the man is no longer "ashamed" of his impotence, and he now has the courage to consult a doctor. Success depends largely on the doctor's tact. In the first place, he must not minimize the patient's complaint, and he must also be careful with his interrogation, lest he should uncover a particularly painful wound. In a great many cases it is comparatively easy to enlighten him as to causes, and enlightenment alone may produce a cure. However, the doctor himself, in order to be able to give such enlightenment, must have a clear knowledge of the serious psychological consequences that impotence may produce. He must further know that medicines or injections are very rarely effective.

But the man in the forties must realize that his age has nothing whatever to do with his impotence, real or imaginary. He must further realize that the sole object of sexual intercourse is to satisfy a genuine sexual appetite. If the appetite is present, and cannot be satisfied owing to inadequate erection, it will be worse than useless to buy the pills and other preparations so largely advertised by makers. He should first of all have himself examined by a general practitioner, and if it is found that no physical causes (diabetes, tabes, etc.) are present, and that the prostate is also healthy, then the patient should consult a specialist.

Men in the forties have no reason whatever to despair. An efficient specialist and the will to understand is all that they require.

CHAPTER 51

PHYSICAL CAUSES OF SEXUAL IMPOTENCE

THE section in this book relating to the man in his forties would not be incomplete if we omitted to deal with the physical causes of impotence, since, as we have seen, this is not a deficiency characteristic of middle-age, but one that may occur at an earlier period in a man's life. However, we will pose the problem in this way, that the *consequences* of certain diseases only manifest themselves at a later age, hence it is understandable why men in their forties are driven to seek a cure of physcial impotence.

For instance, we know that tabes is a delayed after-effect of syphilis contracted in youth, which only manifests itself in the forties or later. Thus syphilitic impotence can only be diagnosed in middle-age, and it even happens that the patient consults a doctor on account of potency troubles, and thereby discovers that he is suffering from tabes. The same applies to diabetes, which also may first manifest itself in the forties, and is sometimes similarly discovered by the patient when he consults a doctor on account of his impotence.

We will consider all these phenomena separately, and indicate the possibilities of a cure in each case.

We must begin by investigating the mechanism of erection. Once we know what organs are involved in this phenomenon, we shall find it easier to understand the causes of physical impotence.

The first condition of an erection is the presence of a sexual urge. If there is no sexual urge, i.e., no desire for sexual activity, then no erection can take place. Complete absence of the sexual instinct has never been observed in otherwise healthy individuals. The desire for intercourse may be slight in certain individuals, or it may be repressed owing to psychological causes, but its complete elimina-

352

tion is improbable. On the other hand, it happens all the more frequently that the sexual urge is weakened for a longer or shorter period of time. In most cases this is due to physical or mental overstrain, or to illnesses which, though unconnected with the genital organs, have the effect of weakening the organism.

However, the presence of the sexual urge alone is insufficient to bring about erection. The individual must be in a suitable mood; there must be what we will call *erotic tension*. For it is obvious that even an otherwise normally sexed individual will not have an erection while he is engaged in solving a mathematical problem.

Normally, erotic tension arises through tactile excitations, like embraces, kisses, caresses, etc.; through visual impressions, i.e., the sight of the sexual object or of parts of the body connected with sexuality; through the hearing, and even through the sense of smell. But erotic tension may also arise through recollection or imagination, through memories or thoughts of a sexual character, or through reading erotic literature. On the other hand, mental discomfort, nausea, fear and other disturbing elements may destroy erotic tension.

But if erotic tension is present, it is conveyed from the brain through certain nerves to the lower part of the spinal cord, where the so-called *erection-center* is situated.

From this center other nerves lead to the blood-vessels of the male member, conveying the impulses to it. The cells or cavernous bodies of the penis are thereby congested with blood, which is prevented from flowing back by muscular action. The cavernous bodies absorb more and more blood, thus increasing the volume of the penis and causing it to become rigid, until a maximum of volume and rigidity is attained.

The sexual act itself causes an excitation of the terminal nerves of the glans penis, which continues until orgasm and ejaculation occur. Ejaculation is effected through the contraction of certain muscles of the sperm reservoirs and of the prostate.

Now, there are two forms of impotence. The one is represented by incapacity to perform the sexual act (*impotentia coeundi*), due to the failure of some part of the above mentioned mechanism and

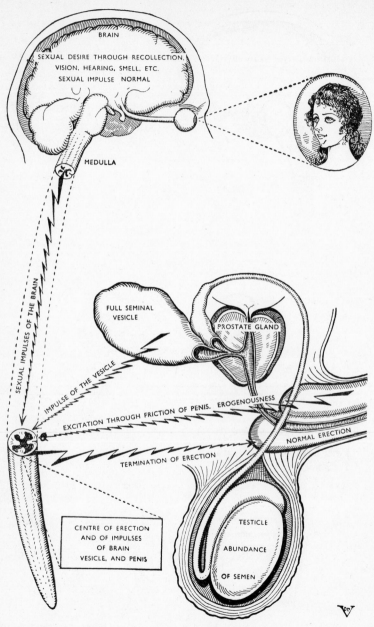

Fig. 126—Picture story of normal physical and psychological potency.

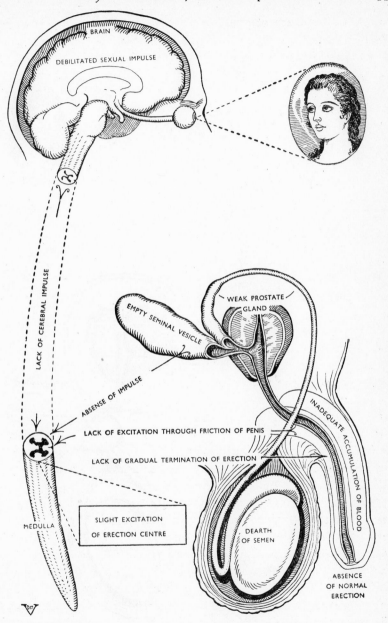

F<small>IG</small>. 127—Picture story of impotence due to functional defects, psychological and organic.

consequent absence of erection, so that the penis cannot be introduced into the vagina. In this type of impotence the production of semen may be quite normal. The other kind of impotence consists in the *incapacity to procreate* (*impotentia generandi*). In this case there may be normal erection, the man may be able to perform the sexual act normally, and may even derive voluptuous enjoyment from it, but he can never impregnate the woman, as his testes produce no fertile spermatozoa. The fluid that is injected into the vagina in such cases is only the secretion of the prostate.

In this chapter we will only deal with the incapacity to perform the sexual act, i.e., the kind of impotence in which no erection takes place, or only an inadequate erection, which leaves the penis too soft to be capable of penetrating into the vagina.

As we have already mentioned, in addition to the sexual urge, the following conditions are indispensable in bringing about erection: (1) Sexual tension; (2) a properly functioning brain and erection center mechanism conveying the impulses; (3) a healthy penis.

Let us examine these three factors separately. We already know what sexual tension is—a mood induced by our senses or by the memory or the imagination. But our senses and the imagination can only evoke the process of erection if the glands supply a sufficient amount of hormones to the blood. In other words, sexual tension can only occur if the blood is sufficiently charged with the endocrine product of the sexual glands. But if these organs for some reason produce too few hormones, or none, then no sexual tension can arise, and no erection can take place. This form of impotence is called *hormonal impotence*.

In the absence of sexual hormones the sexual excitability of the brain and the erection center diminishes, so that there is no inner urge, and the tension cannot be induced even by external excitation. Deficient hormone production is rarely due to a disease of the testes, but mostly to some affection of the pituitary or the suprarenal gland. (See chapters on Glands.) Impotence caused by glandular deficiency is usually also accompanied by *impotentia generandi*, as the affected germinal glands cannot produce any sperms.

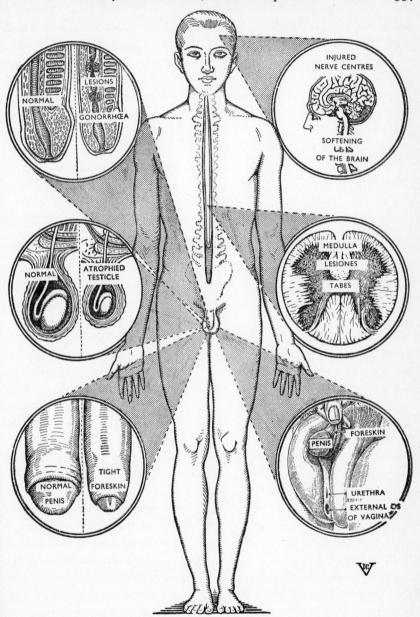

FIG. 128—Picture story of most important causes of impotence in comparison to normal sex potency in man.

There are many forms of injury to the testes involving impotence. If the testes have been completely eliminated, as through castration, a war wound, etc., then, of course, no sexual hormones can be produced. However, cases have been recorded in literature of males being born without testes. The testes may also be infected or affected by various diseases. For instance, gonorrhoea may cause inflammation of the testes, or the testicular tissues may be invaded and destroyed by tubercular bacilli. The action of poisons like alcohol on the testes is dealt with in a separate chapter.

Another form of impotence is caused by diseases of the centers of erection in the brain and the spinal cord and in the connecting nerves. The most important of these diseases are the after-effects of syphilis, such as paralysis of the brain and tabes in the spinal cord. Both these diseases at their inception entail increased potency, as they excite the erection centers and thereby produce automatic erections. At a later stage, however, the erection centers are destroyed and no erection can then occur. (It should be noted, however, that paralysis, and even tabes, is frequently curable.)

As regards the connecting nerves, these may become involved if the rest of the nervous system is attacked by disease. Here again, alcohol is the great danger, and may easily lead to serious damage.

The effect of morphine on potency is similar to that of alcohol. As in the case of alcohol, small doses of morphine may produce a *temporary* intensification in sexual excitability, but experience has shown that any considerable amounts of either of these two poisons inevitably leads to sexual impotence.

Cocaine also affects potency. Chronic lead poisoning has also been proved to produce impotence. The effect of nicotine on the sexual functions is best expressed by the dictum of the famous French novelist, Goncourt: "Tobacco and women are enemies; a taste for the one spoils the taste for the other." On the scientific side, several investigators, including Magnus Hirschfeld, have found that heavy cigarette smokers—more than cigar smokers—frequently suffer from reduced potency. There have been cases in which potency could only be restored when cigarette smoking was given up altogether.

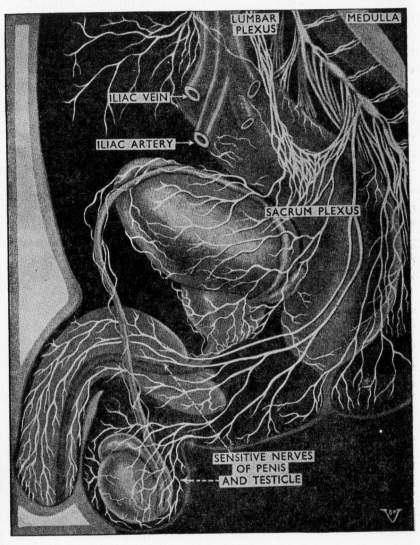

FIG. 129—Showing all the sensitive network of nerves of genital apparatus which conveys external impressions to the internal nerve centers.

Illnesses involving fever, diabetes and diseases of the kidneys also reduce potency.

A third category of physical impotence is due to organic irregularities in the sexual apparatus, though cases of this type are extremely rare. They include total lack of a penis, or abnormal smallness of that organ. In the latter case the genital apparatus as a whole, and particularly the testes, are also small, but sometimes the scrotum and its contents may be perfectly normal, while the penis is rudimentary. However, it frequently happens that the inadequacy of the penis is only imaginary, and the individual concerned is afraid to approach a woman for that unfounded reason. The same applies in cases where an individual thinks his penis is too large to enable cohabitation with a woman. Indeed, it is impossible to establish a standard of size in this connection. Certain it is that the corresponding female organ is sufficiently flexible to render cohabitation possible even with a very voluminous penis, at any rate after a time, unless the woman is suffering from some irregularity.

An extremely rare phenomenon, which we only mention for the sake of completeness, is the congenital double penis. In such cases the two members generally lie side by side, hardly ever on top of each other.

A comparatively frequent irregularity of the penis is the so-called phimosis. Phimosis is present when the foreskin is too tight, or adheres to the glans, so that erection is impeded and rendered

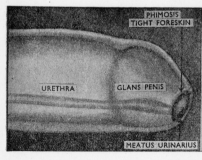
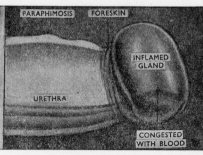

Fig. 130—Showing transparently the glans penis and urethra. Tight foreskin completely covering the glans.

Fig. 131—Showing inside male organ with inflamed glans. If glans is uncovered, the foreskin strangulates the penis, and paraphimosis arises.

painful. Phimosis can be cured by means of a minor operation.

In addition to congenital anomalies, there are also acquired defects of the penis, caused by injuries and diseases. The erect penis may be fractured through the malicious application of force by the woman. This consists in the bursting of the cavernous bodies of the penis. Cases of an erect penis being fractured by a jealous woman have been recorded in literature, as well as cases where the penis was bitten by a horse, a dog, or a rat, or where it was caught in the hinge of a door.

It has been established that it requires a pressure of from 525 to 570 lbs. to sever the penis in the flaccid state, but only from 85 to 130 lbs. in the erect state.

The practice of bandaging or constricting the penis and its consequences deserve special mention. This is usually done in play. Hirschfeld records the case of a woman who drew her wedding ring over her husband's penis, and was then unable to remove it, so that a jeweller had to be called to saw it off, and certain sensitive parts of the organ were injured.

However, bandaging or constriction of the penis is far more frequently effected in order to prevent pollutions, masturbation and nocturnal wetting. There are many recorded cases of parents or guardians tying ribbons, rubber bands, string or wire round the

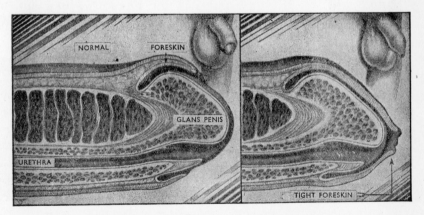

Comparative study of normal penis and tight foreskin.

FIG. 132—Section of normal penis.   FIG. 133—Section of penis with tight foreskin.

penis of their charges for this purpose, and even iron rings have been used. Such devices may injure the tissues by cutting them, or produce other damage through congestion. It is obvious, however, that erection is thereby rendered impossible.

The above are the most important physical causes of impotence and, as the reader will note, none of them has any special connection with age. Thus we repeat: If one or other of these phenomena only manifests itself in the forties, then this is due to the fact that some disease that is otherwise unconnected with sexuality has only reached its full development at that age, producing impotence as a *secondary* phenomenon.

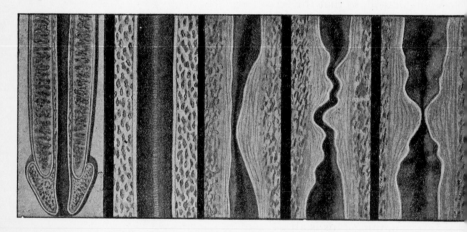

Five sections of the urethra in normal and abnormal conditions.

Fig. 134—Normal.   Fig. 135—Normal.   Fig. 136—Narrowing. Fig. 137—Narrowing.   Fig. 138—Narrowing

It is obvious that such impotence cannot be cured by means of preparations designed to increase potency, but that the disease entailing impotence must be first attacked. If, for instance, impotence is due to diabetes or kidney trouble, then the diabetes or kidney trouble must be taken in hand. Once the disease is cured, potency will automatically be restored. The same applies to the general exhaustion of the nervous system as a result of physical or mental overstrain. If the body is given sufficient rest, potency will reappear, so that in such cases a shorter or longer holiday, with plenty of fresh air and recreation, is indicated.

In cases of impotence caused by the excessive use of alcohol and the like, the obvious remedy is the giving up of these poisons.

Finally, we come to the form of poisoning that is caused, particularly in the forties, by irrational diet.

Since science discovered the influence of vitamins on health (see Chapters 15 and 16) our views on correct diet have undergone a considerable change. We now know that the diet of civilized man is too rich in protein substances and too poor in vitamins. Now, protein, if consumed in excessive quantities, produces a considerable amount of acid, so that the blood becomes charged with acid, which, by way of the bloodstream, injures the entire glandular system, including of course, the sexual glands.

Meat, fish, bacon and cured foods are particularly rich in protein, and very apt to produce acidity in the blood. This does not imply that these foods should be abandoned altogether, but when it is a matter of de-toxicating the organism, it is advisable to use them in great moderation. Indeed, it is best, at first, to abstain from protein foods for some time, say, a month, and to substitute vegetables and fruit in large quantities. Wholewheat bread is very nourishing and helps to purify the blood of acids. Nuts of all kinds, such as walnuts, hazelnuts and almonds are also highly recommended.

We have already referred to the importance of a vegetarian diet rich in vitamins. This is all the more advisable in the case of middle-aged men, as one vitamin, known as *Vitamin E*, produces a favorable effect on potency. Experiments have proved that animals deprived of this vitamin soon become incapable of reproduction. Natural (unpolished) rice, wheat, rye, oats, etc., are rich in vitamins when made to swell in water. Soup prepared from any of these contains an abundance of Vitamin E, which may also be found in cauliflower, turnip, beetroot, celery, spinach, tomatoes and radishes.

Once the blood has been purified of acids by means of a diet on the lines indicated above, the consumption of foods with a greater protein content may be resumed on a moderate scale.

As regards the eroticizing effect of individual foods, this is lost in all cases where the food concerned is frequently used, as the organism becomes accustomed to it. Thus such foods should be reserved for those occasions, when excitation for the sexual act appears to be necessary.

The following is a summary of the dietetic rules designed to promote potency:

1. Purification of the blood of acids by abstaining from the use of meat, cured foods, bacon and fish for at least one month. Thereafter the consumption of these foods in small amounts may be resumed.

2. Diet of vegetables, fruit, nut and wholewheat bread, all of which are rich in vitamins.

3. Use of foods containing Vitamin E.

4. Alcohol, nicotine, coffee and tea to be eliminated during the first month, but may be resumed later in small amounts. It should be noted that the poisons contained in all these substances produce an eroticizing effect if taken in small quantities, by persons whose organism is not inured to them through constant use. However, once the body is accustomed to them, their effect is to reduce potency.

5. The same applies to spices, and all the foods which we have described as eroticizing.

We will deal with the beneficial effect on potency of cold baths elsewhere in this work.

CHAPTER 52

The Woman's Menopause

This is popularly known as the "change of life," the period in the life of a woman when her reproductive capacity stops, the ovaries ceasing to mature ova and ceasing to render them capable of fertilization. Just as, during puberty, the preparation of the entire organism for the phase of sexual maturity is gradual, so the transition to the changes characteristic of the menopause takes place gradually, producing a serios of symptoms known as climacteric symptoms.

Just as the commencement of ovarial activity during puberty is concluded from the first menstruation, it is customary to diagnose the beginning of "the change," at a suitable age, from the most obvious phenomenon, the gradual or sudden cessation of menstruation. This is not a wholly correct conclusion, for the limits of the climacteric are defined by the first and last ascertained climacteric phenomenon, and menstruation is not the most important symptom. In accordance with this temporal definition, we also speak of the climax as the commencement of the menopause. The disturbances occurring before the climax are designated as pre-climacteric, and those occurring after the cessation of the menstruation, as post-climacteric symptoms, or post-menopausal.

The duration of this transition period varies a great deal. Usually a period of from one to two years is sufficient to establish the new equilibrium. Sometimes, however, the process may take several years, though in these exceptional cases the undue gradualness is generally attributable to some pathological condition.

It would be difficult to establish that the period of change in all cases precedes old age, as the climacteric often reaches into old age.

It marks the commencement of the ageing of the entire body, and particularly of the genital organs.

Statistical investigations of the subject have provided us with more accurate information concerning the average age of the menopause. Thus a considerable amount of polyclinical material has been sifted with a view to establishing the commencement, duration and cessation of menstruation. What we are interested in here are the data concerning the time of the menopause, in respect of which we investigated 903 cases. The average age was 47.26 years, which tallies with the general view that the change in our latitudes usually takes place between the ages of forty-five and fifty. The range of this fluctuation is indicated by Schaffer's detailed table. According to his investigations the cessation of sexual maturity and the cyclical activity of the genital apparatus occurs:

In 3.65%	of cases	at	the	age	of	40	years	
" 20.5	"	"	"	"	"	40 to 44¾	years	
" 44.19	"	"	"	"	"	45 " 49¾	"	
" 30.01	"	"	"	"	"	50 " 54¾	"	
" 1.64	"	"	"	"	"	55 " 57¾	"	

Kleinwachter, who investigated the data concerning 373 women also observed the occurrence of the climax between the ages of forty-five and fifty in 54.15% of cases; in 18% of the cases the menopause occurred later, in 34.85% before the age of forty-five. Stratz calculated on the basis of 86,000 observations occurring in literature that the average age for the first menstruation in Europe is the fourteenth, and for the cessation of the menses, the forty-sixth year. The normal range of fluctuation in respect of menstruation is, according to this author, from the tenth to the twenty-first year, and in respect of the menopause, from the thirty-sixth to the fifty-sixth year.

It has long been known that the time of the change is influenced by a number of factors. Climate, race, heredity, mode of life and constitutional characteristics all play a part in this connection.

However, with regard to the importance of climatic conditions the various authors do not appear: to be in agreement. Whereas Montegazza concluded from investigations carried out in Italy that a warm climate frequently delayed the menopause, Bruce and Oppenheim hold the contrary view, namely, that in warm climates the menopause usually occurs earlier. The latter view seems to be borne out by the fact that women of the South reach sexual maturity and also lose their attractiveness earlier than women of the North. However, other investigators have been unable to discover any variation. In our view it is far more probable that differences in the ages when the menopause occurs depend not so much on climatic as on racial and hereditary characteristics. Wiesel is of the same opinion. He writes: "For instance, if a woman born in the South, who has reached puberty at an early age, gives birth to a daughter in a northern climate, the latter will not follow the native rule in those regions as regards the commencement of menstruation, but will also menstruate earlier. The daughters of these children, though they may also be born in the North, will similarly menstruate considerably earlier, just like their grandmother. The same applies to the climacteric, which as a regular rule follows the family type, and is unaffected by purely local factors."

That the menopause in different races occurs at different ages has been known for a long time. Thus Chinese women menstruate not longer than until the age of forty, and the climax frequently occurs even earlier. The time of climax in the Japanese women is towards the end of the forties, while an investigation as to the time of the menopause in North American Indian women has shown that it often occurs as late as the early fifties, and that these women continue to menstruate at an age when women of our own race have long passed the climacteric. The menopause comes particularly early in women of the black races. For instance, the women of the Woloff tribe have their climax between the ages of thirty-five and forty. The women along the Sierra Leone Coast are also said to cease menstruating at an average age of thirty-five. The reproductive capacity of the women of some Indian peoples is also said to cease earlier than in Europe. Marshall has compiled a table concerning the women of the Todas, according to which they cease to bear children at an average age of thirty-seven. In Tungus and Ostiak women productivity similarly ceases between the ages of thirty and thirty-five. Generally, it is safe to say that the climacteric occurs the earlier the more primitive the race to which a woman belongs, and that "the earlier life develops the earlier it decays."

We have already referred to the influence of heredity in connection with the time of the climax. Actually, this is a concomitant of racial peculiarity in this connection. Von Jaschke emphasizes the significance of heredity in this sense, and the present writer himself was able, in a number of cases in which menstruation persisted for a long time, to establish that the climacteric was late in the mother and any sisters as well. The cases in which the temporal limit of the change is low, will be dealt with in the section on *climacterium praecox*, or early climacteric.

Certain observations confirm the view that the mode of life also influences the time of the menopause. It has been asserted that menstruation frequently ceases earlier in the poorer working women. Mayer found that in Berlin, the age of the menopause in idle well-to-do women was 47.138 years, and in the less prosperous working women 46.976 years, which gives an average difference of one month and twenty-eight days. That undernourishment and overstrain, which frequently occur among hard working women, are conducive to an earlier menopause, is, of course, obvious. Nevertheless, cases are not rare in which overworked women experienced the menopause later than usual.

Constitutional factors naturally play an important role in the earlier or later appearance of the climacteric, but comparatively little is known on this subject. Some authors hold that menstruation continues longest in big-boned, not too fat women with dark hair. That the menopause frequently comes early in the case of infantile individuals, is comprehensible, since impeded general development would naturally lead to an early cessation of the inadequate function of the ovaries. Women with masculine characteristics, as well as the intersexual type, also frequently incline to early menopause.

There is one more question to be considered in this connection. It has been said that the early appearance of menstruation involves late appearance of the menopause and *vice versa*. This assertion is contrary to the facts. It is true that the duration of the period of sexual maturity is usually somewhat longer in women who start to menstruate early, while women who start to menstruate late generally menstruate for a shorter period than the average. In both cases, however, the menopause—in the absence of other factors, such as constitutional irregularities, etc.—occurs at the same age.

A further factor affecting the time of the climacteric is represented by a series of diseases of the genital organs.

That severe illness of any kind or other exhausting occurrences may bring about an early change of life is, of course, only natural. But traumas—violent impressions—of a physical or psychical nature may also lead to a sudden menopause, as has been observed in numerous cases. Sudden fright, fear, grief and worry are the psychical traumas which may cause a temporary cessation of the menses even at the age of sexual maturity, but at an advanced age they may bring about a final menopause and a definite cessation of the menses.

CHAPTER 53

Normal Progress of the Menopause

As already mentioned at the outset, the most striking symptom indicating the change of life is the sudden or gradual cessation of the menses at a suitable advanced age. As regards the manner of this cessation of the menses, the most varied types have been observed. In some cases where menstruation ceases gradually, this occurs in such a manner that the menstrual flow recurring regularly every four weeks becomes less and less intense, and finally ceases altogether; while in other cases not only are the duration and intensity of the menstrual flow reduced, but the interval also becomes longer and longer, until the menses finally cease and the menopause occurs. It may even happen that the menses apparently cease completely for a longer or shorter period (from nine months to a year), then recur at regular intervals, and finally cease altogether. However, experience has proved in connection with the latter type of case that the resumption of menstruation is due to a pathological process, so that a thorough examination and careful observation of the patient concerned is advisable.

Sometimes there is a sudden and final cessation of the menstrual flow, mostly accompanied by more or less serious general complaints. The woman concerned may interpret the absence of the menses, in conjunction with other, subjective, phenomena of the climacteric period, as a sign of pregnancy, and this may be accompanied by all the symptoms of "nervous pregnancy." A medical examination in such cases will immediately reveal the truth. Sudden and final cessation of the menses may often be observed in cases of premature climacteric.

The various forms of the cessation of the menses described above are all physiological, that is to say, part of the normal process of ageing; all the other forms, which are accompanied by an increased flow must be regarded as pathological. These will be dealt with later.

However, although the cessation of the menses is the most obvious symptom, it is not the only one that appears during the period of the change. There are, in addition, changes in the genital apparatus of the woman, consisting in processes of retrogression due to the stoppage of ovarial activity, the ultimate cause of which is still wrapped in mystery. In this connection it should be noted that although the shrinkage referred to above commences with the stoppage of ovarial activity, it only concludes very late in life, steadily increasing from this starting point.

With the climax the layer of fat in the region of the mons veneris and in the large lips of the vulva starts to shrink. The vulva becomes smaller and flabbier, the small lips become withered and change into thin folds. The fatty glands, formerly present in more than adequate amounts, disappear almost completely, so that there are only remnants of them left.

The vagina generally loses its internal folds and becomes smooth. Its membrane looks dry. It is thinner and less muscular than before. In the course of the further process the vaginal tube gradually shrinks, becomes narrower, shorter and less elastic.

The uterus at the beginning of the change of life frequently contains an increased supply of blood, so that this organ increases in volume. Soon, however, the uterus also shrinks, and its muscles gradually perish as a result of slow degeneration at certain points. The uterus consequently becomes considerably smaller, thinner and narrower, and acquires a flat appearance.

The shrinkage of the oviducts is characterized by the fact that the tubes become thinner and shorter, their cross section gradually decreasing.

The principal change in the ovaries of a woman during the climacteric consists in the fact that they cease to produce follicles. The connective tissue predominates and is strikingly coarse. Further, there are certain changes in the blood vessels, and from the blood vessels this degeneration progresses to the tissue, which assumes a peculiar glassy appearance. The ovaries become smaller and coarser and are frequently flattened. Their surfaces become furrowed, so that they sometimes resemble the stone of a peach.

The changes in the genital organs are accompanied by changes in the appearance of the woman concerned, which start during the climacteric and almost imperceptibly develop into those changes which are commonly known as senility. In a few cases the climacteric coincides with incipient senility, but in the majority of women at this age there is a series of characteristics that have nothing in common with senility. They vary according to the individual, and are frequently connected with constitutional factors, which are of decisive importance. It should be noted, however, that in view of the merging of constitutional characteristics, which are only rarely crystallized as types in the individual, the changes appearing during the climax cannot be divided into distinct classes, as here, too, transitions have frequently been observed.

As regards the sexually clearly differentiated form of the so-called status pycnicus, this refers mainly to small, rotund women, with short necks, low foreheads and supple skin. The general changes in these women during the climacteric are very slight, and the "crisis" passes over them almost unnoticed. The fat deposits all over the body increase, but without disturbing the shape of any part. Even the face remains smooth and even, resembling during this period that of a child.

Ploss-Bertels in describing the appearance of feminine forms during the climacteric states that all the soft curves, which are the result of fat deposits, and which men find so attractive in women, become repulsive during the climax, in that they literally slide down, and that, in particular, the cheeks, throat, breasts, abdomen, hips and buttocks become flabby, distorting the body. This relates to a definite type, which is comparatively frequent. Some authors are of the opinion that the external changes indicated above represent a constitutional or hereditary anomaly, characterized by the undue flabbiness of the tissue, which leads to the sinking not only of the abdomen, but also of the chest. During the climax this congenital flabbiness becomes intensified. The tension and elasticity of the skin is reduced so that it is incapable of bearing the peculiar fat deposits collected under the skin. The form of the fat that forms during the climacteric is also characteristic. It appears in the form of lumps of fat, and differs very considerably from the continuous layers of fat of previous years. These accumulations of lumps of fat usually occur on the cheeks and under the chin, the temples usually remaining free. The result is the characteristic shape of the face, with pendant fat cheeks and a lump of fat under the chin, covered with atrophied, wrinkled skin. Frequently there is also an accumulation of fat on the neck, but the skin usually remains more supple than on other parts. Similarly, there are accumulations of fat in the supra-clavicular grooves—on the shoulders—which persist even if the rest of the body is lean to the point of emaciation. On the arms, however, the roundness of previous years usually disappears, the skin becoming flabby, pendent, and the muscles soft. The breasts also become considerably fatter and pendent, the areola or court diminishes and loses its original shape. The accumulation of fat in the buttocks and hips, accompanied by loss of suppleness in the skin, causes these groups of muscles to move sideways and downwards, thus distorting the form of the feminine body.

Women belonging to the intersexual type show very different symptoms during the climax. These women, in accordance with their classification as above, have certain heterosexual characteristics even during the period of sexual maturity; during the period of the change of life they develop definitely virile characteristics which give them their peculiar impress. They are generally tall, lean, big-boned women, who even during the climacteric incline to leanness rather than to the accumulation of fat.

The face assumes a distinctly masculine character, the features becoming sharper and more distinct, and an abnormal growth of hair may also appear, or, alternatively, a darkening of the existing growth. The precise cause of the growth of hair at this period is not known.

Other symptoms in the intersexual type are, in some cases, the coarsening of the voice, due to changes in the larynx, and, in the majority of cases, an almost complete disappearance of the mammary glands. The nipple, on the other hand, becomes more prominent, and the areola becomes darker and, sometimes, studded with hair. The growth of hair over the rest of the body, including the sexual organs and the legs, becomes intensified, and dirty-brown spots appear on the back and elsewhere.

However, during the period of the climax, in addition to the changes in the body in general and in the sexual apparatus in particular, there are a number of other disturbances, the so-called climacteric complaints. The cause is the cessation of ovarial activity. The ovary being both an endocrine and an exocrine gland, its function is not restricted to ovulation; it also collaborates with some of the other endocrine glands. The cessation of this endocrine activity during the climacteric may therefore lead to disturbances involving all the endocrine glands, as happens when any other endocrine gland ceases to function.

The deficiency symptoms thus arise through the cessation of all the ovarial functions. In normal circumstances these complaints are far from serious. The strong women of the primitive tribes hardly experience them at all, but the woman of the civilized races will suffer from them according to the extent to which she is affected by neurasthenia and psychopathic inclinations.

A sudden climax in the case of ovaries that have previously functioned normally and efficiently will produce more serious complaints than a gradual transition, because the endocrine system requires a certain amount of time to re-establish its equilibrium after the elimination of ovarial activity.

These general complaints, as we have already mentioned, frequently commence before menstruation has ceased, and may continue long after the menopause. Finally, the body becomes accustomed to the elimination of ovarial activity, a new equilibrium establishes itself among the endocrine glands other than the ovaries, and the complaints disappear.

There is a great variety in the forms in which the deficiency symptoms during the menopause may appear. We shall first consider those forms that may be regarded as normal. It should be noted, however, that just as in the case of the disturbances occurring at the beginning of pregnancy, the boundary between that which may still be considered as normal, and that which must already be designated as pathological, is not sharply defined.

Prominent among the general complaints are usually disturbances relating to circulation, known as flushing. Practically every woman during the period of the climacteric suffers from this complaint, which consists in a suddenly arising local sensation of heat. This may last several seconds or several minutes at a time, and may occur a number of times per day. It may even happen at night, disturbing the patient in her sleep. The face may also flush. The skin at such times is warmer to the touch. Frequently the "heat waves" suddenly give way to the opposite phenomenon, causing a deathly pallor. These attacks are often accompanied by considerable perspiration, followed by slight shivering.

Perspiration, like flushing, comes spontaneously, and may be confined to the night hours. These attacks, particularly if they extend over a considerable area of the body, are usually followed by a feeling of exhaustion, languor and depression.

In some cases these attacks of flushing are accompanied by giddiness and ear noises of various kinds, which may be extremely painful. Similarly, there may be attacks of "dazzle," i.e., the patient sees lights, spots, etc., before her eyes, and this frequently causes considerable anxiety. Again, the action of the heart may sometimes be affected in a manner that the patient can feel subjectively, and may be verified objectively, like palpitations, acceleration of the pulse and rhythmic irregularities. This is accompanied by a sense of oppression and anxiety, which is experienced by the patient at the moment of flushing.

Women also not infrequently complain of circulatory troubles in the extremities. These consist in the sensation of "pins and needles" and numbness in the arms and legs. The fingers and toes are often cold to the touch and look bluish, while the rest of the body is warm.

Cramp in the muscles of the extremities are also a not infrequent symptom, particularly in the calves. This is caused by the contraction of the peripheral blood vessels and may be very painful, particularly if it occurs at night.

To the same category of complaints may be counted the headaches from which many women during the period of the climacteric suffer, and which may assume a cramp-like character, manifesting itself as pressure on the head, a feeling of oppression, frontal and cerebellar headaches. Sometimes these headaches partake of the character of migraine, that is to say, they are to some extent accompanied by stomach-ache and vomiting.

Disturbances may sometimes be found in the intestines which in some women are of a very obstinate character. In particular, during this period very severe constipation may develop. Women during the climacteric also frequently complain of pain in the abdomen and in the small of the back.

Another frequent complaint is insomnia. This is often generally caused by flushing and perspiration occurring at night, but sometimes insomnia may be present without these causes.

The changes and complaints at this period relate not only to the body, but psychological disturbances are frequent. In this connection the influence of the climacteric period is probably overrated, and there can be no doubt whatever that the cessation of the menses does not depress women to the extent that many people believe. Nevertheless, the cessation of ovarial activity quite certainly affects the mental attitude of women. In normal cases the psychological disturbances will probably manifest themselves to the woman's environment by increased irritability of the central nervous system, extreme fluctuations between gaiety and depression, with a tendency to prolong the latter moods and general capriciousness. However, the degree of these disturbances in a normal case depends very considerably on the individual's capacity for self-control, and her general temperament. Nervousness and irritability may be brought about by the deficiency symptoms described above. However, in the case of a large number of women the climacteric is psychologically favorable. It has frequently been observed that nervous individuals who during the period of sexual maturity have suffered from all sorts of abdominal complaints have been relieved of all their complaints as soon as the menses ceased, and have benefited physically and mentally.

In the case of a number of women the period of the climacteric is characterized by intensified sexual excitability and libido. That may be due in many cases to the process of decay that starts with the climacteric in the vagina and the uterus. However, in other cases increased excitability is caused by inflammation of the vulva, which has frequently been observed in recent years. Finally, in the case of naturally sensuous women the fear of the approaching end of their sexual life, or the thought that pregnancy is now out of the question and they therefore have greater freedom as regards sexual intercourse, may be the cause of increased sexual excitability.

Although in normal cases no specific medical treatment is necessary, it is nevertheless the task of the doctor during those critical years in the life of a woman to counteract the changes in the circulation, the disturbances in the nervous, alimentary and digestive systems, and to regulate the patient's mode of life in such a manner that the climacteric should be passed with as few complaints and fluctuations of the general health as possible.

In order to avert or combat all the many deficiency symptoms of the climacteric, it is above all necessary to regulate the patient's diet and mode of life. To avoid complaints arising from a disturbed circulation, it is advisable to abstain from all food, drink, etc.. that affects the action of the heart. Alcohol in any form, tea, coffee and tobacco should be avoided. It is also best to avoid all foods with a particularly abundant protein content, as well as meat extracts. Instead, a preponderance of vegetarian elements in the patient's diet may be recommended, as these impose less strain on the now weakened intestinal activity. Naturally, vegetarian dishes that produce a considerable amount of gas, like beans, peas, etc., must be avoided.

Generally speaking, at this period it is advisable to moderate the diet altogether. In numerous cases the increase of fat deposits during the period of the climacteric is due to over-eating. In cases of severe circulatory disturbances, Prof. Sellheim recommends a milk diet prescribed by Kisch, according to which milk is given four times per day in progressive quantities of one-third, three-fourths and up to one cup, with a more solid meal only at midday.

Water cures have proved particularly effective for perspiration and flushing during the climacteric period. In many cases repeated baths of a temperature of approximately blood heat—lasting from fifteen to twenty minutes each time—will produce a considerable improvement. Pine, oxygen, light and sun baths may be recommended. In other cases, cold compresses and the rubbing down of the upper part of the body with cool water, preferably mixed with a little vinegar or eau-de-Cologne, will reduce the frequency and intensity of the attacks.

Saline purgatives may also be recommended. Such purgatives force the blood towards the intestines, thus counteracting the surge of blood towards the brain. They counteract the weakness of the intestines and constipation, and produce a favorable effect on the flatulence which frequently appears during this period, but they should not be taken too habitually or too frequently.

It is of considerable importance that the patient should take suitable physical exercise, with plenty of fresh air, regular, not too strenuous, walks, and careful gymnastic exercises.

The latter may be recommended for flushing, as they draw the blood away from the brain, and at the same time strengthen the heart and promote the suppleness of the skin. It is also possible, by means of such systematic physical culture, to prevent the excessive accumulation of fat deposits during the period of the climacteric, which leads to slowness of movement and love of comfort, and these again conduce to a further increase of weight and consequent complaints in connection with the sinking of various groups of muscles. However, in cases of climacteric obesity all forced reducing must be avoided, as this frequently leads to a complete breakdown of the central nervous system and may, if carried on with the aid of thyroid preparations, cause serious injury to the heart and produce lasting complaints. *But a careful course of exercises and systematic dietetic treatment will generally succeed in preventing the accumulation of excessive fat during the climacteric.*

The psychical disturbances and excessive nervous irritability must also receive attention. These conditions may be most effectively combated by some physical and mental work. Literature, art or social welfare work frequently afford opportunities for the type of light occupation that will prove beneficial to a woman during the climacteric. Such preoccupations, in particular, counteract the tendency of a woman at this time to think constantly of herself. In addition, enlightenment and reassurance on the part of the doctor, and avoidance of irritating factors in the patient's environment, are indicated. Sexual intercourse during the critical period must be restricted to the frequency compatible with the individual concerned.

By means of the general hygienic and dietetic measures it is possible to mitigate the complaints usual at this period to a considerable extent, and to make life more tolerable to a woman during the climacteric.

Once this important, and sometimes stormy, period is safely over, there usually follows a quiet life unaffected by the influence of the genital apparatus, and this condition continues far into old age.

CHAPTER 54

Physical Disturbances of Menopause

Apart from the fact that certain complaints and difficulties are almost inevitable even in normal circumstances, the climacteric is a period during which the subject is particularly prone to diseases and pathological conditions, so that it may rightly be described as the critical period in the life of a woman.

In particular, pathological menstruation is very frequent during this time of transition. There are data available to show that 65% of all excessive menstruation occur at the beginning and end of the period of sexual maturity. The incidence of excessive discharges of blood during the period of the climacteric is such a general phenomenon, well known even to lay people, that a great many women ignore them, and omit to consult a doctor even when they reach a serious degree. Hemorrhages during the climacteric may occur without any serious changes in the organs and solely through the cessation of ovarial activity. However it frequently happens, just at this time, that these discharges conceal some severe affection of the sexual organs.

Thus in cases of excessive menstruation during the climacteric a doctor should be consulted at once, as this may prove to be a symptom of incipient cancer in the uterus.

In the majority of cases of excessive menstruation at this period, this phenomenon is accompanied by a temporal irregularity. Sometimes the menstruation is delayed, and occurs after six or eight weeks, and even after several months. At the same time, the duration of the flow is also longer, and may continue throughout an entire interval. As regards quantity the menstruation may amount to a veritable hemorrhage, with a considerable discharge of coagulated

380

blood clots. In other cases the interval between menstruations is shortened to three weeks or two weeks, and even less, and here again the duration of the flow may be lengthened. Further, there are cases in which abundant and inadequate menstruations alternate, the interval between menstruations being longer, shorter or normal. And finally, in a not inconsiderable number of cases there is no menstrual cycle at all, the flow appearing irregularly.

During the climacteric period it frequently happens that the subject's life is made almost intolerable by the itching of the external genital organs. We know today that this may be a symptom of some disease, like diabetes, and it is therefore indispensable for a woman so affected to consult a doctor immediately.

However, whatever the cause of the itching in individual cases may be, in most cases it appears not as a continuous irritation, but rather in the form of periodical attacks. At night it may be brought on by the warmth of the bedclothes, after a long walk by contact of the external genital organs with the clothes, and at other times after relieving the bladder, or through sexual excitement. The irritation is sometimes so intense that the woman so affected is unable to sleep, and there are cases in which the torment of it evokes thoughts of suicide.

The treatment of this irritation is naturally governed by its causes, and this must be ascertained before a cure can be devised. There is one point, in particular, that must be cleared up at once; namely, whether there is any sugar in the urine. That is not an infrequent cause of the irritation in the external genital organs at this time, and if sugar is present the woman concerned must be treated for diabetes.

If, however, the irritation has been caused by local factors, then a local treatment of the external genital organs is indicated. Most women try to soothe the irritation by bathing the affected parts with cold water, but although cold water affords temporary relief, it only aggravates the complaint in the end. The use of water should therefore be avoided at all costs. In order to protect the sensitive skin from the effects of urine, perspiration or vaginal secretion, it is advisable to apply an ointment which should preferably contain some menthol, as this gives a sensation of coolness. Once a day the genital organs may be washed with soap and water, in order to clean off the stale ointment. After this the affected part should be dabbed with salicylic spirit (1%) and powdered with talcum powder. In severe cases operative intervention may be necessary. In any case medical advice should be sought to preclude more serious local disease.

Women during the climacteric period frequently complain of an increased vaginal flux (discharge). In some cases this may only be noticed through the soiling of the woman's underwear, but very often the increased flux leads to an irritation of the skin. There may be a sensation of soreness over the affected area, which may be intensified after walking, and may cause such severe pain during sexual intercourse that the sufferer prefers to avoid it. However, particularly after urine is passed there is a burning sensation, and this has given rise to the view that the urine at this time is particularly "strong" and has a corrosive effect. In other cases traces of blood in the vaginal flux cause the sufferer to consult a doctor.

The cause of the increased vaginal flux is partly due to the changes occurring in the vagina, to which we have already referred above, but mainly to the process of changes provoked by the cessation of ovarial activity, which leads to the secretion of the thin, light gray discharge. The flux may be so heavy that it may set up irritation and inflammation of the lining membrane of the vagina, as well as the external genital organs and even the thighs.

A good remedy for this vaginal flux is douching with a solution of ordinary vinegar (one or two tablespoonfuls to a quart of warm water).

We have already dealt with the changes and regressive processes taking place in the uterus as a result of the climacteric. But the uterus may also change its position. Not infrequently there is a sinking and forward tilting of the uterus and even the vagina. Where this condition has existed before the climacteric, it may appear in an aggravated form during this critical period. The reason is that during the climacteric the fibrous tissue relaxes and is incapable of withstanding the pressure of the intestine and the bladder.

How great is this disposition for the displacement of the uterus and the vagina during the climacteric is evidenced by the many cases in which this change has occurred in a woman after a sudden strain on the abdominal muscles, e.g., after the lifting of a weight.

In concluding this chapter, let us briefly consider the question of uteral cancer.

The statistical data on the subject show that uterine cancer, like cancer of the other organs, in the majority of cases develops at an advanced age. There have been cases in which, for instance, a girl of eight developed uterine cancer, but it is nevertheless an undeniable fact that age has a decisive influence in this connection. The great majority of cases falls between the ages of forty and sixty, that is to say, the age of the climacteric.

Unfortunately, little is known concerning the causes of cancer, though it is safe to assume that there is some connection between the functioning of the endocrine—or internal secretory—glands and the development of cancer. However, as in the present state of medical science there can be no question of prevention, we must concentrate on recognizing the presence of this pernicious growth as early as possible. In many cases early diagnosis renders a complete cure possible, and the woman suffering from uterine cancer may be saved from the horrible end which neglect entails.

We will therefore describe the early symptoms of uterine cancer, and call particular attention to the fact that a woman observing in herself the least sign of any of the symptoms mentioned below, must immediately consult a doctor. Every hour's delay may involve irreparable injury.

Abnormal menstruations and an increased vaginal flux during the climacteric deserve special attention. Menstrual anomalies of all kinds and, in particular, a flow of blood after sexual intercourse or after vaginal douches, or a watery flux stained with red, are a distinct indication that there may be cancer in the genital organs. That cancer is present may be assumed with certainty if a woman resumes menstruation months or years after the menopause. Uterine cancer can today be diagnosed with considerable certainty. In such cases operative intervention is unavoidable. It frequently happens that small cancerous growths are treated by a woman herself by means of corrosive substances. This may lead to tragic consequences owing to the waste of time, as a case of cancer that is operable today may not be so after a few weeks.

In addition to cancer in the genital organs, cancer of the mammae (breasts) is also tragically frequent. Any hardening or lumps of the mammary glands spell danger, and a doctor should be consulted immediately.

Having outlined the pathological changes occurring during the climacteric in the genital organs, we will now consider those symptoms of the climacteric which may appear in a pathological form in the rest of the organism, frequently causing grave general disturbances.

It has long been known that psychological factors play a considerable role in judging climacteric complaints. Whereas women with sound nerves generally suffer but little during this period, neurasthenic women are often seriously affected. It is also universally known and acknowledged that women in a simple environment with a regular occupation absorbing the whole of their time complain far less of difficulties during the climacteric, than women who have a great deal of leisure to worry about their health. The latter type of woman frequently overrates certain temporary complaints, about which she may have heard that it heralded the change of life.

Prominent among these complaints are the disturbances commonly known as flushing. But this complaint, which occurs with particular frequency during the climacteric, is not confined to that period. It has been established that it is, in particular, fat, short-necked women with palpable thyroid glands who complain a great deal about flushing during the climacteric period, whereas women with a small thyroid gland are at first less affected by this complaint. This observation points to the conclusion that the thyroid plays a part in the causation of this complaint.

The complaints associated with flushing have already been mentioned, and it has been pointed out that they often arise in connection with physical strain or agitation. In most cases the sudden flushing of the face, which is caused by a rush of blood to the head,

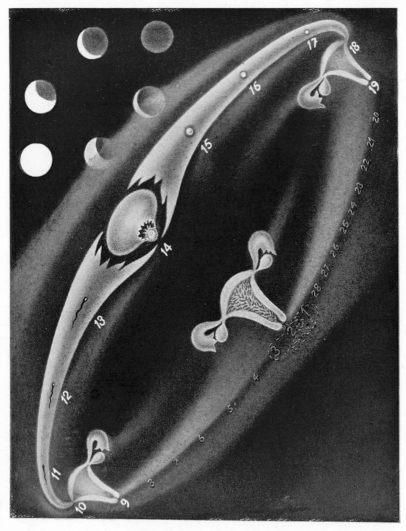

Fig. C-20—Pictorial representation of menstsrual cycle and woman's days of immunity from conception.

This illustration is according to Professor Ogino's theory that there are a total of 7 to 11 fertile days. However, this is incorrect, as proved by exact scientific tests carried out by Professor Knaus, according to whom the total number of days on which fecundation might take place is only five.

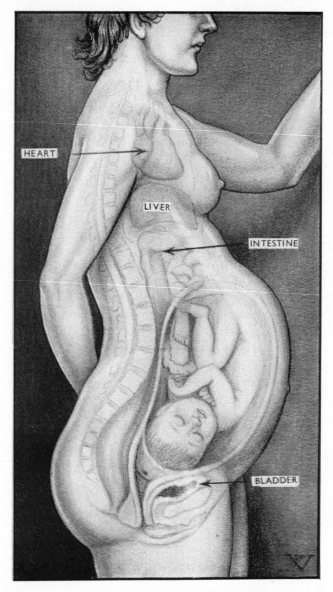

FIG. C-21—Picture of woman's body, transparently
revealing end of pregnancy.

Showing position of the child towards the end of pregnancy, as well as the displacement of the various
organs, like the intestine, liver, etc.

is accompanied by dizziness and followed by an outbreak of perspiration. However, sometimes there is also either a dryness in the mouth or an increased production of saliva. The rush of blood to the head can mostly be observed objectively, together with the subsequent pallor, though in some cases no change of color in the face can be discerned, only an outbreak of perspiration after the attack.

The outbreak of perspiration following upon an attack of flushing mostly affects the upper part of the body, and particularly the head. Perspiration appears over certain areas, such as the forehead, nose, lips and sometimes even the scalp. However, it sometimes happens that the perspiration appears on the back or over the abdomen, and cases have been observed where the subject perspired on one side only. At the same time the intensified secretion of perspiration may be observed not only in connection with attacks of flushing; there is a pronounced tendency to perspiration even apart from these attacks. Frequently, the entire body is affected, though mostly the perspiration is confined to the upper part of the body, and particularly to the upper extremities, the palms being often unpleasantly moist. However, even though outbreaks of perspiration are today regarded as a concomitant symptom of the climacteric period, it should be remembered that increased secretion of moisture may also be observed apart from the climacteric, in cases of goiter and the over-activity of the thyroid gland.

Flushing is very frequently accompanied by severe dizziness and imaginary ear noises. However, both these symptoms may appear without flushing. Where the dizziness appears as a concomitant of flushing it is caused by the sudden increase in the amount of blood, and often causes fear of a "stroke"; the attacks of dizziness detached from flushing mostly occur upon waking in the morning, and are frequently repeated during the day, generally when the subject is in a certain position, particularly bending down. This dizziness is either a "round-and-round" one, or it appears in the form of a sensation of uncertainty when walking, or in the form of the sensation that the ground is slipping from under the feet.

The head noises appearing now and then during the climacteric are among the most painful symptoms of this period, particularly as they frequently appear to defy treatment. In the great majority of cases the subject hears a buzzing, roaring noise, and sometimes a ringing noise, and these noises may come not only periodically, but also as a continuous, tormenting noise. During the night these phenomena usually become intensified, as they always do when there are no actual, external noises, and this condition frequently leads to insomnia and to severe nervous conditions. In many cases, particularly where the head noises appear from time to time by way of periodical attacks, they may be due to a local complaint. At all events, it is advisable to consult an ear specialist in all such cases, which are sometimes hereditary.

Sometimes, particularly during an attack of flushing, women complain that their eyes are "swimming." This may be accompanied by headache and nausea. The cause of this disturbance has long been known to be due to circulatory irregularities of central origin.

Women during the climacteric frequently complain of heart troubles. They complain of palpitations, which occur in the form of periodical attacks, independently from any physical effort, and sometimes at night. This may be accompanied by "stitches" in the region of the tip of the heart. Sometimes there is an acceleration of the pulse, or the pulse may miss a beat now and then during these attacks. The duration of these attacks is usually short, and they are followed by an interval of perfect well-being. We emphasize that these "heart attacks" have no connection with real heart trouble (angina pectoris). There is no doubt whatever that the common chatter about the inevitability of heart trouble during he climacteric and the reading of imperfectly understood medical works by women during that period, is the cause of many complaints of heart trouble. The pain at the tip of the heart so frequently complained of by women during the climacteric is usually absent in the case of genuine angina pectoris.

A frequent complaint during the climacteric period relates to inadequate intestinal activity. Women are particularly prone to constipation at all times, and this trouble may be aggravated during the climacteric. This is probably due partly to the increase of weight occurring during this period, but an alternation of normalcy and severe constipation is in some cases a striking feature. In cases where the sense of taste is affected and the nourishment taken is consequently inadequate, this may be regarded as a contributory cause.

Diarrhea during the climacteric period is very frequent. Sometimes this is accompanied by pains resembling colic, but there is no inflammation or irritation of the organs concerned. However, the diarrhetic stools may be associated with intestinal hemorrhages, and in all such cases, even during the climacteric, it is necessary to make sure whether the hemorrhage is not caused by some organic complaint, such as carcinoma. In nearly all cases of diarrhea at this time there is intensified intestinal activity, with loud rumbling noises in the abdomen, which occur particularly in women with weak abdominal integuments. The diarrhetic condition occurs in the form of periodical attacks, sometimes at regular monthly intervals. It is characterized by the fact that in the case of women with sound intestines it appears as the first sign of the climacteric. It is an obstinate condition and very difficult to influence in any way. This diarrhea was in former years regarded as a substitute for menstruation, and many authors have strenuously opposed any interference with it.

Wiesel also mentions cramp in the anus as a tormenting complaint of the climacteric which may occur with or without hemorrhoids.

Another complaint that sometimes occurs during the climacteric is an unpleasant urge to urinate. This may be due to an abnormally irritable bladder. This is a purely functional, nervous irregularity of the bladder, which may also be observed during menstruation before the climacteric, and to which neurasthenic individuals, in particular, are predisposed.

Perhaps the most frequent complaint during the climacteric period relates to insomnia, which is in many cases very serious and, in turn, may lead to further nervous complaints. Insomnia is frequently caused by the complaints already described, such as flushing, outbreaks of perspiration, pain in the joints, etc., but it may also be the consequence of sexual excitability, which is sometimes intensified during the climacteric. Another possible cause is the increased psychical sensibility that is characteristic of this period and may lead to depression, and even to a state of fear. Two different kinds of insomnia have been observed. Sleep is either interrupted by the complaints occurring in the form of periodical attacks, or it is delayed by many hours. The latter type of insomnia may be observed mainly in cases where the cause is excessive nervous irritation, which in turn may be called forth by the various complaints from which sensitive individuals suffer.

These are the principal and most painful subjective complaints from which women may suffer during this period of intensified sensitiveness and irritability. The objectively provable changes to which these complaints may be ascribed are frequently insignificant or even entirely absent. But even where objective changes can be established it is very difficult, and frequently impossible, to decide to what extent they can be causally related to the cessation of ovarial activity.

As already mentioned in dealing with the normal course of the climacteric, the objective changes are not uniform. Whereas many women during the climacteric period put on flesh, assuming the well-known "comfortable" appearance of the middle-aged woman, other women, on the contrary, lose flesh, and look lean and bony. The reason for this difference lies in differences of constitution, which in addition to physical appearance also determine in the various types differences in the complaints and other objectively provable phenomena of this period. This connection with the climacteric becomes comprehensible when we consider that the type of constitution is not determined by the generative apparatus alone, but also by the activity and varying influences of the germinal cells on the organism as a whole.

We have already mentioned that during the climacteric, even if it takes a normal course, temporary disturbance of the individual's nervous and emotional equilibrium is in most cases inevitable. This applies to a far greater extent where the climacteric takes a pathological course, and it is an undoubted fact that the psychical phenomena and the numerous physical troubles occurring at this time exercise a mutual influence upon each other. At all events, it is certain that in the case of neurotic individuals the intensified irritability of the central nervous system, characteristic of the climacteric period, leads to a considerable overrating of the troubles accompanying the climacteric, which in turn leads to increased sensitiveness and a sensation of pain in every part of the body. It is neurasthenic patients, women who in earlier years were also irritable, moody, sensitive and hypochondriacal, who suffer from the most serious complaints during the climacteric.

These psychical troubles, which manifest themselves by an intensified fluctuation of temper with a distinct inclination to depression, are frequently due to the fact of the cessation of sexuality alone. This realization may, in particular, produce a serious effect on childless women who have not created a sphere of activity for themselves, and were always sensuous. Especially does this apply when the individual concerned is in the erroneous belief that with the cessation of the menses the sexual life of a woman ceases altogether, in the same way as when castration or impotence in a man evokes a deep sense of inferiority and depression, which may often lead to suicide.

It may further be regarded as an established fact that the dangers and sufferings attendant upon the climacteric, as they are known to women from hearsay and from the reading of medical works, are bound to make a deep impression on neurasthenically inclined individuals, who overrate these troubles and thereby lose their mental equilibrium. In particular, the belief, widespread even among the many educated people, that the cessation of the discharge of menstrual blood leads to the accumulation of poisonous substances in the body, producing a variety of diseases in a woman's body, are apt to produce such depressive conditions. This depressed, anxious condition is accompanied by a general sensation of fatigue, lassitude, indecision, apathy, sluggish activity of the brain, and a deterioration of the memory. In addition, increased irritability, impatience, and restlessness may also appear.

We have now reached the conclusion of our description of the subjective and objective changes which may occur in the organism as a whole during the climacteric period where it takes a pathological course. As we have seen, there is a great variety of pheno-

mena at this time, and nearly every organ of the body may be affected. Thus this phase in the life of a woman may be beset with
difficulties.

However, it would be a grave error to assume on the basis of
the above descriptions that the period of the climacteric is always,
or even in the majority of cases, accompanied by such complaints.

On the contrary, since the cessation of ovarial activity represents
a normal, physiological process, it is correct to assume that the great
majority of women pass through the climacteric without trouble,
or that at any rate the troubles attendant upon the climacteric are
not in any way serious.

CHAPTER 55

SEXUAL INTERCOURSE DURING MENOPAUSE

IN the previous chapter we have dealt in some detail with the climacteric period both in its normal and in its pathological course. We will now discuss the delicate subject of sexual intercourse during this period. We consider this all the more necessary because married people, precisely because the subject is of such a delicate nature, are reluctant to raise it with their doctor. It must be remembered that a woman at this age generally has grown-up children, or may even be a mother-in-law or a grandmother, hence a frank discussion of the question of sexual intercourse is naturally painful both to her and her husband.

The situation is rendered all the more difficult by the fact that the sexual instinct of a woman, and her desire for sexual pleasure, become intensified prior to and during the climacteric, and even for a long time after the climacteric. As against the increased sexual desire of a woman at this time, there is the fact that the husband, who is usually a few years older than the woman, is in most cases less potent sexually than in former years, so that the temporarily intensely sensuous wife is faced by a scarcely potent husband, with possibly tragic results to conjugal harmony. The fact that this difficulty arises after decades of happy married life, renders the situation all the more tragic.

The statement that women during the climacteric period experience an intensification of sexual desire may strike the reader as paradoxical, since, as has been explained in the preceding chapters, the sexual life of women is governed by activity of the ovaries, and the climacteric consists in the diminution, and finally in the total cessation of ovarial activity, accompanied by a general degeneration, a "withering" of the entire genital apparatus. Thus, logically, this retrogression of the genital apparatus should involve a corresponding retrogression of the sexual instinct and sexual desire. What, then, is the explanation of this apparent contradiction?

In the first place, it should be remembered that—as already explained elsewhere in this book—the sexual instinct is composed of two factors, the physical and the psychological.

The physical component has already been explained. We have mentioned the itching of the genital organs, which is an almost universal phenomenon during the climacteric. Now, this itching alone would be sufficient to keep a woman's attention concentrated on her genital apparatus. The itching manifests itself in almost unbearable irritation and burning of the genitals, frequently accompanied with libidinous sensations, which may be so intense that unless relief can be obtained through conjugal intercourse, excessive masturbation may be resorted to. Dr. Magnus Hirschfeld in his *Sexual Pathology* records the cases of women who were driven to nymphomania as a result of this tormenting irritation.

We have also discussed the relaxation of the tissues and the consequent congestion of the genital apparatus. This is further aggravated by the various swellings, and the possible displacement of the uterus which, by causing congestion in the pelvis, may stimulate the genital apparatus.

It will be seen, therefore, that the climacteric must produce an eroticizing effect even when it takes a normal course, and if, in addition, we take into account the psychological component, the causes of a woman's intensified sexual excitability during the climacteric will become clear.

Everyone possessing the least knowledge of feminine psychology is aware that physical beauty plays a considerable role in the psychical life of a woman. Now, with the climacteric comes the realization that she must lose her physical attractiveness, and that age is creeping on. Fear of the passing of her own sexual desirability, and even of her own desires, therefore becomes a characteristic feature of her thoughts and outlook—and the reaction may assume a very grave form. The sudden mania during the climacteric period of some women, even when they have a number of grown-up children, to be youthful in dress and appearance, is nothing but a conscious or unconscious manifestation of the struggle against the extinction of sexuality, against the "dangerous age." And the danger lies in the fact that a woman at this time may forget everything that she previously regarded as sacred, merely in order to delay the time of final renunciation.

Unfortunately, there are many cases of women during the climacteric period going to ridiculous or dangerous excesses, which bring them into conflict with their husbands and society. Such acts may wreck their marriage and make them impossible socially. The desire for satisfaction of the sexual impulses sometimes appears with such vehemence that even morally disposed individuals may be incapable of resistance. It happens again and again that women during the climacteric cause amazement and consternation in their own circle by the manner in which they forget or throw away everything, sacrificing not only money but also love and friendship in order to obtain one more passionate experience. Such women generally choose young men, sometimes even mere boys, as their partners for this funereal dance of their love life. Very frequently this is accompanied by a critical attitude towards their previous married life, regret over a "wasted life," which leads to mental restlessness.

The love of an ageing woman desperately clinging to her departing youth, who flouts social convention in order to experience one final adventure with an immature youth, has been the subject of many novels.

One of the best known of these novels is *The Dangerous Age,* by the Danish authoress, Karin Michaelis. It deals with the love of an ageing woman who sacrifices everything in order to secure the love of a youth of twenty.

Naturally, it would be a grave error to regard the process outlined here as the general rule. It is, for instance, obvious that a married woman with a number of children, who is burdened with their care and education, in addition to her tasks as a housewife, or a woman actively engaged in work or a profession, will not be carried away as easily as a woman without any definite sphere of activity, whose mind has always been filled with thoughts of amusement, luxury, fashion and constant preoccupation with her own body.

In contrast with the cases indicated above, the majority of women, after a happy married and family life, pass through the climacteric without serious inner conflicts. And once the period of the climacteric has been safely passed, and a woman has had time to resign herself to the inevitable, there follows a state of well-being, of peace and cheerfulness. In some cases it is precisely at this stage that a real friendship and camaraderie develops between husband and wife—and sexual relations are not precluded even until late into the sixties. Then, with the appearance of old age, all sexual desire passes.

In conclusion, we must deal with the question whether sexual intercourse during the climacteric period can be injurious to the health of a woman. The answer is that, as a rule, and despite intensified desire on the part of the woman, sexual intercourse in moderation at this time may not be injurious. In this connection it should be remembered that the internal sexual organs during the climacteric are relaxed, and are therefore less resistant than formerly to injury. The husband must therefore exercise extreme care during sexual intercourse. If, however, despite every precaution sexual intercourse should nevertheless produce an injury or a flow of blood from the genital apparatus, then it must be completely eliminated. In such cases greater tenderness on the part of the husband may to some extent replace sexual intercourse, and help the woman over the difficult period of the climacteric.

BOOK VI

Diseases—Alcoholism—Sterility

CHAPTER 56

NOCTURNAL EMISSIONS AND LOSS OF SEMEN

NOCTURNAL emissions (pollutions) are involuntary emissions of semen during sleep. There are two forms of pollutions, the physiological or normal, and the pathological.

The normal form occurs in healthy persons and is caused by an excess of seminal fluid. It is observed mostly in men who are either easily excitable or lead abstemious lives, and also in full-blooded men who regularly overfeed, while at the same time avoiding physical exercise. In such cases the loss of semen is a natural reaction of the organism, a normally accumulated surplus of semen being ejected, mostly during a nocturnal dream, in the absence of discharge through sexual intercourse. Thus nocturnal pollutions in such circumstances are not harmful. The frequency of their occurence depends entirely on the individual circumstances. Normally they occur at intervals of several days, or even weeks.

It is only when the pollutions occur too frequently that they are of a pathological nature, and not due to an excessive accumulation of seminal fluid. In such cases the pollutions are caused either by a diseased condition of the genital apparatus, or by a conscious or subconscious nervous erotic sur-excitation. During sleep the subject has erotic dreams with visions of voluptuousness, which find release in a discharge of semen.

It is important to know what erotic dreams mainly come to persons who during the day too frequently think erotic thoughts or nurse erotic desires, for it is only natural that these thoughts should be reflected in the subject's dreams. At all events, it is certain that nocturnal discharges of semen may be due either to organic or psychological causes. Thus, when there is a combination of the two, i.e., when a man has erotic dreams at a time when his germinal glands are full of semen, a nocturnal discharge is bound to result. Pollutions are only pathological when they are caused solely by an unhealthy sur-excited imagination, without a super-abundance of semen in the glands. In this connection it is thought that sensuous thoughts which lead to erection during the day intensify the production of semen, so that erotic thoughts and desires may indirectly lead to nocturnal pollutions. It is clear that in cases where frequent sexual excitement during the waking hours is not followed by sexual intercourse, the discharge of the accumulated semen must occur during sleep. Thus enforced sexual abstemiousness may easily cause pollutions.

Now, if the discharge of semen is normal and due to physiological causes, then the voluptuous sensation the subject experiences during his dream is also quite normal, and may be just as intense as during sexual intercourse in the waking state. Erection is also complete both before and during the discharge, as may be observed by any man who—as is normally the case—wakes up immediately after the ejaculation. But if erection during ejaculation is inadequate, or if the subject does not wake up after it, that may be suspected as a sure sign of functional trouble in the genital apparatus. In such cases the pollutions are of a pathological nature, and the voluptuous sensation is also less pronounced than in normal cases.

The organic causes are frequently represented by distensions or inflammations of the seminal tubules and the urethra, or by overstrain of the prostate.

However, sur-excitation of the nerve centers through erotic fancies also enter into the causation of the complaint. All abnormal sexual practices, such as interruption of coitus shortly before ejaculation, and also excessive masturbation, inevitably lead, sooner or later, to psychological damage which finds expression in irregularities of the genital organs, and may result in pathological pollutions.

Masturbation itself is not, as was formerly believed, organically injurious, and its harmfulness lies mainly in its phychological effects. These effects are produced by fears concerning the disastrous consequences of masturbation, which are further aggravated by the sense of guilt associated with this practice. In addition, there is a lack of psychological satisfaction, a deficiency that is bound to affect emotional life.

Treatment of Pathological Emission (Pollution). In view of the fact that this complaint frequently leads to serious psychological disturbances, it is advisable to consult a specialist. If the pathological character of the pollutions is not pronounced, it is not difficult to eliminate them, and in most cases a radical change in the patient's mode of life is sufficient.

It is advisable, during the period of treatment, to live on a preponderantly vegetarian diet rich in vitamins and nutritive salts. Stimulating foods should be avoided. Thus game, fish, eggs, cheese, mushrooms, as well as alcohol, must be eliminated from the diet, and milk and coffee must be taken in moderate quantities only. On the other hand, wholewheat bread, potatoes, vegetables, salads, fruit, etc., are very beneficial, as such a diet also eliminates possible constipation. Normally, evacuation should occur in the morning and evening. Excreta retained in the rectum exercise pressure on the prostate, and may thereby cause pollutions.

A regime suitable for the purpose would produce the following results:

1. Prevent the production of excessive amounts of seminal fluid, thereby giving the germinal glands a rest.

2. Eliminate the harmful effect of unnatural stimulating foods.

3. Prevent the accumulation of excreta in the rectum.

4. Prevent the accumulation of blood in the abdomen and in the genital organs.

All these dietetic measures must be linked with a careful sexual hygiene. In addition, it is useful to sleep only as long as is absolutely necessary, and preferably on a hard mattress. It is advisable to avoid taking fluids before bedtime and to empty the bladder several times during the night, as a full bladder during the night usually leads to erections. Regular exercises will also prove to be beneficial and will hasten a cure.

At the same time, however, a radical change in the patient's psychological attitude is also indispensable. Only then will it be possible to regulate the sexual impulses and fantasies in a normal manner. All the impressions, fancies and desires which are conveyed to the brain through the eyes, ears or the senses of smell and touch, produce certain effects in the central nervous system that may not always manifest themselves immediately. Erotic ideas that take root in the subconscious mind, accumulate there, only to reappear later, sometimes in very peculiar forms, as when waking impressions return with greater intensity during sleep.

But if the requirements outlined above with regard to a change of the mode of life and the psychological attitude are carried out, then the patient's health will gradually be re-established, as a reward for his purposeful effort of will.

The basic causes of loss of semen, which almost invariably occurs during the day, are the same as those of nocturnal pollutions. Nevertheless, there is a fundamental difference between the two complaints. Loss of semen is even more unnatural than nocturnal pollution, because an erotic thought or a slight touch or friction of the genital organs is sufficient to bring it about, and it may even occur without any evident cause.

In some patients the semen flows out slowly, and is not ejected or ejaculated. Frequently, the loss of semen occurs during evacuation of the bowels, owing to the pressure on the prostate, or immediately after urinating. At first the loss of semen is usually slight, but increases in time.

Whereas loss of semen accompanied by chronic constipation may sometimes be cured by curing the constipation, a cure becomes difficult where the complaint is chronic or where it appears in connection with urination. In such cases a doctor must be consulted, as there are diseases of the urethra that produce similar phenomena.

Treatment. The measures recommended for nocturnal pollutions should also be applied here. As this complaint is sometimes very obstinate, the patient must not be discouraged by initial failures into stopping the treatment. Patience and doggedness in the application of the treatment play a decisive role here.

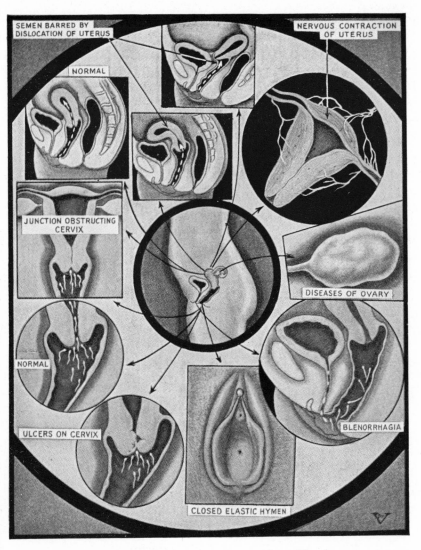

FIG. C-22—11 pictures revealing causes of sterility in women.

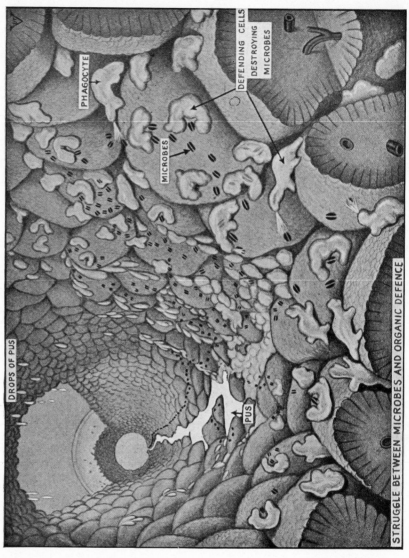

FIG. C-23—How woman's sex organs fight venereal disease.
Schematic illustration showing invasion of the gonococci (microbes of
gonorrhea) opposed by the defending cells in the urethra. The dead
bodies of the latter, together with those of the microbes, compose the
mucus that is discharged through the urinary meatus. If the defense
is good, the microbes are conquered, and formation of mucus ceases,
i.e., the gonorrhea is cured.

CHAPTER 57

Diseases of the Female Genital Organs

Inflammation of the Vagina (Colpitis)

This may be either acute or chronic. There are various causes, including masturbation, parasites in the rectum, pessaries, etc. However, it may also be caused by infection (gonorrhea), anemia and general debility. Chronic vaginal inflammation sometimes arises in consequence of an inflammation of the uterus. Infection with a parasitic organism, called the Trichomonas, is often a persistent cause of irritating vaginal inflammation. Another cause of vaginal inflammation is infection with a yeast-like organism called Monilia. The diagnosis and treatment of these conditions is best managed by a gynecologist.

Symptoms.—More or less considerable white flux, at first itching of the skin and a sensation of pressure, and later, pain in the region of the rectum, local rise of temperature, irritation and swelling of mucous membrane. In the chronic stage the mucous membrane shows a tendency to harden, while the acute symptoms become less pronounced.

Inflammation of the Uterus (Endometritis)

Inflammation of the uterus may arise from many causes. Gonorrhea, tuberculosis, syphilis, anemia, and probably most often abortions and infections before and after child-birth. Inflammation of the uterus may also be a complication of scarlet fever and measles or a consequence of operations (as for uteral ulcers, etc.).

However, the causes are not always evident, and inflammations of this type may occur in a healthy organism. For instance, the regu-

401

lar practice of coitus interruptus prevents the proper abatement of the excitement of the genital nerves, and an irritation is left behind which causes the uteral blood supply to circulate in a jerky manner. It is easy to understand that such irregularity may cause inflammation.

Symptoms.—Irregularities in menstruation, white flux or suppuration, bleeding outside the period, a feeling of pain, pressure or fullness in the abdomen, backache, nausea, and general nervous symptoms. During the acute stage the symptoms are very frequently accompanied by a rise of temperature; the uterus is swollen and extremely sensitive. The chronic forms are less pronounced. The symptoms are the same as in the acute form, but considerably toned down.

DISPLACEMENT OF THE UTERUS

The uterus is normally kept in position by strong ligaments between the bladder and the rectum. But there are irregularities which consist in an alteration of the position of this organ, resulting in various pathological symptoms.

The uterus may bend forwards or backwards, or it may drop, but these displacements frequently occur in various combinations. If the sinking of the uterus is so serious that the uterus penetrates into the vagina, we speak of a prolapse of the uterus.

The causes of the displacement of the uterus are either hereditary or acquired. Displacements of the uterus may be caused, in particular, by chronic constipation, inflammation of the uterus, oviducts or ovaries, ulcers of the uterus or the adjacent organs, as well as by the scars of former ulcers. The wearing of corsets that are too tight may also be a contributory factor. Inexpertly attended deliveries (child-birth), or even several normal deliveries, are a common cause of prolapse of the uterus, usually associated with more or less prolapse of the bladder and rectum at the same time.

Symptoms.—There are a large number of symptoms, including pain, bleeding, white flux, discharges of blood during pregnancy, abortions, sterility through the barring (bending) of the oviducts, a sensation of pressure in the region of the bladder and rectum,

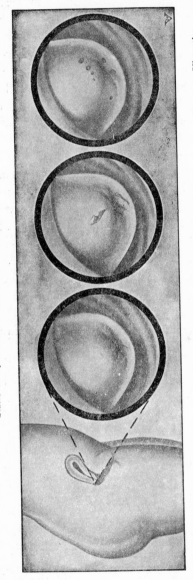

States of injured uterus and the female figure transparent.

FIG. 139—Uterus and vagina.   FIG. 140—Mouth of uterus; normal.   FIG. 141—Very slight ulceration.   FIG. 142—Ulceration.

constipation, pain during sexual intercourse, difficulty in urination, nervous troubles, fainting fits, vomiting and hysteria, all of which occur with varying intensity, according to the seriousness of the displacement. Frequently there are no symptoms.

Ulcers at the mouth of the uterus mostly appear as a complication of inflammation, unless there has been an external infection. Irritation owing to intense excitation, mechanical irritation through impact or through the wearing of pessaries may also produce such ulcers. The symptoms are similar to those of inflammation of the uterus, but are usually less pronounced.

Tumors in the uterus generally occur after the age of 25-30.

Symptoms.—Irregular discharges of blood are characteristic of this condition. The discharges may occur either after menstruation, or at other times. If the tumors are large, then there is sometimes a flux, and also a sensation of pressure in the region of the rectum and bladder. This painful sensation may radiate upwards and affect the large ischium nerve, in which case walking involves considerable pain. Sometimes the tumors, in a purely mechanical manner, lead to congestions, which may easily produce swellings and varicose veins on the legs. At the least suspicion of a tumor a specialist must be consulted, as early treatment may prevent the development of cancer.

Inflammation of the Oviducts

The causes of inflammation in one or both of the oviducts are essentially the same as inflammation of the mouth of the uterus. This condition may be either acute or chronic. Untreated gonorrheal infection is often a cause.

Symptoms.—In the acute stage the oviduct concerned is swollen. It produces a secretion which is discharged through the uterus. Local pains in the abdomen, fever, headaches and irregularities in menstruation, are further symptoms. The chronic form may develop from an imperfectly cured acute case, but it may also arise without any previous acute stage. If the treatment of this condition is unsuccessful, then the oviduct may become narrower, and may even be closed altogether, in which case the woman concerned naturally

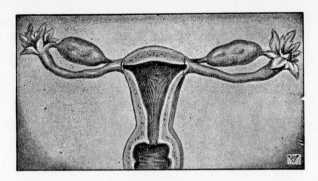

FIG. 143—Normal uterus, ovaries and oviducts.

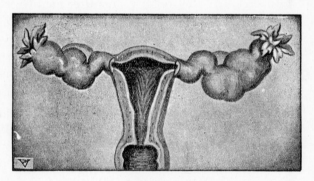

FIG. 144—Inflammation of both oviducts.

becomes sterile. The symptoms of the chronic form are similar to those of the acute form, but less pronounced. Sometimes a flux, abdominal pain, and menstrual irregularities may be observed.

INFLAMMATION OF THE OVARIES

Inflammation of the oviducts may spread and reach the ovaries. Resistance of the tissues is reduced by the entry of bacilli.

Symptoms.—In the acute form there are abdominal pains, a disturbance of the general health and temperature. The pain may radiate as far as the thighs, but it is usually more intense in the region of the anus and the rectum. Menstruation is also painful, and frequently lasts several days longer than normal. If the acute inflammation is not treated in time it may develop into chronic inflammation. The latter form is less painful, and the symptoms less pronounced. Painful menstruation is in most cases the only symptom, but it may lead to the shrinkage of the ovaries and consequent sterility. Infections of the tubes and ovaries produce very similar symptoms, and usually occur together. A common consequence is the production of painful adhesions. Surgical removal of all or part of these organs is often necessary for relief of symptoms, particularly in long unattended or recurrent flare-up of the inflammatory process.

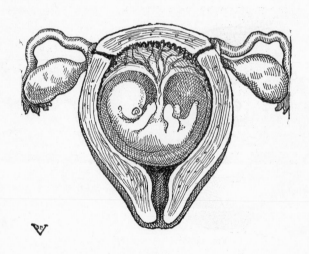

FIG. 145—Normal foetus in uterus.

We have already mentioned the important influence of the endocrine secretions and their action on the nervous system. This explains the nervous disturbances, headaches, restlessness, moodiness and hysterical phenomena that sometime accompany the chronic form of ovarial inflammation. In order to prevent its development, it is of great importance to take the acute form in hand immediately, as chronic ovarial inflammation may make the life of the patient one of constant misery.

Extra-Uterine Pregnancy (Ectopic Pregnancy)

Cases in which pregnancy occurs outside the uterus are quite rare. They are usually due to narrowness of the oviducts, which prevents the progress of the ovum towards the uterus, but nevertheless enables the spermatozoa to reach the abdominal cavity, where fertilization and subsequent development of the embryo take place. These pathological anatomical irregularities may be congenital, but are frequently acquired through such diseases as inflammation of the oviducts or ovaries.

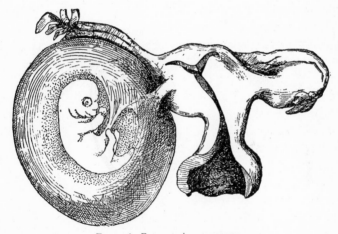

Fig. 146—Extra-uterine pregnancy.

Common or Non-infectious White Flux (Fluor Albus or Leukorrhea)

The fact that few women have escaped this minor trouble suggests that white flux is a consequence of our "civilization." This complaint reflects an unnatural mode of life.

We are of the opinion that complete health is impossible without a strictly hygienic mode of life, and the correctness of this view is confirmed by wild animal life. Animals have no complaints of this kind, otherwise such phenomena would have been observed long ago. In the case of wild animals, Nature is relied upon both for nourishment and protection, and if disease is nevertheless wholly, or almost wholly, avoided, that shows the perfection of Nature. From that fact we must conclude that Nature has not implanted disease in us, and that it is only a consequence of our infringements of her laws.

The glands of a healthy cervix and vulva produce secretions all the time, but in such minute quantities that they are not noticed. But during or as a result of weakening general illness, or in the case of obstinate constipation, pathological changes frequently occur in the lower genital tract, and this is manifested through intensified activity of the glands and an increased production of secretions, which appear in the form of a flux. We know that the vagina is permanently inhabited by certain harmless bacteria. This settlement of bacteria may undergo certain changes for various reasons. Their condition in most cases depends on a rational and natural diet, apart from cases of acute illness. Thus the presence of bacteria in the vagina is ordained by Nature, both as regards kind and quantity. It is only through the damaging of the mucous membrane of the vagina and the adjacent organs by the poisoning of the juices of the body—particularly through acidity—that a pathological change can occur in the bacteria. In that case the normal settlement of bacteria may easily be suppressed by invading bacteria, such as streptococci. Trichomonas and Monilia infections have been mentioned previously. The cause and proper treatment of most vaginal discharges and infections can be promptly managed in short order by the gynecologist. Self-treatment with unprescribed preparations can lead to more serious troubles.

CHAPTER 58

DISEASES OF THE PROSTATE

Acute Inflammation of the Prostate. The prostate is approximately the size of a chestnut. It encloses the urethra, and is situated at the outlet of the bladder. Its secretion plays an important role during the sexual act, in that it exercises a favorable influence on the chemical conditions of the semen.

Acute inflammation of the prostate is in most cases the consequences of neglected gonorrhea, or urethral inflammation of a different character. There is a sensation of heaviness in the region of the rectum. There is pain, which may radiate right down into the calves. Owing to the pressure of the prostate on the urethra, difficulties may arise in connection with urination. When emptying the bowels the sensation of pressure and pain is intensified, and there may be a discharge of prostatic fluid from the urinary passage.

Treatment.—A doctor must be consulted, in order to discover the cause of the inflammation and to carry out or prescribe the proper treatment.

Chronic Inflammation of the Prostate. The causes are varied. In some cases there is an acute inflammation which is not amenable to treatment. In others, it may be induced by repeated infections with gonorrhea. In very rare instances it may be the result of sexual overstrain. Abuse of alcohol, premature impairment of potency, the regular practice of coitus interruptus, may all produce a predisposition for prostatic disease.

In contrast with acute inflammation, the symptoms are not so pronounced in the case of chronic inflammation. There is a slight sensation of pressure in the region of the anus and in the rectum. There may also be pain from time to time. After urination there may be a sensation of burning in the urethra. However, the principal symptom of the disease is a drop of whitish fluid that can be squeezed out of the urinary meatus in the morning, or becomes noticeable when emptying the bowels. This secretion has the typical odor of semen, which, as we know, is given to the semen by the secretion of the prostate. The drop may become viscous and form a sort of stopper. Sometimes the secretion may be yellowish, with the odor of semen. If there is pain in the urethra during urination in the morning, this is frequently a sign that the inflammation of the prostate is due to gonorrhea.

Potency may diminish, as well as the sexual urge. Owing to the disease, ejaculation becomes difficult and the voluptuous sensation whose center is the part of the urethra that pierces the prostate, is absent. In severe cases the mucous secretion may be mixed with a few drops of blood originating from the prostate itself, or from the diseased parts of the urethra. In some cases a severe swelling of the glands may close the urinary passage.

The organic symptoms mentioned above cause more or less severe depression in some patients. This arises from the fear that potency may be prematurely lost, or that the disease may get worse. However, there is no reason for such fear, as the complaint can be considerably influenced by means of the proper treatment.

Treatment.—A thorough examination by a specialist, in order to devise the treatment according to the cause of the disease. A suitable diet will assist the treatment. Meat, fish and spices should be completely avoided, and replaced by fruit, vegetables and salads. Warm abdominal baths (twice daily) are strongly recommended. Sexual intercourse should be restricted as far as possible. If the treatment is begun early, and carried out correctly, a cure can be effected in most cases.

Enlargement of the Prostate. (Hypertrophy). This is a disease of middle or advanced old age. According to the appearance of the symptoms, it may be divided into three stages.

At first there is an increased urge to urinate, so that the patient must strain himself in order to empty the bladder. If the enlargement of the prostate continues, then complete relief of the bladder becomes impossible. This is the second phase of the disease. In the third phase urination is still more difficult, and urine is only discharged involuntarily and in drops. The urine, owing to the blocking of the urethra, is retained in the bladder, which leads to an enlargement of that organ.

Treatment.—Some experts hold that the enlargement of the prostate can only be dealt with by operative means, or by irradiation. We are more optimistic, and believe that a consistently observed natural treatment may improve the condition sufficiently.

The chances of a cure are all the better, the earlier the treatment is started. It is in the initial stages, when the disease is not yet really troublesome, that it must be taken in hand. If the disease has progressed so far that the urethra is partly blocked, and the bladder must be relieved daily by means of a catheter, then an operation cannot be avoided. In addition, the frequent introduction of the catheter may cause a slight infection of the bladder, which may further aggravate the disease.

In conclusion, we would particularly point out that the difficult urination entailed by enlargement of the prostate must not be confused with the complaint which often arises some decades after an infection with gonorrhea. In the latter case the impediment to urination is caused by scars in the urethra. To avoid any erroneous treatment, the diagnosis and advice of a specialist should first be obtained.

CHAPTER 59

Alcohol and Sexual Potency

It would be futile to investigate the effect of alcoholic beverages on sexual life without first deciding the larger question as to the influence of alcohol on health in general, since, evidently, the proper functioning of the genital apparatus depends on the condition of the rest of the organism.

But first of all, we must settle the problem whether alcohol is a food or a poison, whether it should be included in a rational diet, or completely eliminated. This problem has been, and still is, hotly disputed. However, the controversy is largely due to an initial error. For whereas the theoretical advocates of alcohol only recommend wine and beer, and these only in very moderate amounts, the advocates of temperance condemn all beverages containing alcohol, and make no distinction between wine, spirits, liqueurs, apertifs, etc., so that the two camps are not debating on the same ground; the former are far from advocating what the latter so fiercely oppose.

Taking a sane view of the question, a distinction must be drawn between wine and fermented beverages on the one hand, and spirits, whose effect is far more violent, on the other. Wine and beer taken in moderate amounts cannot cause serious harm, whereas the habitual consumption of spirits, i.e., alcoholism proper, frequently leads to all kinds of physical and moral troubles, and, at worst, to the dreaded delirium tremens.

There remains to be decided where moderation ends and abuse begins. However, that is an entirely individual question, since what is moderation in one case may be excess in another. There are people in whom a small glass of wine causes giddiness and a feeling of malaise; it is in this manner that the organism issues its warning against that which is harmful to it. On the other hand, there are those who thrive wonderfully well and live long, though they take a glass of wine, or more, at each meal. The permissible dose depends not only on the individual's constitution, but also on the climate and on his mode of life. Thus a manual worker may absorb without harm far larger doses than an intellectual worker leading a sedentary life. Naturally, alcoholic beverages are less potent when diluted, so that in determining the dose, strength as well as quantity counts.

All these factors render the suggested rules as to the permissible amount of alcohol, such as that a person may take one-sixth of an ounce of alcohol for every pound of his weight, rather illusory.

This brings us to the question: Does the moderate use of alcohol, i.e., in a manner that does not affect the general health, produce any particular influence on sexual life? The answer is decidedly in the affirmative. Alcohol stimulates the entire nervous system, and it is undeniable that it produces a slight excitement which partly manifests itself in the temporary intensification of the sexual appetite. Needless to say, it is not necessary to become actually intoxicated in order to rouse the body to erotic desire. Married couples who use wine moderately, are bound to find that a little alcohol may liven up conjugal relations. Certain women of antiquity are said to have deliberately employed this innocent means, as well as slightly aphrodisiacal foods, when they found that their husbands were "not up to the mark," and it is not at all improbable that they have many imitators in modern times.

Naturally, the dividing line that exists between the elation produced by a glass of good wine and actual intoxication is easily overstepped. And the degree of intoxication that manifests itself in a sense of blissful gaiety, an optimistic outlook and an immense self-confidence, may be changed to a state of hopeless inebriation by a few more ounces of drink. In that condition the subject loses control of himself, his moral sense becomes completely blunted, his frenzied imagination conjures up extravagant erotic images, and he may be led to acts which would cause him to burn with shame in his sober state.

The high percentage of crimes committed in a drunken state is outside the scope of the present work. What we are concerned with here is the fact that sexual excesses under the influence of alcohol are very frequent. The orgies of the Dionysian feasts in Greece and of the bacchanalia in Rome, are classic examples. In all ages alcohol has been the most faithful ally of adultery. King Solomon summed up the effects of drunkenness in one sentence: "Thine eyes will look at strange women, and thy heart will speak in a confused manner."

Men and women of absolutely normal sexual morality may, under the effect of drink, discover in themselves undreamed of erotic tendencies. Is not there an element of sadism in the conduct of drunkards towards their wives or sweethearts, whom they beat unmercifully when in that condition? Every criminologist knows that in a considerable proportion of cases the crime of incest is committed under the influence of drink. As regards what is described in the newspapers as "certain offenses," these are nearly always committed, in public, by drunken men.

Naturally, however, what might be described as accidental drunkenness is from the sexual point of view far less disastrous than chronic alcoholism. The sexual crimes committed by these two categories differ very considerably. Among other things, it has been noted that whereas rape of adult women is frequently due to an "accidental" drunkard, rape of children is a crime peculiar to dypsomaniacs. In other words, whereas in the first case drink only intensifies to unreasoning frenzy a fundamentally normal sexual impulse, in the second it deflects the normal urge and imposes upon it the character of senile dementia. For the rest, it has been scientifically established that in about half the cases of infantile rape, the victims are the criminals' own children.

However, the sexual aberrations of chronic alcoholics are generally not of long duration. For if, up to a point, alcohol acts as a stimulant, in the end it proves to be a dangerous narcotic that paralyzes all the sensations, and particularly the sexual impulse, in that it causes a veritable torpor in the genital apparatus. It is well known that drink stimulates amorous enterprise, but lames the power of satisfaction. Many scientists have found that the genital tissues are particularly susceptible to the effects of alcohol and soon become atrophied, once they become saturated with this poison. Long before the grave effects of alcohol manifest themselves, a still young and healthy-looking drunkard may already be affected by a disease of the testicles that renders him impotent. Van de Velde writes in this connection:

"Alcoholism causes incurable lesions in the testicles, which ultimately prevent the production of spermatozoa. The spermatic cells

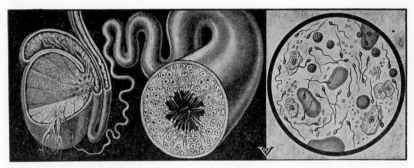

Fig. 147—Normal testicle, shown in section in order to show interior. A very considerably enlarged seminiferous tubule to show the manner in which the spermatozoa are born.

Fig. 148—Normal semen under the microscope, showing numerous healthy spermatozoa.

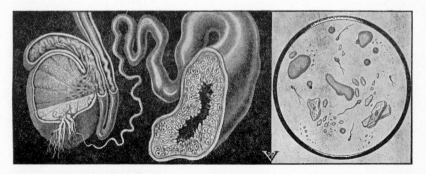

Fig. 149—Degenerated testicle of a habitual drunkard. The seminiferous tubule, similarly degenerated, produces hardly any spermatozoa.

Fig. 150—Semen under the microscope; there are few spermatozoa, and those are defective, so that such a man would produce degenerate offspring.

change under the effect of alcohol, and the spermatozoa progressively diminish, and finally disappear altogether, so that many dypso-maniacs, if not suffering from impotentia coeundi, suffer from impotentia generandi, or sterility."

In the case of women, the ravages of alcohol are no less serious from the sexual point of view. It causes menstrual irregularities, a disposition to abortion, internal hemorrhages, and other similar accidents. There is also a connection, though an indirect one, between alcohol and venereal disease. As Forel, the great sexologist, wrote, alcohol promotes the spread of venereal disease by leading to thoughtless intercourse.

Nature in her wisdom deprives the drunkard of the power of reproduction because, as we shall see in the following chapter, he hands on a terrible legacy to his descendants. Unfortunately, Nature does not always take this precaution in time, and many dypso-maniacs bring children into the world who bear the tragic stigma of their parents' vice all their lives.

CHAPTER 60

ALCOHOLISM AND HEREDITY

"Corrupta sunt semina ebriosorum"—the seed of drunkards is corrupt. This Latin saying shows that the danger of the transmission of a terrible legacy by drunkards to their descendants was well known in antiquity. But there are many other references to the subject in Greek and Roman literature. Thus Diogenes one day said to a debauched young man, "So your parents were drunk when they conceived you?" Which shows that the great Greek philosopher regarded drunken parents as the prime cause of degeneracy.

The legislation of the ancients also provided against the danger represented by the procreating activity of drunken people, and Lycurgus, for instance, introduced a law in Sparta, where physical perfection was cultivated more than anywhere else, forbidding married couples to have sexual intercourse when in a state of inebriation. In Carthage, the consumption of wine was prohibited on the days of conjugal cohabitation. Many centuries later the same idea appeared in literature, as for instance in the works of Molière, the great French dramatist.

Today, when science disposes of exact means of verification, the view of the ancients has been strikingly confirmed. It has been proved by means of laboratory experiments that the spermatozoa of inveterate drunkards, even when they are still fertile, are literally poisoned, and cannot possibly evolve into a sane and normal being. That the descendants of chronic alcoholists are degenerate, has been placed beyond doubt by certain experiments carried out by French scientists on dogs. The dogs, which animals are least affected by alcoholic intoxication, were given considerable doses of alcohol until a state of chronic intoxication was produced. The very few bitches which remained fertile under this treatment gave birth to puppies that were so weak that they soon perished. When the "alcoholization" of the dogs ceased to be chronic, but was still maintained by means of occasional doses, the bitches became less sterile, but 75 percent of their puppies died soon after birth, while the rest were weak and sickly. Finally, when the administration of alcohol was stopped altogether, the puppies that were born afterwards were somewhat stronger, but they still bore traces of their parents' earlier alcoholism, and mortality among them was higher than among normal dogs.

Other scientists have produced in dogs physical defects, such as club-foot, atrophy of the toes, and general debility, by "alcoholizing" the parents, and these defects returned even after several generations.

It will be noted that the hereditary defects due to alcoholism are transmitted mainly by the mother. The foetus of women alcoholists already bears the indelible impress of degeneracy. It frequently happens that pregnancy is interrupted, i.e., an abortion takes place, because the foetus is not strong enough to last to the end. Among the children of such mothers who do come into the world, the mortality rate is extremely high, due, in many cases, to causes connected with nursing, for the milk of an alcoholic mother is itself poisoned. Thus where alcoholism among women is rife, artificial nursing is far more successful than natural lactation.

Those who are accustomed to deal with infants and young children, have no difficulty in recognizing which child has drunken parents. Malformations of the skull, squinting, debility and an appearance of age, are all eloquent signs.

The malformations of the body of a child conceived by its parents in a state of inebriation, may be so serious that the child may be regarded as a monster. In mythology we see a drunken Jupiter caressing Juno, who soon afterwards gives birth to a monster. According to certain authors, if there are in one and the same family normal and abnormal children, it is correct to assume that the latter were conceived when the parents were in a state of inebriation. Thus a temporary drunkenness is sufficient to produce defective children, and this happens not only when the parents are inveterate drunkards. It would take us too far to enumerate all the anomalies and diseases that may affect the descendants of drunkards, and we will only mention a few of the most frequent symptoms. These include hydrocephaly ("water on the brain") in infancy, and nervous troubles, perhaps even epilepsy, later; also considerable mental debility, and incapacity to support alcohol, associated with an irresistible desire for it.

At the end of the eighteenth century, Erasmus Darwin, father of Charles Darwin, formulated a theory according to which the hereditary defects arising from alcoholism are transmitted down to the fourth generation, unless the intervening generations rigidly abstain from alcohol.

More recently, Professor Morel, in his essay, "Physical, Intellectual and Moral Degeneracy of the Human Race," established the following table on alcoholic heredity:

1st generation.—Immorality, excesses, depravity, brutality.

2nd generation.—Hereditary drunkenness, fits, manias, general paralysis.

3rd generation.—Sobriety, tendency to hypochondria, persecution mania, homicidal tendencies.

4th generation.—Under-developed intelligence, stupidity, transition to idiocy, and finally, probable extinction of the line.

Another author found that the descendants of drunken parents suffer from a peculiar nervousness, an early desire for stimulants, a strange character and, in early childhood, from convulsions and the frequent incidence of tuburcular meningitis. Further, it is generally known that alcoholism leads to degeneracy of the race, the children of drunkards being stunted, with badly developed chests and an inclination for tuberculosis.

A great many family histories of dypsomaniacs have been compiled, of which we mention one, the data of which have been collected by a professor at the University of Bonn. The subject, a woman named Adda Jurcke, was born in 1840 and died at the beginning of the present century. She had a total of 834 descendants.

Of her children, grandchildren and great-grandchildren, 106 were born illegitimately, 142 were beggars, 64 inmates of workhouses; 181 of the girls became prostitutes; 79 were sentenced for various crimes, including seven for murders.

Unfortunately the historian of Adda Jurcke's family confines himself to the social aspect of the matter, and fails to mention the physical defects of the family, though it does not require a particularly powerful imagination to guess how terrible they must have been.

Alcoholism is indeed one of the greatest evils.

CHAPTER 61

SEXUAL STERILITY—MALE AND FEMALE

STERILITY means the inability to bear children, and it may be due to either the inability to properly conceive, or continue a pregnancy to a viable (sufficiently developed to live) stage of the foetus. Most gynecologists (physicians who specialize in female disorders) define sterility as lack of ability to conceive. We are concerned with several types of sterility. *Absolute* or *primary* sterility is that type wherein the woman concerned has *never* conceived. *Secondary* sterility is that which follows a previous pregnancy, whether or not it resulted in a viable foetus. Decreased but not entirely absent conception ability is called *relative sterility* or *impaired fertility*.

The fact that an estimated ten percent of all marriages in the United States are barren indicates the magnitude of sterility in general, and the necessity of a scientific medical approach to the problem. Nowadays some gynecologists devote their entire time to this one field of practice, with increasingly gratifying results in recent years. The popular conception has been, until very recently at least, that sterility is the misfortune or fault of the woman alone. This is not true by any means, because medical records show that barrenness can be attributed to defect or faulty function in the husband in over one-third of all childless marriages. So sterility is really a problem of *sterile mating*, and the fertility of *both husband and wife* must be ascertained in an honest approach to the problem.

Normal conception requires certain prerequisite conditions. Essential, of course, is the regular production of normal ova (egg cells) by the female and of normal healthy sperm cells by the male. Careful history, examination, and study of both man and wife by the physician can determine this. A factor frequently overlooked is that copulation must take place at the time of ovulation (extrusion of the egg from the ovary of the female). Ovulation in the normal healthy woman with regular menstrual cycles usually occurs sometime about the tenth to fifteenth day of the cycle, though this may vary greatly. (See Chapters 23 and 24.) Despite the great work of Professors Ogino and Knaus, a somewhat disconcerting fact is that in a series of some 1400 cases observed by an accredited gynecologist where the exact date of copulation resulting in conception was known, more conceptions occurred on the eighth and ninth days of the cycle than during the above-mentioned days, and, equally as important, none of the 28 days of the average normal cycle of this group were free of conceptions occurring.

The well-trained physician can usually determine the date of ovulation by certain points of the history (such as a slight pain on one side or other occurring regularly each cycle as the ovum is extruded, or occasionally a spot of vaginal bleeding occurring regularly at the time of ovulation), by certain signs on examination (the ovulating ovary may be slightly enlarged or tender, as compared to other times of examination), and by special laboratory tests (such as the type and acidity or alkalinity of the mucus secreted by the cervix—mouth of the womb, or the type of cells seen through a microscope in specially prepared smears taken at the time of examinations or by the woman herself at home). Another frequently used method is the daily taking of the vaginal, or rectal, temperature; this must be done at the same time and under the same conditions (rest, state of mind, etc.) each day. A slight but definite temperature change can be noted near the time of ovulation.

Since most authorities agree that the life of the unfertilized ovum is brief, not more than about 24 hours, and the fertilizing ability of the sperm cell is only about 24 hours, it is obvious that copulation and subsequent impregnation must take place within 24 hours of ovulation.

The genital ducts must be open. In the male this is proven by the presence of sperm cells in the semen. In the female, the potency of the fallopian tubes, which conduct the ovum from the ovary to the cavity of the uterus, where pregnancy normally develops, can be

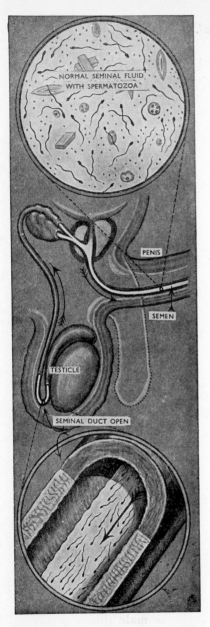

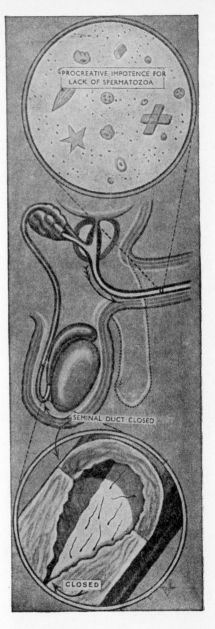

Fig. 151—Picture story of normal sexuality in man.
Seminal fluid is rich in spermatozoa capable of fecundation.

Fig. 152—Picture story of procreative impotence.
Sterility. Owing to former inflammations in the epididymis (mostly arising from gonorrhea) the seminal duct may be closed, so that the spermatozoa cannot reach the urethra, and impregnation is impossible.

determined by a simple test. This, the Rubin or Carey Test, is performed by injecting air under pressure into the cervix, and listening over the lower abdomen with a stethescope to determine whether air bubbles out through the fallopian tubes into the abdominal cavity. If no air passes through at a certain pressure, blockage of the tubes is indicated—the ovum cannot get to the uterus, nor can the sperm get to the ovum. Further information as to the condition of the passages of the genital tract can be determined by taking X-ray pictures, called Utero-salpingograms, after injecting a harmless dye into the uterine cavity via the cervix.

In sterility studies, the health of the female genital tract must be ascertained and corrected where necessary. Often a simple infection or inflammation of the vagina or cervix producing secretions injurious to sperm can be cleared up by simple treatment. Frequently a condition called Erosion (chronic inflammation) of the cervix can be healed by application of the electro-cautery and mild acid douches thereafter. These and similar conditions often produce secretions that kill the sperm cells or impede their progress through the cervical opening to the uterus on the way to union with the ovum. (Out of the millions of sperm deposited at one time, it takes only one to fertilize an ovum and achieve conception.) Small tumors of the cervix or uterus, such as polyps of the mucous lining, or fibroid tumors of the muscle wall, may impede conception. These, when treated by surgical removal, are often followed by the gratifying result of a pregnancy thereafter.

Often the physician may find a simple displacement of the uterus, such as retroversion (tipped backwards), or anteversion (tipped too far forward)—the body of the uterus may be bent upon itself in such a way as to block the canal and hence prevent conception. Such mal-positions can be corrected frequently simply by replacement of the uterus to proper position by the physician at the time of examination, followed by special exercises which he may prescribe thereafter.

Frequently the only obstruction to impregnation is a thick hymen with only a small perforation, causing improbability, if not impossibility, of conception, as well as pain on attempt at coitus. This is treated easily and simply by incision and dilation of the hymen under a light anaesthesia with rapid healing thereafter.

Infection in the fallopian tubes (salpingitis), resulting in adhesions and strictures blocking their opening, is perhaps the greatest cause of sterility in the female. The most frequent cause of "blocked tubes" is gonorrheal infection, damage to the tubes remaining long after the acute infection has cleared up. Other infections, however, such as ruptured appendix, peritonitis, or tuberculosis of the female genital tract, and infections such as those which occasionally develop during or following child-birth under unsanitary conditions, and especially after an unclean or instrumental abortion (usually the criminal or illegally done), may be the cause of blocked tubes. We have mentioned above methods for establishing whether tubes were open or closed.

Various operations for plastic surgery of the tubes, such as splicing and re-attachment into the cavity of the uterus, or re-opening of the closed outer ends, have been devised and tried; but these, for the most part, have not turned out very satisfactory as far as results in achieving conception.

Other and more rare causes of sterility include those which occur on a congenital or a developmental basis, such as the infantile type of uterus, which is *abnormally* small and undeveloped. Tubes and ovaries may likewise be undeveloped to the extent necessary for proper conception. Hormonal (endocrine) disfunctions also come into this category of sterility causes. Here, the female organs and the menses may be or appear to be normal, but certain hormonal imbalances, or deficiencies, may preclude pregnancy. The so-called anovulatory cycle is that type of menstrual cycle in which the woman may menstruate regularly, but no ovum is discharged from the ovary into the tube as should occur normally. Such conditions can be frequently improved, if not completely corrected, upon careful study and institution of the proper treatment with hormones. Wide research continues at present in this very important field of Female Endocrinology or Gynecology.

Sterility sometimes may exist as a result of a general hormone

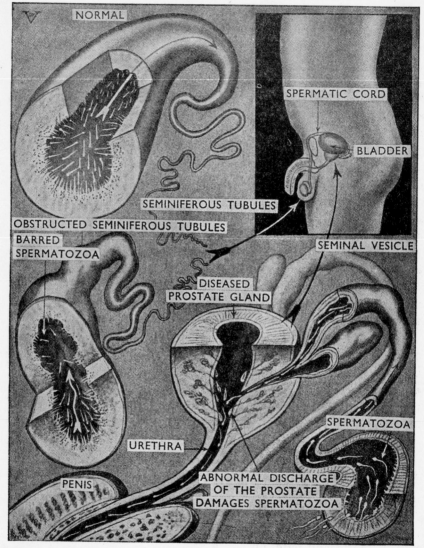

Fig. 153—Picture story of normal genital apparatus of man, compared to obstructions which cause sterility.

deficiency complicated by obesity. In such cases, controlled weight reduction and careful use of thyroid extract, or certain other hormones as indicated, have often proved successful.

Now we must include sterility-causing abnormalities of the male. These are impotence, certain constitutional factors, and defects in the sperm and semen. It is a relatively simple matter to examine recently collected semen under a microscope in order to study and count the sperm. If no sperm are present because of some obstruction of the spermatic ducts, yet the male organs are otherwise normal, a plastic operation on the ducts is sometimes of value. If the matter is one of functional impotence, then simple psychological readjustment, rest, and a more rational mode of living will usually overcome the difficulty. In the male, as well as in the female, infertility may be improved by the elimination of conditions such as anemia and chronic systemic infections, and by developing proper habits of living and reasonable sexual temperance. Sometimes, endocrine deficiencies in the male are amenable to treatment with special male hormones.

A recently widely discussed treatment of infertility in married couples is that of *artificial insemination*. This may be resorted to where there is an incorrectible defect in the husband of a normal woman, proven by careful medical examination and study. The method consists simply of obtaining donor sperm from a healthy male of proper social, physical, and eugenic background, and placing a specimen of same into the cervix of the woman in question by the physician, at the time of ovulation. Though this method of impregnation has not been widely used or accepted, it has proven very satisfactory in a number of cases. Many uncertain legal aspects must be carefully considered, according to existing laws on the subject, though there are virtually no specific laws at present. In general there must be a witnessed written permission for the procedure by both husband and wife. Of course, the identity of the male donor should be unknown, for obvious reasons, to both husband and wife, and precaution should be taken that it never be disclosed. Likewise, the identity of the recipient couple must be unknown to the donor. The physician must carefully select the proper time, that of ovulation, for placing the donor semen, recently obtained and properly preserved, into the cervix. Often several attempts may be necessary before pregnancy is achieved.

The time-honored routine of legal adoption of one or more children is, under present conditions, perhaps still the best way of satisfying natural desires for offspring in cases of incurable sterility in either husband or wife. Curiously enough, there are frequent cases on record of women conceiving and bearing normal children soon after adoption of a child because of supposed infertility. This may well be considered a result of release of certain psychological inhibitions which previously prevented conception.

A CONCISE DICTIONARY

OF SEXUAL TERMS

A

Aberration, sexual—Deviation from normal sexual activity and practices.

Abortion—Expulsion, from the womb, of the unborn child before its term, or due time, either spontaneously or through induction by medical or surgical means.

After-birth—The placenta and membranes which are expelled from the womb after the birth of the child.

Accocheur—A man who acts as a midwife.

Accoucheuse—A midwife.

Acyesis—Female sterility.

Adolescence—The period of growth from childhood to womanhood or manhood.

Adultery—Sexual intercourse with one who is married to another person.

Algolagnia—Abnormal sex desire to receive pain from person of opposite sex.

Ambiosis—Miscarriage.

Amenorrhea—Absence of the monthly periods of a woman.

Androphobia—A fear of man.

Animal love—Same as Zoolagnia.

Anther—In plants, the male sexual organs.

Anus—The rectum.

Aphoria—Female sterility.

Aposthia—Penis with no prepuce, due to congenital condition.

Aphrodisiac—A drug or other means, the chief purpose of which is to stimulate and arouse sexual desire.

Areola—The ring around the nipple.

Artificial insemination—Same as Test-tube baby.

Ascheim-Zondek test—To determine whether the woman is pregnant.

Asexual—Having no sex.

Aspermia—A lack of male seminal secretion during the sexual act.

Asynodia—Sexual impotence.

Atocia—Sterility, when applied to women.

Auto-erotic—Pertaining to methods of self-gratification sexually. This is used to include such practices as masturbation.

Azoöspermia—A lack or absence of spermatozoa in the seminal fluid.

B

Bagnio—House of prostitution.

Balanic—Pertaining to the *glans penis* or *glans clitoris* (head).

Balanitis—An inflammation of the *glans penis*.

Balanoblennorrhea—Balanitis due to gonorrhea.

Balanoplasty—Plastic surgery performed on the *glans penis*.

Baptorrhea—Same as gonorrhea.

Baptothecorrhea—Gonorrheal infection in women.

Barren—Sterile; incapable of producing offspring.

Bartholinitis—An inflammation of Bartholin's glands, a pair of small glands situated on each side of the vagina.

Bastard—A child born out of wedlock.

Bestiality—Sexual relations of a human being with an animal.

Biogenesis—The normal process of reproduction.

Biparous—Giving birth to twins.

Birth control—Voluntary limitation of size of family.

Bisexual—Having sexual craving for both sexes; an equal mixture of hetersexualism and homosexualism.

Blennelytria—Catarrh of the vagina.

Blennorhagia—Profuse discharge from vagina.

Bradyspermatism—Very slow ejaculation of the seminal fluid.

Bromidrosiphobia—Morbid dread of body odors.

C

Carey test—To determine sexual potency of a woman.

Castrate—A person who has been deprived of his sexual organs, such as an eunuch.

Catamenia—The monthly periods.

Celibate—One who is unmarried. Often used to describe a person who takes a vow against sexual life.

Centromere—The narrow, neck-like region of the spermatozoön.

Cervical—Pertaining to the neck or narrow region of the womb.

Cervix—The neck of the womb.

Cesarian section—Child-birth by extraction of foetus through abdominal incision.

Change of life—The period of menopause. Cessation of the menses.

Chastity—The state of being chaste, or untouched by sexual practices.

Chemicogenesis—Use of chemicals to fertilize the ovum.

Chlorosis—Anemia due to menstrual irregularities.

Circumcision—Minor operation to remove part of foreskin of the penis.

Climacteric—Pertaining to the change of life period in both men and women.

Climacterium preaecox—Change of life which occurs too early.

Climax—Arriving at orgasm in sexual intercourse.

Clitoris—The seat of a woman's sexual feeling, quite similar to a small penis, located in the vagina.

Cohabitation—Performance of the sex act.

Coitophobia—A morbid fear of coitus.

Coitus—Same as cohabitation, sexual relation, sexual intercourse.

Coitus interruptus—Withdrawal of the penis from the vagina before emission of the semen has taken place.

Coitus more ferarum—Act of coitus in which the woman assumes the above or superior position.

Coitus prolongatus—Prolonged sexual intercourse.

Coitus reservatus—Sexual relations brought to an end before the male orgasm has occurred.

Coleocele—Hernia in the vagina.

Colpitis—Inflammation of the vagina.

Colpoptosis—Vaginal hemorrhage.

Conception—The beginning of pregnancy following fertilization of the ovum by the spermatozoön.

Concubitus—Same as Copulation.

Congenital—Existing from birth; born with.

Conjugal—Pertaining to marriage.

Contraceptive —A device or medicine designed to prevent conception.

Copulation—Sexual intercouse; coitus.

Cryptorchism—Failure of the testes to descend into the scrotum.

Cunnus—The vulva.

Cycle—The recurrent periodical time of menstruation.

Cyophoria—The period of pregnancy.

Cypridophobia—An excessive fear of having sexual relations.

D

Deferentectomy—Removal of the *vas deferens* by surgery.

Defloration—Act of rupturing the hymen during the first intercourse.

Detumescence—Restoration of the penis to a state of flaccidity after erection.

Didymodynia—Pain in the testes.

Discharge—Same as Leukorrhea.

Dotage—Same as Senility.

Dysgenesis—A term including sterility and infertility.

Dysmenorrhea—Painful monthly periods.

Dysovarism—Internal sections of ovary not functioning properly.

Dyspareunia—Painful sexual intercourse in women.

E

Ectopic pregnancy—Pregnancy taking place outside the womb.

Edea—The reproductive organs.

Edeoptosis—Prolapse of the genital organs.

Effeminate—A term applied to men having woman-like characteristics.

Egomania—Abornal admiration and esteem of self.

Ejaculate—To discharge the seminal fluid during sexual intercourse.

Ejaculatio ante portem—Ejaculation occurring before the penis has entered the vagina.

Ejaculatio precipitata—Immediate ejaculation occurring upon erection.

Ejaculatio praecox—Premature ejaculation of semen.

Elytritis—Same as Vaginitis.

Embryo—Developed ovum in womb up to the fourth month.

Embryotrophy—Nutrition of the foetus.

Emissions—Same as Nocturnal emissions.

Enciente—Pregnant.

Endometritis—An inflammation of the uterus.

Epididymis—Tube leading from testicle, through which spermatozoa. travel in process of ejaculation.

Episiorrhagia—Profuse bleeding from vulva.

Erection—The state of rigidity and enlargement of the penis, due to sexual excitation.

Erethism—Stimulation of the genital organs.

Eros—The Greek God of Love.

Erotic—Pertaining to sexual love.

Erotophobia—An aversion to listening to a discussion of sexual topics.

Eunuch—A man who has been deprived of his genital organs.

Eunuchoid—Pertaining or resembling eunuchism.

Evirate—Same as Castrate.

Exhibitionist—In sexual terms, one who abnormally exposes the genital organs, seeking admiration from the onlooker.

Extra-uterine pregnancy—Same as Ectopic.

F

Fallopian tube—Passage through which ovum travels from ovary to uterus.

Fecundate—To fertilize, to impregnate.

Fertility—Capability of producing offspring.

Fetishism—The endowment with sexual qualities of a non-sexual object.

Thus gloves or shoes may arouse sexual feeling in certain men. The gloves or shoes are then called fetishes.

Flagellation—Arousing sexual desire by being whipped or spanked.

Flux—Same as Leukorrhea.

Foetus—Unborn child in the womb, after the third month.

Folliculin—The female sex hormone which regulates the monthly periods.

Foreplay—Petting and caressing which precedes the sex act.

Frigidity—A condition of partial or complete indifference to sexual matters. Lack of sexual feeling.

Frustration—In sexual matters, a real failure or a feeling of failure.

Funiculitis—Inflammation of the spermatic cord.

Furor uterinus—Same as Nymphomania.

G

Galactorrhea—Excessive milk flow from the breasts.

Gamete—A cell capable of reproduction; sperm; ovum.

Gamophobia—A fear of marriage.

Genitals—The reproductive sex organs.

Gestation—Pregnancy.

Glans clitoris—The bulbous tip of the clitoris.

Glans penis—The bulbous extremity (head) of the penis.

Gonococcus—The germ that causes gonorrhea.

Gonorrhea—Inflammation of the mucous membrane of the genital organs, which is contagious.

Graafian follicle—Covering which envelops the ovum, and bursts when ovum is matured.

Gravida—A pregnant woman.

Gynecomania—Excessive sexual desire in men.

Gymnophobia—A fear of being seen naked.

Gynandrite—Same as Hermaphrodite.

Gynecology—The scientific study of the functions of a woman's body and the treatment of female diseases.

Gynecophobia—Dread of women.

Gynoplastic—Plastic surgery on female genital organs.

H

Haphephobia—A fear of being touched by anyone.

Hermaphrodite—A person having the sexual characteristics of both a man and a woman.

Hernia—A rupture.

Heterosexual—Sexual feeling for the opposite sex—normal sexual love.

Hiatus—The vulva.

Homosexual—Sexual feeling for members of the same sex—abnormal sexual love.

Hormones—Substances produced by the endocrine glands to influence activity of the other organs, or of the body as a whole.

Hymen—A thin membrane at the entrance of the uterus, found in most virgins.

Hypergonadism—An excessive flow of secretion from the ovaries or testes.

Hypertrophy—Enlargement of the prostate.

Hysterectomy—Surgical removal of the womb.

I

Immissio penis—The act of introducing the penis into the vaginal canal.

Impotentia coeundi—Inability of the male to have sexual relations.

Impotentia erigendi—Lack of power of the male to have an erection.

Impotentia generandi—Sterility: the inability to beget children.

Incest—Sexual relations between very near blood relations, such as brother and sister, father and daughter, etc.

Infantilism—Childish characteristics retained by an adult.

Inhibition—To hold back or curb desires.

Intercourse—The sexual act between male and female.

Isogamy—A sexual mating of similar gametes.

K

Karezza—A method of prolonged sexual intercourse during which time ejaculation is voluntarily withheld.

Kleptolagnia—Stealing for the purpose of obtaining sexual gratification.
Kysthitis—Same as Vaginitis.

L

Labia majora—The outer lips of the vagina.
Labia minora—The inner lips of the vagina.
Lesbianism—Homosexual love among women. Other terms used are tribadism and sapphism.
Leukorrhea—A mucous discharge (or flux) from the vagina.
Libido—Sexual desire and all its implications.
Lochia—The discharge from the womb following childbirth.
Love—A strong emotion between a man and woman, based on a feeling of mutual admiration and pleasure in one another's presence.
Lubric—Lewd, lustful, sexual.
Luetic—Pertaining to syphilis.

M

Maidenhead—Same as Hymen.
Maiensiophobia—Fear of going through child-birth.
Mammary glands—The breasts.
Marital—Pertaining to marriage.
Masochism—Sexual satisfaction derived from being beaten, humiliated and harshly handled in a variety of ways.
Masochist—A person suffering from masochism.
Mastitis—Inflammation of the breast.
Mastomenia—A false menstruation from the breast.
Masturbation—Sexual stimulation derived from self-manipulation of genital organs.
Meatus, urinarius—External opening of the urethra.
Membrum virile—The penis.
Menopause—Same as Change of life.
Menses—The monthly periods.
Metrodynia—Pain in the womb.

Metorrhagia—Bleeding between menstrual periods.
Midwife—A woman who delivers a child obstetrically.
Miscarriage—A premature birth.
Miscegenation—Marriage between two persons of different races.
Misogamy—Fear of marriage.
Monogamy—A marriage with one mate.
Monorchid—Man who has only one testicle.
Muliebria—The female sexual organs.

N

Narcissim—Love of one's self.
Neurotic—Affected by a nervous ailment.
Neuter—Having no sex; being neither male nor female.
Nocturnal emissions—Man's involuntary loss of semen, while he is asleep.
Nubility—Fitted for marriage sexually.
Nullipara—Woman who has never given birth to a child.
Nycturia—Involuntary passing of urine during the night.
Nymphitis—Inflammation of the labia (lips) of the vagina.
Nymphomania—Suffering from excessive sexual desire, on the part of a woman.

O

Obstetrician—A physician who treats women during pregnancy and child-birth.
Oligogenics—Practice of birth control.
Oligospermia—A decrease in the number of spermatozoa present in the seminal fluid.
Omotacia—A miscarriage (premature birth).
Onanism—Masturbation.
Oophoritis—Inflammation of the ovary.
Oophoromania—Insanity resulting from disease of the ovaries.
Oosperm—An ovum which has been fertilized by sperm.
Orchectomy—Testicle removed by surgery.

Orchialgia—A pain in the testes.

Orchitis—Inflammation of the testicle.

Orgasm—The height of sexual feeling.

Orgasmus praecox—Premature orgasm; orgasm occurring before the normal time.

Osmolagnia—Sexual desire aroused by odors.

Ovaralgia—Pain in the ovary.

Ovariectomy—Removal of ovary by surgery.

Ovaries—The organs in a woman's body wherein the ova (eggs) are developed.

Ovariocentesis—A punctured ovary.

Ovariocyesis—Pregnancy occurring in the ovary.

Ovaritis—Same as Oophoritis.

Oviduct—Part of woman's genital organs, where the ovum is fertilized by the male sperm.

Ovulation—The process of producing ova by the ovaries in the female.

P

Paramenia—Menstrual irregularities.

Parametric—Inflamed condition surrounding the womb.

Paroniria—Dreams of a morbid nature.

Parturition—The process of giving birth to a child.

Pectoral—A muscle of the breast.

Pederasty—Abnormal sexual intercourse with boys, through the anus.

Penis—The male sex organ.

Penitis—Inflammation of the penis.

Perispermatitis—Inflamed sheath of the spermatic cord.

Phallitis—Inflammation of the penis.

Phalloncus—Swelling or tumor of the penis.

Phallus—The penis.

Phimosis—Abnormal tightness of prepuce or foreskin of penis, often causing strangulation of penis.

Pineal gland—A contributing factor, through its extract, to precocious sex development.

Placenta—The afterbirth.

Platonic—In matters of love, an attachment between two people which is purely spiritual, and has no passion.

Pollution—Involuntary emission of seminal fluid, occurring usually during sleep.

Polyandry—A type of marriage wherein the woman has more than one husband at a time.

Polygamy—The type of marriage wherein there is more than one wife or one husband, at one time.

Polymastia—More than two normal breasts.

Poplymenorrhea—An excessive menstrual bleeding.

Polyspermia—More than the usual amount of seminal secretion.

Polythelia—More than one nipple on a breast.

Pornographic—A term applied to literature, paintings, dramatic and cinematic shows which aim to arouse sexual desire.

Pregnancy—The state of a woman carrying a child within her body.

Prepuce—Foreskin of the penis.

Prevenceptive—Same as contraceptive, aimed at preventing pregnancy.

Priapism—A nabnormal and painful erection of the penis, independent of sexual desire.

Priapitis—An inflammatory condition of the penis.

Priapus—The penis.

Primigravida—A woman in her first pregnancy.

Privates—The external genital organs.

Procreate—Produce offspring.

Proiotia—Precocious sexual development.

Prolapse—The falling down of an organ (such as the uterus) from its normal position.

Prolific—Capable of producing many offspring.

Prostate gland—Situated at the base of the bladder in the male body.

Prostatitis—Inflammation of the prostate gland.

Pseudocyesis—A false pregnancy.

Psycholagny—Achieving sexual satisfaction by conjuring up in one's mind erotic scenes.

Puberty—The period of life when the young person develops into womanhood or manhood, and is capable of producing offspring.

Pubic hair—Growth of hair around the genitals.

Pudenda—The external genitals of the female.

Pudendagra—Painful genital organs.

Pudic—Relating to the sexual organs.

Pyometra—Pus in the uterus.

Pyoovarium—An abscess in the ovary.

Q

Quickening—The movement of the child within the body of the pregnant woman.

R

Rabbit-test—Same as Ascheim-Zondek test, to determine pregnancy.

Rape—A violation of a woman's chastity by force, and without her consent.

Rectophobia—Morbid fear of disease of the rectum.

Retifism—A form of fetishism in which the shoe is endowed with sexual significance.

Rhythm—Same as *Tempus ageneseos*.

Ridgel—A man whose testes have been removed.

Ridgling—Man who possesses only one testicle.

Rubin test—Same as Carey test.

Rugae—The transverse vaginal folds which allow the vaginal canal to expand during childbirth.

Rutting time—Sexual excitation. This term is used mainly for animals' mating time.

S

Sadism—A form of sexual perversion in which gratification is obtained sexually by inflicting pain on another person.

Sadist—A person practising sadism; a sexual pervert.

Salpingitis—Inflammation of the Fallopian tube.

Salpingocyesis—Pregnancy which occurs in the Fallopian tube.

Sapphism—Homosexual relations between women.

Sapphist—A woman homosexual.

Sarcocele—Tumor in the testicle.

Satyriasis—Morbid and excessive sexual craving in men.

Scrotitis—Inflammation of the scrotum.

Scrotum—The pouch, situated on each side of the penis, which contains the testis.

Scythian disease—Male genital organs become atrophied.

Seduction—Enticing a woman to surrender her chastity in sexual intercourse.

Semen—The male's fecundating fluid.

Semenuria—Leakage of the seminal fluid into the urine.

Seminal vesicle—Pouch between the base of the bladder and the rectum, which is the reservoir for the male semen.

Semination—The process of introducing semen into the vagina and womb; insemination is also a term for the same process.

Senility—The state of dotage, or feebleness of the mind, in old age.

Sex—The character of being either a male or a female.

Sexologist—An expert in the science of sexology.

Sexology—The scientific study of sex and its phenomena.

Sexual aberrations—A term which includes all sexual abnormal practices.

Sexual anesthesia—Complete absence of all sexual feeling and emotion.

Skene's Glands—Two glands situated in the urethra of the female. Together with Bartholin's glands they furnish the lubricating fluid for the genital tract.

Sodomy—Abnormal sexual intercourse in which the anus is employed.

Spado—A person suffering from sexual impotence.

Spay—Surgical removal of ovaries or testicles.

Spend—Ejaculate semen in sexual intercourse.

Spermatozoa (sperm) —Male reproductive cell which fertilizes the female ovum.

Spermatic cord—The cord which hangs suspended from the testicle, carrying lymph and blood vessels, the *vas deferens,* and the nerves.

Spermatism—The act of discharging semen.

Spermatorrhea—An emission of semen which is involuntary.

Sterilize—To deprive, by medical or surgical means, the power of producing offspring.

Sublimation—Diversion of sexual energy into non-sexual channels.

Summa libido—The greatest height of sexual feeling.

Superlactation—Over-abundant milk secretion in the breast.

Syngamy—The process of union of the gametes during fertilization.

Syphilis—A communicable venereal disease, contracted by direct contact with the germ, or due to heredity.

T

Tempus ageneseos—The safe period, taken advantage of in natural birth control.

Tenigo—Extreme sexual desire.

Teratrophobia—Fear of giving birth to a monster.

Testicles (testes) —The two glandular bodies in the scrotum (one on each side of the penis) that secrete the semen.

Testicond—The condition of having undescended testes.

Test-tube baby—A baby born as the result of artificial insemination.

Thelalgia—A pain in the nipples.

Thymus gland—An endocrine gland (situated in the chest) that impedes sexual development.

Tribade—A woman homosexual, same as Lesbian.

Tumefaction—The process of erection of the penis.

U

Umbilical cord—The connection, within the mother's body, between the foetus and the placenta.

Urethra—The duct through which the urine is discharged from the bladder.

Urethritis—Inflammation of the urethra.

Urning—A male homosexual.

Urnism—Male homosexuality.

Uroclepsia—Involuntary discharge of urine.

Uterine anteversion—Uterus displaced so it tips forward.

Uterine frenzy—Nymphomania; excessive sexual desire in women.

Uterine retroversion—Uterus displaced so it tips backward.

Uterus—The womb.

V

Vagina—The female sexual passage or canal.

Vaginal—Pertaining to the vagina.

Vaginismus—Convulsive contraction of the vaginal muscles.

Vaginitis—Inflammation of the vagina.

Vampirism—A condition in which sexual excitement is accompanied by scratching and blood-letting.

Vas deferens—The duct of the testis through which the semen is ejected.

Venereal—Pertaining to diseases communicated through sexual contact with an infected person.

Venery—Sexual intercourse.

Virginity—The state of being a chaste (unmarried) woman.

Virilia—The male sex organs.

Virility—The state of manhood in its sexual maturity.

Viripotent—Sexual maturity applied to men.

Vita sexualis—The sex life of the individual.

Voyeurism—A sexual abnormality in which the person afflicted obtains sexual gratification by looking at the sexual organs of another person.

Vulva—The female external sexual organs.

Vulval—Pertaining to the vulva.

W

Wasserman test—A serum test to determine if syphilis is present.

Whites—Same as Leukorrhea.

Womb—The organ in a woman's body where the offspring is developed.

Y

Yard—The penis.

Z

Zoanthropist—One who (because of a distortion of the mind) thinks he is an animal.

Zoolagnia—Sexual attraction to animals; a form of sexual aberration.

Zoosperm—A spermatozoön.